D1297164

# Math INNOVATIONS COURSE 3

*MOVING MATH FORWARD THROUGH CRITICAL THINKING AND EXPLORATION*

## Solve It

## Focusing on Equations, Inequalities and Exponents

M. Katherine Gavin

Linda Jensen Sheffield

Suzanne H. Chapin

Ann Marie Spinelli

**Kendall Hunt**

publishing company

# ACKNOWLEDGMENTS

## Math Innovations Writing Team

### Authors

M. Katherine Gavin

Linda Jensen Sheffield

Suzanne H. Chapin

### Project Manager

Janice M. Vuolo

### Teacher Edition Team

Ann Marie Spinelli

Alice J. Gabbard

Jacob J. Whitmore

### Writing Assistants

Kathy Dorkin

Jane Paulin

### Mathematics Editor

Kathleen G. Snook

### Assessment Specialist

Nancy Anderson

### Advisory Board

Jerry P. Becker

Janet Beissinger

Diane J. Briars

Ann Lawrence

Ira J. Papick

Page 2 © SSPL/Science Museum/Art Resource, NY. Page 85 Roman glass photo is in the public domain. Page 143 Gordon E. Moore, Co-founder, Intel Corporation. Copyright © 2005 Intel Corporation. Page 146 Photo © Jim Callaway. Used by permission. See *www.jimcallaway.com*. Cover photo of girl with marker by TSI Graphics. Unless otherwise noted, all images on cover and interior used under license by ShutterStock, Inc. Portions of *Curriculum Focal Points* have been reprinted with the permission of the National Council of Teachers of Mathematics.

## Kendall Hunt
publishing company

www.kendallhunt.com

Send all inquiries to:

4050 Westmark Drive

Dubuque, IA 52004-1840

1-800-542-6657

# Solve It:
## Focusing on Equations, Inequalities and Exponents

# Table of Contents

# Teaching and Learning Strategies

## Think Like a Mathematician Daily Record Sheet

*Think Like a Mathematician* is a unique feature of the Kendall Hunt *Math Innovations* program. This daily record sheet is a learning tool designed to help students organize and keep track of their daily work and notes throughout the lessons and for reference during class discussions and homework. In addition to offering students a place to record their work and the key ideas presented in each lesson, the *Think Like a Mathematician Daily Record Sheet* also provides students with easy access to important notes when studying for quizzes and tests. Organizing work and establishing productive study habits are critical skills that need to be developed in the middle school years. Using this tool daily not only encourages students to keep a record of their own innovative results, conjectures, arguments and questions, but it also provides them with notes that can be polished or refined as well as studied. It is yet another way in which *Math Innovations* helps students reflect on their thinking process as they mature mathematically.

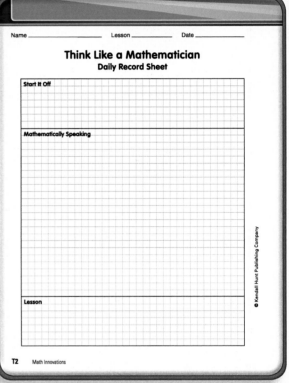

The *Think Like a Mathematician Daily Record Sheet* is partitioned into labeled sections, with one section for each component of the lesson, and has a grid paper background. Most teachers and students will use more than one *Think Like a Mathematician Daily Record Sheet* for multiple-day lessons.

An important habit of mind that this program develops in students is careful note-taking during mathematics class. Initially, teachers may need to demonstrate this to students by recording important information related to the key ideas of the lesson on the board or on an overhead for students to copy. Students should be encouraged to record other key information in their notes, such as their individual mathematical work, strategies and insights; mathematical terms and their definitions; important formulas; and examples or drawings that explain or illustrate new concepts.

It is recommended that students keep their *Think Like a Mathematician Daily Record Sheets* in a 3-ring binder. This 3-ring binder will serve as the student's mathematics notebook.

Name _____     Lesson _____     Date _____

# Think Like a Mathematician
## Daily Record Sheet

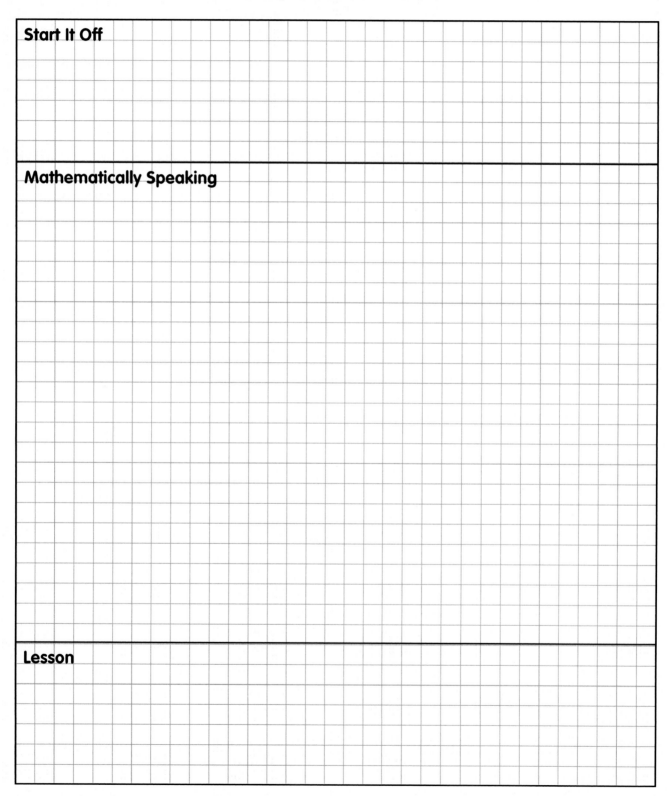

**Start It Off**

**Mathematically Speaking**

**Lesson**

© Kendall Hunt Publishing Company

**Lesson (continued)**

**Wrap It Up**

**Start It Off**

1. Identify the place value of ea
2. Determine the value of each in words.

$10^6 = 1,000,000$   Ten

# Start It Off

*Start It Off* is a short problem or series of problems found at the beginning of each lesson. It is designed to be a quick warm-up at the start of class that helps students build upon previous learning and connect it to new concepts that are being introduced. It usually contains a metacognitive question to help students deepen their mathematical understanding. This leads students to make connections to previous knowledge as they discover relationships among specific mathematical concepts, skills and procedures.

Using the *Start It Off* questions as a daily mathematical warm-up helps establish a classroom routine and will smooth the transition time as students enter the classroom. Students should be instructed to begin work on the *Start It Off* as soon as they enter class. This allows the teacher to take attendance, distribute materials or attend to individual students' needs. *Start It Off* problems only take a few minutes to complete, but the discussion about these problems will build skills and knowledge over time. Approximately 5–10 minutes should be used during each class to discuss the questions. For multi-day lessons, teachers may assign a part of the *Start It Off* each day.

**Sorting Fractions**

Have students use calculators and wor
pairs or groups of three to complete th
activity. They should find the decimal
representation of each fraction by divi
the numerator by the denominator (not using
fraction-decimal key) and record their results
Lesson Guide 1.5: *Sorting Fractions*. Then they
should look for patterns in the fractions and
answer Question 2 on the Lesson Guide. Discu
Question 2 as a class. Do not be surprised if
students' observations are very general at this
point in the lesson.

# The Lesson

## Guiding the Lesson

The lessons presented in *Math Innovations* have students learning mathematics using interesting, age-appropriate, hands-on investigations, tasks, problems and games. A conversational tone is used throughout the series as a motivational tool and to demonstrate respect to students' as mathematical thinkers who are capable of reading and understanding the material. Embedded in each lesson are questions that encourage students to use critical and creative thinking and mathematical reasoning as they solve problems and discover key mathematical concepts. Examples are often presented for the students to discuss and study. *Lesson Guides*, found in the Teacher's Edition, help students to record their data and organize their work as they engage in lesson activities. Using these guides will save time and enable students to focus more of their attention on developing a deeper understanding of the key mathematical concepts presented in the lesson.

Teacher notes provided in the Teacher's Edition offer assistance for the teacher in guiding and navigating students through the lesson activities. These notes include tips on teaching strategies, recommended classroom instructional arrangements, questions to further develop student understanding, key student responses and possible student misconceptions. The teacher's role during lesson exploration is to circulate, observe and ask questions, but not to explain procedures. It is important to cultivate independent student thinking during activity exploration. This provides an opportunity for students to gain self-confidence by discussing their ideas with other students as they work to gain understanding.

## Guiding the Discussion

Classroom discussion is a key component in *Math Innovations*. Discussions can include the whole class, small groups or partners. Classroom discussions are especially effective in moving student thinking forward and developing students' collective understanding of key mathematical ideas. Teachers are strongly urged to allow time for students to share and discuss ideas, discoveries and solution strategies at several points throughout the lessons. Sometimes students are asked to discuss errors or incorrect procedures. While some think this will confuse students, the opposite occurs! Students clarify their understanding of the material when they have had to address their preconceived notions and misconceptions.

Teachers are also encouraged to be mindful of key vocabulary terms and symbols highlighted in the Student Edition and to emphasize their appropriate use in class discussions. Students must not only understand the meaning of these terms, but must also become fluent in the precise use of mathematical language. Teachers should expect students to use this mathematical language on a daily basis during class discussions and in their writing. As they explicitly encourage students to use this language, teachers should remind students that this helps them think and talk like mathematicians, which is a recurring goal of the *Math Innovations* program.

## Talk Moves

Several strategies can be used to facilitate meaningful classroom discussions. Chapin, O'Connor, and Anderson (2009) refer to these strategies as *talk moves*. The *Math Innovations* program recommends teachers use the following six talk moves:

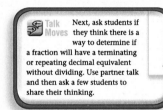

Talk Moves: Next, ask students if they think there is a way to determine if a fraction will have a terminating or repeating decimal equivalent without dividing. Use partner talk and then ask a few students to share their thinking.

### Revoicing

The teacher *restates/revoices* a student's words as accurately as possible and then verifies whether the student's response was correct. This move can be used when a student's response is unclear or confusing. It also can be used when a student's contribution is unique and brilliant, but not understood by the majority of the class. For example, a teacher might ask, "You said that triangle was equilateral and scalene? Did I get that right?" The student then has a chance to restate what he or she meant. Often the next utterance is much more succinct; "No, I meant that if the triangle is equilateral, then it cannot be scalene too." This talk move helps students to clarify their thinking.

### Repeat/rephrase

When using *repeat/rephrase* the teacher focuses the discussion on the main ideas of the lesson. After a student has made a particularly important point or comment, the teacher asks another student to restate the point by asking, "Would you repeat what he/she said in your own words?" It is important to use this move to highlight ideas that are foundational, no matter how small, or ideas that are not well-understood. For example, many students are confused by how the size of a denominator of a fraction affects the size of a fractional piece. This talk move can be used to ask a number of students to repeat a classmate's explanation for why $\frac{1}{8}$ is less than $\frac{1}{3}$. Do not ask students to repeat information that everyone already understands. Teachers can also follow up with the student who contributed the original thought to ensure that the idea was heard as intended. This not only validates the idea, but also gives the class another version of the idea. This talk move slows down the instruction in order to give students enough time to process what they are learning and helps students stay engaged and involved in the lesson. Many teachers have found that the use of this talk move especially benefits English language learners.

## Agree/disagree and why

*Agree/disagree and why* is the most important talk move, as it asks students to reason about another's contribution. It is used after the teacher makes sure that students heard and had time to process the mathematical idea. By posing questions like, "Do you agree or disagree with that idea? Why?" teachers can draw out student thinking by having them apply their understanding to someone else's thoughts. It is important that teachers do not offer their positions, but instead allow students to wrestle with their own ideas. Teachers can help students focus on the correct concepts after they have had the chance to develop their own reasoning.

## Adding on

Teachers encourage students to participate further in a class discussion by using *adding on*. Posing a question like "Would someone like to add on to what was just said?" solicits more input to the discussion. Surprisingly, students are not bored when more than one student contributes the same information. In fact, for many students hearing the same information a number of times helps them fully process the new content. Students also learn new approaches and problem-solving strategies when teachers elicit additional contributions. When students have to make sense of different solution methods, they must consider how these methods are similar or different from their own.

## Wait time

*Wait time* involves waiting at least ten seconds before calling on a student for an answer once a question has been posed. This move gives students an opportunity to think about and organize their ideas. It also serves to encourage all students to contribute, not just those who process their thoughts quickly. Wait time should also be used once a student has been called upon to share an idea or respond to a question. A comment like, "We'll wait...take your time," usually serves this purpose. It is important for all students to become active in class discussions to reap the learning benefits.

### Partner talk

*Partner talk* enables students to put their thoughts into words by discussing their ideas with a partner. It provides an opportunity for hesitant or unsure learners to clarify and practice their contribution with just one person before sharing with the whole class. Partner talk is also helpful when students do not fully understand an idea. Students can raise their questions to their partners and together decide on the best way to pose them to the rest of the class. Teachers have found that this is an effective move when few students volunteer to answer a question; asking students to discuss the question with their partner increases the likelihood of their contributions in the future!

In addition to promoting a deeper understanding of important and significant mathematical ideas, these classroom discussion strategies encourage more active student listening, enhance the quality of verbal discourse, build students' vocabulary, help students view problems from different perspectives, and foster student appreciation for a variety of thinking and problem-solving styles.

## Questioning Techniques

A variety of questions designed to stimulate rich class discussions in the *Math Innovations* program are listed in the Student Edition as well as in the teacher notes found in the Teacher's Edition. These questions encourage students to delve deeply into important mathematical ideas. Students are often called upon to make and explore mathematical conjectures, analyze patterns and formulate generalizations, develop and evaluate mathematical arguments, select and apply a variety of representations, use and make connections among mathematical ideas, and reflect on their thinking and problem-solving strategies. Teachers should be aware of the type of questions they ask, and avoid *funneling* questions, which may elicit their own predetermined, restrictive answer. A better questioning strategy is the use of *focusing* questions. These allow students to explain their thinking and to develop creative solutions and understanding for internalization of concepts (Herbel-Eisenmann & Breyfogle, 2005).

- Examples of ***funneling*** questions (less effective for supporting deeper student thinking):

  "How many sides does that shape have?"

  "Which angle is larger?"

  "What is the product?"

- Examples of ***focusing*** questions (more effective to guide student thinking):

  "What have you figured out?"

  "Why do you think that?"

  "Does that always work?"

  "Is there another way?"

  "How are these two methods different? How are they similar?"

## Five Ws and an H Mathematical Questions

While the focusing questions encourage students to become investigative mathematicians as they explore problems and new mathematics concepts, students may also find the following question types helpful in nudging their thinking forward and deepening their mathematical understanding. Just as students answer questions of "who, what, when, where, why and how" in writing articles for the school newspaper, they can answer these same questions as they investigate and extend mathematical problems (Sheffield, 2006). As students begin to think like mathematicians, they will realize that the most interesting mathematical concepts often begin after they answer the initial question.

- **Who?**
  *Who has another method? Who has another solution? Who is right?*

- **What or what if?**
  *What sense can I make of this problem? What is the answer? What are the essential elements of this problem? What is the important mathematical concept? What patterns do I see in this data? What generalizations might I make from these patterns? What if I change part of the problem? What if I use a different representation?*

- **When?**
  *When does this work? When does this not work?*

- **Where?**
  *Where did that come from? Where should I start? Where might I go next? Where might I find additional information?*

- **Why or why not?**
  *Why does that work? If it does not work, why not?*

- **How?**
  *How is this like other mathematical problems or patterns that I have seen? How does it differ? How does this relate to "real-life" situations or models? How many solutions are possible? How do I know that I have found all the possible solutions? In how many ways can I represent, simulate, model, or visualize these ideas? In how many ways can I sort, organize, and present this information?*

##  Differentiation

### Think Differently

*Math Innovations* recognizes the importance and challenge of differentiated instruction in today's diverse middle school classroom. As a result, this program not only includes differentiated teaching strategies and tips, but also provides some ready-made tools that will meet the needs of students at different levels of learning. Where appropriate, these differentiated strategies and tools can be found in the teacher notes labeled *Differentiation: Think Differently*. Two unique features, *Accommodation Guides* and *Think Beyond Questions*, are specific to the content of the lesson and provide teachers with alternative strategies and differentiation materials that will make mathematics meaningful for all students.

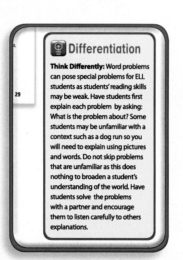

**Differentiation**

**Think Differently:** Word problems can pose special problems for ELL students as students' reading skills may be weak. Have students first explain each problem by asking: What is the problem about? Some students may be unfamiliar with a context such as a dog run so you will need to explain using pictures and words. Do not skip problems that are unfamiliar as this does nothing to broaden a student's understanding of the world. Have students solve the problems with a partner and encourage them to listen carefully to others' explanations.

*Accommodation Guides,* found at the end of a lesson in the Teacher Guide, are designed to provide additional support for those students experiencing difficulty with a lesson activity. These accommodation guides often consist of ready-made tables and other graphic organizers that help student structure and organize their work. Some guides may offer different problem-solving approaches or strategies. Accommodation Guides are those Lesson Guides which contain an A after the number.

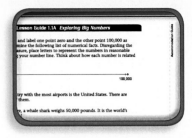

Think Beyond Questions, found in the On Your Own sections of the Student Edition, are extension questions for students that have a firm grasp of the concepts presented in the lesson and are ready for further challenge. Think Beyond Questions expand students' knowledge by asking questions that require more complex reasoning, or by asking students to conduct research or create materials.

## Meeting the Needs of English Language Learners (ELL)

Today there are millions of students in mathematics classrooms who are English language learners (ELL). Research indicates that one of the most effective ways to help ELLs learn mathematics is to provide them with a discussion-rich classroom. Kersaint and colleagues (2009) state "It is through language that ELLs come to understand not only mathematics but English as well. Such classrooms are environments in which teachers and students have built a climate of trust and respect in which everyone's contributions are valued" (p. xii).

Math Innovations' emphasis on discussion and vocabulary will help your ELL students learn. To get started, you and your students need to discuss the rules for how you will talk together respectfully. If students think they might be teased or laughed at, they will be unwilling to participate. Go over body language, actions and words that are not allowed such as rolling one's eyes or tapping one's foot impatiently. Remind everyone how difficult it is to learn mathematics in a different language and how important it is to give individuals time to compose an answer. In addition, work to include all students, especially English language learners, in the mathematical conversations. When you pose a question, first have students turn and talk to a partner so they can vocalize their ideas in a safe way. Then open up the conversation to the whole class. Many English language learners have attended elementary school in another country and can enrich discussions by sharing a variety of mathematics algorithms and strategies that they learned in their home countries.

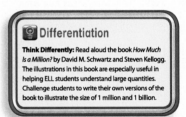

**Differentiation**

**Think Differently:** Read aloud the book *How Much Is a Million?* by David M. Schwartz and Steven Kellogg. The illustrations in this book are especially useful in helping ELL students understand large quantities. Challenge students to write their own versions of the book to illustrate the size of 1 million and 1 billion.

There are many strategies you can use to enhance the learning experience for ELLs. When possible, use visuals, physical models, manipulative materials, drawings, charts, tables and graphs to support the communication in the classroom. Write important words on the board and/or create a word wall, and link these terms with drawings and materials. Take a minute to explain idiomatic expressions or culturally based terms (e.g., blue ribbon job) and to identify important features of the text. Also help connect the mathematics of the lesson to real life, even if it means taking the time to explain a particular context. Provide opportunities for students to work with others to solve problems and use talk moves, especially revoice and repeat/rephrase discussed in this section, to enable students to hear something explained more than one time. ELLs benefit from being able to practice articulating their understanding in mathematics. A related strategy involves having students explain to their partners their solution methods prior to having to present them in front of the whole class. Dramatic gestures, speaking and enunciating clearly, and providing support around note taking will also help ELLs.

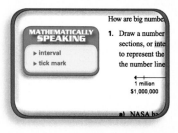

Vocabulary is especially important in mathematics and receives significant attention in *Math Innovations*. Make vocabulary learning part of every lesson by regularly discussing words, their meanings, and how we use them in a sentence. *Math Innovations* provides students with easy access to new vocabulary by highlighting new terms when they are introduced in the student text and by listing new vocabulary terms at the end of each section and lesson. Every time you discuss a Wrap It Up question, help students to use the correct terms, referring to these terms in the Mathematically Speaking section. A word wall containing these terms prominently placed in the classroom will benefit all students in speaking and writing like mathematicians using correct and precise vocabulary.

Be sure to explain the difference between the social meaning and the mathematical meaning of many words (e.g., some and sum) and ask students to draw comparisons among terms such as perimeter, area and volume. Many mathematical terms are similar in other languages and students may benefit from translating terms to their native language, especially if it is a concept that is well-understood and only the English word that is new. We have found that if students keep a personal dictionary (word, definition, picture, application or examples and non-examples), they refer to their dictionaries when confused. It also may be useful for students to have a dictionary with translations from English to their native language, especially if one is available with mathematical terms. Remember also that it is through the sustained use of these strategies that achievement gains are realized. These and additional strategies are elaborated upon in the Think Differently sections of the Teacher Edition.

## Student Snapshot—Lesson Observation Tool

The Student Snapshot observational tool is another unique feature of *Math Innovations*. It is designed to be used during lesson activities in which students work in groups to explore key mathematical ideas and solve problems. One of the teacher's roles as a facilitator is to move from group to group and listen in on student conversations. This provides an opportunity to determine which students to call on for contributions during class discussions. It also enables the teacher to observe and informally assess students' depth of knowledge and understanding of major mathematical concepts; their mathematical communication skills, including the appropriate use of key mathematical terms; the forms of representation students are using; and student problem-solving and reasoning skills. As teachers observe and listen to group conversations, short anecdotal notes can be recorded to provide a snapshot of student learning. These snapshots will be helpful in assessing students' mathematical understanding and will provide insight that will be useful in guiding future instruction.

Unit _____

# Student Snapshot

| Name | Major Concepts/ Connections | Communication | Problem Solving |
|------|------------------------------|----------------|------------------|
|      |                              |                |                  |
|      |                              |                |                  |
|      |                              |                |                  |
|      |                              |                |                  |

It is recommended that teachers focus on a few students per lesson (not necessarily from the same group) when using the Student Snapshot observational tool. Having a clipboard and a pad of sticky-notes handy is helpful when attempting to record anecdotal observations as the teacher moves from group to group. It is important to date the notes and to file them at the end of the class period or school day using the Student Snapshot sheet provided on page T11 or a teacher's grade book.

##  Wrap It Up

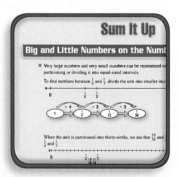

Each lesson contains Wrap It Up discussion questions, which provide an opportunity for the entire class to reflect on the major mathematical concepts presented in the lesson. A Wrap It Up discussion may include students sharing their discoveries from the lesson or may focus on the summary questions. During the Wrap It Up section, teachers should encourage students to use talk moves (explained above) as they share their thinking with other students. The *Think Like a Mathematician Daily Record Sheet* provides space for students to record important ideas offered during the Wrap It Up class discussions. In the beginning of the year, teachers may need to model how to record Wrap It Up comments and responses, but with daily practice students will become more independent note takers. It is important that students record their own insights and problem-solving strategies as well as those offered by their classmates or the teacher. Following each Wrap It Up discussion, students will have an opportunity to write about their mathematical understanding individually as they respond to a similar reflective question located at the beginning of each *On Your Own* section. This question is labeled *Write About It*, and provides accountability to each student for their learning, as well as a method for teachers to assess students' understanding of the major concepts of the lesson.

## Sum It Up/Study Guide

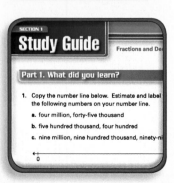

The *Sum It Up* feature provides students with a resource for reviewing and summarizing their learning at the end of each section. This feature consists of an outline of the major mathematics concepts that students have learned within a given section and includes examples of procedures and skills. *Study Guides* located in the student book provide students with questions and exercises to review the concepts and skills presented in the section. This is another example of how *Math Innovations* helps students develop study skills and encourages them to take ownership of their learning as well as to prepare for the quizzes on each section. There also is a unit Study Guide to help students prepare for the unit test. Students might use the Sum It Up section along with the Study Guide when they have missed a mathematics class or when they want to share what they are learning with their family members or guardians.

# Mathematically Speaking

Mathematically Speaking emphasizes vocabulary words that are important mathematical concept anchors that students should use to develop their mathematical proficiency and communication skills. Students are encouraged to think about and use the new vocabulary words that are introduced and highlighted in each lesson. As students work on their homework, they can then refer to the vocabulary words that are organized for emphasis in the Mathematically Speaking box at the end of each lesson. Teachers should guide students to develop an understanding of the Mathematically Speaking terms before referring students to the glossary at the end of each unit. They should also make sure that students use their new vocabulary terms with precision as they explore the important mathematical ideas and relationships in each unit.

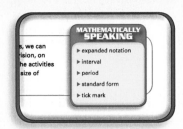

## Word Wall

Teachers can post the Mathematically Speaking vocabulary words on a word wall so that students will have access to the words they learn throughout the unit. Words can be written in large print on sentence strips and affixed with magnet tape for posting on a magnetic surface. Magnetic posting allows for flexibility in word grouping and removal, as needed for individual or group use.

## Vocabulary Activities

Motivational activities can be incorporated into lessons to make students more comfortable with the vocabulary words in Mathematically Speaking.

- **Vocabulary Scramble:** Write each word and its definition on separate cards. Shuffle the cards and give one to each student. Students then walk around the room, looking at other students' cards, trying to find their match.

- **Word/Definition Game:** "I have _____. Who has _____?" Give each student a card that has a word and a definition to a different word. Each student listens for the definition that matches his or her word, and then reads the next definition as a prompt for another student. For example, Student One: "I have <u>parallel</u>. Who has <u>the word that means a five-sided figure?</u>" Student Two: "I have <u>pentagon</u>. Who has the <u>word that means all sides have the same length?</u>"

  The rest of the class continues to read the cards, each containing a vocabulary word answer and a definition prompt for a different vocabulary word held by another student.

- Have students illustrate the Mathematically Speaking words using drawings, graphs and symbols and place these next to the vocabulary word on the word wall.

- Use free online services or software to create paper and pencil games such as crossword puzzles, word finds and word scrambles. Helpful websites include *puzzlemaker.school.discovery.com* and *www.crosswordpuzzlegames.com/create.html*.

- **Twenty Questions:** Let one student think of a Mathematically Speaking vocabulary word and answer yes and no questions from the class as they try to guess the word.

- **Pictionary:** Divide the class into two teams. Teams take turns sending students to the board. These students view vocabulary word and attempt to draw images that prompt their teams' correct guesses.

## On Your Own

Each lesson concludes with an On Your Own section that includes independent work that reinforces, reviews and extends that day's learning experience. The On Your Own questions were written to be completed as homework, but a teacher may want students to start on these exercises at the end of class. If class time is limited, teachers may prefer to ask students which questions they had trouble with, or to focus on the most engaging On Your Own problems, as suggested in the Teacher Edition.

###  Write About It

The first question of the On Your Own section has a prompt for reflective writing. This allows students to organize and consolidate the exploration and discussion of the day's lesson. Students can use the notes they recorded during the Wrap It Up section of the lesson as they reflect and respond to the Write About It journal prompts. The Write About It prompts focus on the important mathematical ideas that students should have gleaned from the lesson.

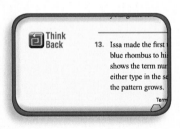

###  Think Back

The On Your Own section includes practice problems that use concepts and skills from previous lessons and/or prior courses. In this way, *Math Innovations* spirals to continually require students to Think Back and reinforce their prior knowledge. This feature is provided to meet the recognized need for students to become mathematically literate and fluent in problem solving and computation. Think Back questions are often presented in formats similar to those found on many standardized tests, including state assessments.

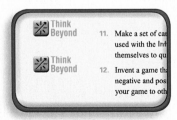

###  Think Beyond

The On Your Own section gives students challenging opportunities to Think Beyond the material covered in the day's lesson. Teachers are encouraged to differentiate the homework assignment by giving these problems to the students who require more challenge.

# Reflect

In recognition of the importance of teacher reflection for enhancing instruction and improving student achievement, *Math Innovations* has incorporated a series of reflective questions designed to support teachers in assessing their instruction and their students' learning for each lesson. The *Reflect* questions are located in the Teacher's Edition following the Wrap It Up discussion notes. These questions not only guide teachers in assessing students' understanding of key concepts in the lesson, but can help them in planning and guiding instruction for future lessons as well. Developing metacognitive habits is an essential component of Math Innovations for teachers and students alike.

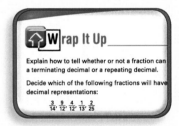

**Reflect**
Use these questions to help you reflect on the lesson and plan for future instruction.
- Are students able to use factors of the denominator to partition a number line to find the location of a fraction?
- How well do students understand that there are infinitely many fractions (or decimal numbers) between any two points on a number line?

# Assessments

The word *assessment* is derived from the Latin phrase "to sit beside". The assessment components in the *Math Innovations* program invite the teacher "to sit beside" each student as a guide along his or her mathematics journey. The assessment data gives teachers information about how each student is progressing. The teacher can use this data to adjust the course of study so that each student continues to progress towards achieving the mathematical goals of the unit.

The following assessment components are included in each Math Innovations unit:

### Questions

Each lesson in *Math Innovations* ends with Wrap It Up questions that measure students' understanding of the mathematical objectives of that lesson. Discussing these questions prepares students to respond to the On Your Own questions, and helps the teacher plan for future instruction. Study Guide questions help students to connect and reflect on the mathematics they have learned within and across sections.

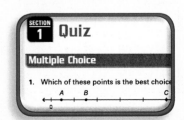

### Study Guide

The Study Guide in each unit in the Student Edition bridges the unit activities and discussions with the unit quizzes and test. The questions in the Study Guide will enable students to target the skills, concepts, and vocabulary terms that they need to review prior to more formal assessments.

### Quizzes

Section quizzes measure a student's ability to transfer what they have learned from the problems posed in the section to extensions or modifications of these problems. Each quiz includes a question similar to the Write About It questions at the end of each lesson. Other quiz question formats include short answer, multiple-choice, true/false, and open response. Quizzes are located in the Assessment Resources.

## Tests

Located in the Assessment Resources, each unit test includes multiple-choice, short-answer, Write About It and open-response items. Test items vary in difficulty as well as in required depth of knowledge. For example, test items will include those that measure students' recall and reproduction, comprehension of skills and concepts and strategic and complex mathematical reasoning.

## Student Self-Assessment

At the end of each Math Innovations unit, students will reflect on their performance prior to, as well as after, the unit test. Students will measure their reasoning, problem solving, and communication skills, identify areas in which they are in need of improvement, and write about *how* they will improve those areas in future study. The Student Self-Assessments are in the Assessment Resources.

## Projects

The projects in *Math Innovations* allow students to develop mathematical understanding through independent exploration. Students will think creatively, make decisions, and write about the mathematical concepts explored during a particular unit. A rubric specific to each project is provided to assess students' work. Projects and rubrics are located in the Assessment Resources.

## Student Snapshot

As students work through a *Math Innovations* unit, the teacher is encouraged to observe students' depth of comprehension, communication, and representations, as well as their problem-solving and reasoning skills. The teacher can write observations on 1.5" × 2" sticky notes to place on Student Snapshot sheets in a 3-ring binder as an authentic assessment of each student's long-term progress. The Student Snapshot sheet is on page T11 in the Teacher Guide.

# References

Chapin, S.H., C. O'Connor, and N.C. Anderson. 2009. *Classroom discussions: Using math talk to help students learn, grades 1–6*. Sausalito, CA: Math Solutions Publications.

Herbel-Eisenmann, B.A. and L.M. Breyfogle. 2005. "Questioning our patterns of questioning." *Mathematics Teaching in the Middle School*, NCTM, Vol. 10, No. 9.

Kersaint, G., D. Thompson, and M. Petkova. 2009. *Teaching Mathematics to English Language Learners*. New York: Routledge Publishers.

Sheffield, L.J. 2006. "Developing mathematical promise and creativity," *Journal of the Korea Society of Mathematical Education, Series D, Research in Mathematics Education*, Vol. 10, No. 1: 1–11.

# Solve It:
## Focusing on Equations, Inequalities and Exponents

## Goals of the Unit

In *Solve It: Focusing on Equations, Inequalities and Exponents*, students will

▶ Solve complex equations by using the order of operations and by combining like terms.

▶ Solve and graph inequalities on a number line.

▶ Use scientific notation to describe very large and very small numbers.

▶ Use rules of exponents to evaluate expressions.

▶ Recognize and graph quadratic and exponential functions.

## Unit Overview

In *Solve It: Focusing on Equations, Inequalities and Exponents,* students continue their study of linear relationships as they use arithmetic properties and algebraic techniques to find solutions to linear equations. They then extend their analysis to include nonlinear relationships. Students model situations using linear equations and inequalities. As indicated in the NCTM Curriculum Focal Points for mathematics in grade 8, students at this level use linear equations to "represent, analyze, and solve a variety of problems." Our emphasis is on understanding the concepts of equality and inequality, solution sets and graphically representing solutions. Students then investigate very large and very small numbers using scientific notation. Finally, students explore functions that do not look or act like the linear ones they previously studied. Exponential and quadratic functions provide students with an introduction to nonlinear functions. In addition to the primary emphasis on the Algebra Focal Point of linear relations, several ideas from the Grade 8 Connections to the Focal Points apply to the latter sections of this unit:

**Number and Operation:** Students use exponents and scientific notation to describe very large and very small numbers.

**Algebra:** Students encounter some nonlinear functions (. . . quadratic and exponential. . . ) whose rates of change contrast with the constant rate of change of linear functions. (www.nctm.org)

The continued study of algebra at this level serves three purposes. First, students solidify their understanding of the basic principles and properties of arithmetic and algebra. The following content expectations from the NCTM *Principles & Standards* link to the Grade 8 Focal Points:

- Use the associative and commutative properties of addition and multiplication and the distributive property of multiplication over addition to simplify computations with integers, fractions, and decimals.
- Understand and use the inverse relationships of addition and subtraction, multiplication and division, and squaring and finding square roots to simplify computations and solve problems.
- Use symbolic algebra to represent situations and to solve problems, especially those that involve linear relationships.
- Recognize and generate equivalent forms for simple algebraic expressions and solve linear equations.

The second purpose of this unit is for students to examine very large and very small numbers. The following content expectation from the NCTM *Principles & Standards* links to the Grade 8 Focal Points:

- Develop an understanding of large numbers and recognize and appropriately use exponential, scientific, and calculator notation.

Finally, students extend their understanding of algebra from linear functions to nonlinear functions. Students examine exponential and quadratic functions and apply basic solution techniques of using square roots to solve quadratic equations. The following content expectation from the NCTM *Principles & Standards* links to the Grade 8 Focal Points:

- Identify functions as linear or nonlinear and contrast their properties from tables, graphs, or equations.

## Section Summaries

 **Algebraic Expressions and Equations**

Students use Mathmagic number tricks to explore arithmetic operations and their inverses. Students make up sequences of operations to apply to any input number that will result in a predictable output value. Through developing and analyzing these "tricks," students review many of the basic arithmetic properties. They are introduced to factoring as the inverse of the distributive property. Students review order of operations and examine several solution procedures as they model and solve linear equations.

 **Inequalities**

Students explore inequalities. Using many of the same properties and principles that they applied to equations, students analyze inequalities. Students find solution sets for inequalities, which contrasts with the single value they found when solving equations. Students graph these solution sets on a number line.

 **Exponents and Scientific Notation**

Students write large and small numbers using scientific notation by investigating distances in space (light-years and astronomical units) and lengths used in nanotechnology (microns). In solving problems that involve exponential notation, students discover the rules for multiplying and dividing expressions with exponents, as well as the rules for raising a power to a power.

**Functions with Exponents and the Curves They Make**

Students investigate the behavior of two different types of nonlinear relationships. First, the quadratic function provides an example of a variable raised to a power. Students graph functions of the form $y = ax^2$ as parabolas. They solve simple quadratic equations by finding square roots. Exponential functions of the form $y = b^x$ then lead to a discussion of growth and decay models. Students compare both types of nonlinear functions with linear functions.

# Unit Mathematics

## Arithmetic Property Review

There are six operations in arithmetic that we can apply to numbers: addition, subtraction, multiplication, division, raising to a power and taking a root. In applying some of these operations, certain behaviors are always present. These are called properties. Understanding the properties of arithmetic is critical to solving problems algebraically. This unit includes use of the following properties to rewrite expressions and solve problems:

- *Associative Property.* In an associative operation, numbers can be grouped in any way without changing the resulting answer. The operations of addition and multiplication are associative. We formally write:
  - Associative Property of Addition:
    For all real numbers $a$, $b$ and $c$, $a + (b + c) = (a + b) + c$.
    Example: $2 + (3 + 4) = (2 + 3) + 4$

  - Associative Property of Multiplication:
    For all real numbers $a$, $b$ and $c$, $a \cdot (b \cdot c) = (a \cdot b) \cdot c$.
    Example: $2 \cdot (3 \cdot 4) = (2 \cdot 3) \cdot 4$

- *Commutative Property.* In a commutative operation, the order of numbers can be rearranged in any way without changing the resulting answer. The operations of addition and multiplication are commutative. We formally write:
  - Commutative Property of Addition:
    For all real numbers $a$ and $b$, $a + b = b + a$.
    Example: $2 + 3 = 3 + 2$

  - Commutative Property of Multiplication:
    For all real numbers $a$ and $b$, $a \cdot b = b \cdot a$.
    Example: $2 \cdot 3 = 3 \cdot 2$

- *Distributive Property.* The distributive property involves two operations: one operation is distributed over another. There are two combinations of operations where the distributive property applies.
  - Distributive Property of Multiplication over Addition:
    For all real numbers $a$, $b$ and $c$, $a \cdot (b + c) = (ab + ac)$.
    Example: $2 \cdot (3 + 4) = 2 \cdot 3 + 2 \cdot 4$

  - Distributive Property of Multiplication over Subtraction:
    For all real numbers $a$, $b$ and $c$, $a \cdot (b - c) = (ab - ac)$.
    Example: $3 \cdot (4 - 2) = 3 \cdot 4 - 3 \cdot 2$

- *Identity Properties.* Identity operations result in no change to the original value of a quantity. Multiplying a number by 1 or adding 0 to a number simply results in the original number.
  - Identity Property of Addition:

    For any real number $a$, $a + 0 = a$ and $0 + a = a$.
    Example: $4 + 0 = 0 + 4 = 4$
    0 is called the additive identity.

  - Identity Property of Multiplication:

    For any real number $a$, $a \cdot 1 = a$ and $1 \cdot a = a$.
    Example: $5 \cdot 1 = 1 \cdot 5 = 5$
    1 is called the multiplicative identity.

- *Inverses.* The inverse of an operation undoes the operation. To solve simple linear equations in this unit we use the inverses of the addition and multiplication operations: subtraction and division. In essence, we use additive and multiplicative inverses.
  - Additive Inverse:

    For any real number $a$, $a + {}^{-}a = 0$ and ${}^{-}a + a = 0$.
    Example: $3 + {}^{-}3 = {}^{-}3 + 3 = 0$
    ${}^{-}a$ is the additive inverse of $a$, and the sum $(a + {}^{-}a)$ is the additive identity 0.

  - Multiplicative Inverse:

    For any real number $a \neq 0$, $a \cdot \frac{1}{a} = 1$ and $\frac{1}{a} \cdot a = 1$.
    Example: $2 \cdot \frac{1}{2} = \frac{1}{2} \cdot 2 = 1$
    $\frac{1}{a}$ is the multiplicative inverse of $a$ and the product $(a \cdot \frac{1}{a})$ is the multiplicative identity 1.

- *Equality Properties.* The equal sign in an equation indicates that the expressions on each side of the equal sign are equivalent. The equality properties indicate that we can perform the same operation on each side of the equal sign and the equation will remain true.
  - Addition Property of Equality:

    For all real numbers $a$, $b$ and $c$, if $a = b$ then $a + c = b + c$.
    Examples: $3 = 3$, so $3 + 2 = 3 + 2$. If $y = 2x$, then $y + 3 = 2x + 3$.

  - Multiplication Property of Equality:

    For all real numbers $a$, $b$ and $c$, if $a = b$ then $a \cdot c = b \cdot c$.
    Examples: $5 = 5$, so $5 \cdot 4 = 5 \cdot 4$. If $t = 3r$, then $t \cdot 2 = 3r \cdot 2$.

## Evaluating and Simplifying Expressions

In order to solve equations and inequalities, we often want to rewrite (by expanding and/or simplifying) one or both expressions. We may also want to evaluate an expression for a particular value of the variable. The following concepts are integral in these processes.

- ***Order of Operations.*** When rewriting or evaluating an expression, following the order of operations is imperative. Recall the mnemonic: **P**lease **E**xcuse **M**y **D**ear **A**unt **S**ally. The order to follow in rewriting expressions is:

  **P**—parentheses—Perform all operations inside the parentheses first.

  **E**—exponents—Raise numbers or expressions to the power indicated.

  $$x^2 = x \cdot x \text{ and } x^{-3} = \frac{1}{x^3} \text{ and } x^{\frac{1}{2}} = \sqrt{x} \text{ and } x^{\frac{2}{3}} = \sqrt[3]{x^2}.$$

  **M & D**—Multiply and divide from left to right.

  **A & S**—Add and subtract from left to right.

- ***Grouping Symbols.*** The mnemonic for the order of operations indicates that the **P** is for parentheses. In reality, the parentheses represent any grouping symbol. Grouping symbols separate one part of the expression from another part. The operations inside any grouping symbol are performed first when evaluating or simplifying an expression. Examples of grouping symbols include parentheses ( ), brackets [ ] and the division bar in an expression represented as a fraction of expressions (a rational expression).

## Example

Evaluate the expression for $x = 5$: $\dfrac{5x + 3[2 + 3(x-3)^2]}{2 - x}$

| | | |
|---|---|---|
| **1.** | $\dfrac{5(5) + 3[2 + 3(5-3)^2]}{2-5}$ | Substitute 5 for all $x$ in expression. |
| **2.** | $\dfrac{5(5) + 3[2 + 3(2)^2]}{2-5}$ | parentheses (inside bracket) |
| **3.** | $\dfrac{5(5) + 3[2 + 3(4)]}{2-5}$ | exponent |
| **4.** | $\dfrac{5(5) + 3[2 + 12]}{2-5}$ | multiplication |
| **5.** | $\dfrac{5(5) + 3[14]}{2-5}$ | addition (inside of bracket finished, go to top of division bar) |
| **6.** | $\dfrac{25 + 42}{2-5}$ | multiplication (start from left and go to right) |
| **7.** | $\dfrac{67}{2-5}$ | addition (top of division bar finished, go to bottom of bar) |
| **8.** | $\dfrac{67}{-3}$ | subtraction (bottom of division bar finished) |
| **9.** | $\dfrac{67}{-3} = -22\frac{2}{3}$ | division; evaluation at $x = 5$ complete |

- *Like Terms.* Like terms are terms that contain the same variable(s) raised to the same respective powers. All terms comprised of only constants in an expression are considered like terms. Collecting like terms assists us in simplifying and/or solving expressions, equations and inequalities.

## Example

Simplify $3x^2y + 10 + 2y^2 - 4x^2y + 5 - 7x^2$.

Use the commutative and associative properties to group like terms:
$(3x^2y - 4x^2y) + (5 + 10) - 7x^2 + 2y^2$.

Combine like terms: $-x^2y + 15 - 7x^2 + 2y^2$.

## Solving Linear Equations

There are several methods for solving linear equations. Many times we can solve simple one-variable linear equations by examination or inspection, and other times it may take a step or two. As equations become more complicated, we use additional techniques. The following are two techniques useful in solving more complicated equations.

- *Bar Diagram.* Similar to the cover-up method, the bar diagram method is used when grouping symbols are present in the equation. Instead of covering up, however, parts of the equation are expanded to visually examine the problem using equivalent bars.

---

### Example

Solve the equation $4 + 2(3x + 1) = 30$.

| 30 | | | | |
|---|---|---|---|---|
| $3x + 1$ | | $3x + 1$ | | 4 |
| 26 | | | | 4 |
| 13 | | 13 | | 4 |
| $3x$ | 1 | $3x$ | 1 | 4 |
| 12 | 1 | 12 | 1 | 4 |

So, $3x = 12$ and $x = 4$.

---

- *Equality and Properties.* Both the cover-up and bar diagram methods use equality and arithmetic properties. We can also solve problems by directly applying these principles to manipulate the equation to find a solution. The goal of these manipulations is to isolate the variable on one side of the equation, thereby revealing its value on the other side of the equation. The most important procedural rule is this: when using the properties of equality, whatever operation you perform on one side of the equation must be performed on the other side of the equation.

## Example

Solve the equation $4 + 2(3x + 1) = 30$.

| | |
|---|---|
| $-4 + 4 + 2(3x + 1) = -4 + 30$ | addition property of equality |
| $0 + 2(3x + 1) = 26$ | additive inverse property |
| $2(3x + 1) = 26$ | additive identity property |
| $\left(\frac{1}{2}\right) \cdot 2(3x + 1) = \left(\frac{1}{2}\right) \cdot 26$ | multiplication property of equality |
| $1 \cdot (3x + 1) = 13$ | multiplicative inverse property |
| $3x + 1 = 13$ | multiplicative identity property |
| $3x + 1 + -1 = 13 + -1$ | addition property of equality |
| $3x + 0 = 12$ | additive inverse property |
| $3x = 12$ | additive identity property |
| $\left(\frac{1}{3}\right) \cdot 3x = \left(\frac{1}{3}\right) \cdot 12$ | multiplication property of equality |
| $1 \cdot x = 4$ | multiplicative inverse property |
| $x = 4$ | multiplicative identity property |

In some cases, the variable appears on both sides of the equation. The same principles apply, but the procedure initially includes gathering like terms. Collect all terms with a variable on one side of the equation and all terms without a variable on the other side. This is called isolating the variable.

## Example

Solve the equation $3x - 4 = 2x + 5$.

$$3x - 4 + (-2x) = 2x + (-2x) + 5$$
$$x - 4 = 5$$
$$x - 4 + (4) = 5 + (4)$$
$$x = 9$$

## Inequalities

Inequalities are mathematical statements that compare two expressions and indicate how they are related by using the following inequality symbols.

$>$     greater than
$\geq$     greater than or equal to
$<$     less than
$\leq$     less than or equal to
$\neq$     not equal to

### Example

| | |
|---|---|
| $a > b$ | the value of $a$ is greater than the value of $b$. |
| $c \geq d$ | the value of $c$ is greater than or equal to the value of $d$. |
| $x < 5$ | the value of $x$ is less than 5. |
| $y \leq 10$ | the value of $y$ is less than or equal to 10. |
| $x \neq 0$ | the value of $x$ is not equal to 0. |

- *Solution Set.* The solution to an inequality is the set of values that make the inequality true. In most equations students have solved so far, there was only one value for the variable that made the equation true. Inequalities are different in that the solution is often a set of values. We call these values the solution set. In the inequality $x < 5$, the solution set consists of all values of $x$ less than 5. We can find solution sets for more complex inequalities using rules similar to those we applied to equations. Again, whatever operation you perform to one side of the inequality, you must also perform it on the other side of the inequality.

  **addition property of inequality** The property that states that adding the same number to both sides of an inequality does not change the inequality. For all real numbers $a$, $b$ and $c$, if $a > b$ then $a + c > b + c$.

  **multiplication property of inequality for multiplication by a positive number** The property that states that multiplying both sides of an inequality by the same positive number does not change the inequality. For all real numbers $a$, $b$ and $c$, if $a > b$ and $c > 0$ then $a \cdot c > b \cdot c$.

  **multiplication property of inequality for multiplication by a negative number** The property that states that multiplying both sides of an inequality by the same negative number reverses the inequality. For all real numbers $a$, $b$ and $c$, if $a > b$ and $c < 0$ then $a \cdot c < b \cdot c$.

As stated above, the one difference in applying properties to an inequality is that if we multiply or divide both sides of an inequality by a negative number, the direction of the inequality sign must be reversed ($>$ and $\geq$ become $<$ and $\leq$; $<$ and $\leq$ become $>$ and $\geq$). The reason this occurs is that the two sides of an inequality are not equivalent. The two sides are related in a specific way; one greater or less than the other as indicated by the direction of the inequality symbol. While the two equations $a = b$ and $-a = -b$ represent the same relationship between $a$ and $b$, the two inequalities $a < b$ and $-a < -b$ do not represent the same relationship. Multiplying or dividing by a negative number reverses the relationship between the two expressions in an inequality (if $a < b$, then $-a > -b$). This is best illustrated by looking at a number line.

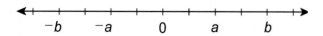

We can check solution sets of inequalities by substituting values from both inside and outside of the solution set to see if the inequality is true or false.

---
**Example**

$$4 + x \geq 10$$
$$(-4) + 4 + x \geq 10 + (-4)$$
$$x \geq 6$$

**Check:**

$x = 6$ must be in the solution set of $x \geq 6$.

$4 + 6 \geq 10$   $10 \geq 10?$                Yes, $x = 6$ is in solution set

$x = 10$ should be a solution since $10 \geq 6$.

$4 + 10 \geq 10$   $14 \geq 10?$               Yes, $x = 10$ in solution set.

$x = 0$ should not be a solution since $0 < 6$.

$4 + 0 \geq 10$   $4 \geq 10?$                 No, $x = 0$ not in solution set.

---

---
**Example**

$$3 - 2x < 9$$
$$(-3) + 3 - 2x < 9 + (-3)$$
$$-2x < 6$$
$$-\left(\tfrac{1}{2}\right) \cdot (-2x) > -\left(\tfrac{1}{2}\right) \cdot 6$$
$$x > -3$$

**Check:**

$x = -3$ cannot be in the solution set $x > -3$ (strict inequality).

$3 - 2(-3) < 9$   $9 < 9?$                     No.

$x = 0$ should be a solution since $0 > -3$.

$3 - 2(0) < 9$   $3 < 9?$                      Yes, $x = 0$ in solution set.

$x = -5$ should not be a solution since $-5 < -3$.

$3 - 2(-5) < 9$   $13 < 9?$                    No, $x = -5$ not in solution set.

---

- *Graphing Solutions.* Once we know the values in the solution set of a one-variable inequality, we can graph them on a number line. We can also check our solution set by examining the graph and analyzing points both inside and outside of the solution set. The following graphs show the solution sets for the examples above.

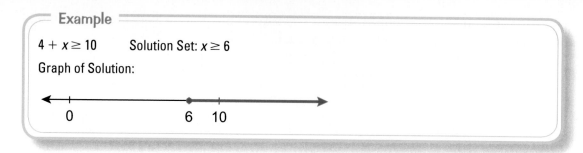

**Example**

$4 + x \geq 10$     Solution Set: $x \geq 6$

Graph of Solution:

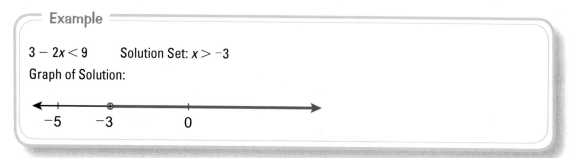

**Example**

$3 - 2x < 9$     Solution Set: $x > -3$

Graph of Solution:

## Large and Small Numbers

In the past, students looked at decimals and fractions and considered the magnitude of large and small numbers. In the world of science, it is conducive to write large and small numbers in a more efficient manner. Investigating our universe and solar system requires use of very large numbers. Developing technology and the new science of nanotechnology require the use of very small numbers. We use exponents and scientific notation to efficiently represent these numbers.

- *Exponent Basics.* We use whole number exponents to indicate repeated multiplication. The exponent indicates how many times a value is multiplied by itself. This value is called the base. Use of an exponent is also called "raising to a power."

    $3 \cdot 3$ is written as $3^2$, where 3 is the base and 2 is the exponent— we say "three squared" or "three to the 2nd power."

    $2 \cdot 2 \cdot 2$ is written as $2^3$, where 2 is the base and 3 is the exponent— we say "two cubed" or "two to the 3rd power."

**Examples**

large numbers:     $12{,}300 = 1.23 \times 10^4$
$45{,}600{,}000{,}000 = 4.56 \times 10^{10}$
$789{,}000{,}000{,}000{,}000{,}000{,}000 = 7.89 \times 10^{20}$

small numbers:     $0.0000123 = 1.23 \times 10^{-5}$
$0.00000000000456 = 4.56 \times 10^{-12}$
$0.0000000000000000000000789 = 7.89 \times 10^{-22}$

- *Properties of Exponents.* There are several properties used to simplify expressions written with exponents.

### Product of powers with like bases.
When multiplying powers with the same base, keep the base the same and add the exponents: $a^b \cdot a^c = a^{(b+c)}$. In this unit students only work with numerical bases. Examples are provided here with numerical and variable bases.

**Examples**

$$2^2 \cdot 2^4 = 2^{(2+4)} = 2^6 = 64$$
$$x^3 \cdot x^5 = x^{(3+5)} = x^8$$

### Quotient of powers with like bases.
When dividing two powers with the same base, keep the base the same and subtract the exponents: $\frac{a^b}{a^c} = a^{b-c}$. $\frac{a^b}{a^c} = aa^{b-c}$.

**Examples**

$$\frac{4^4}{4^2} = 4^{(4-2)} = 4^2 = 16$$
$$\frac{x^6}{x^2} = x^{(6-2)} = x^4$$

### Zero Exponent.
Any number or variable raised to the zero power is 1: $a^0 = 1$.

**Examples**

For $x \neq 0$, $x^0 = x^{m-m} = x^m \cdot x^{-m} = \frac{x^m}{x^m} = 1$
$$10^0 = 1$$

### Negative Exponent.
Any number or variable raised to a negative power is equivalent to the reciprocal of the number or variable raised to the absolute value of the power.

**Examples**

$$8^{-2} = \frac{1}{8^2} = \frac{1}{64}$$
$$x^{-5} = \frac{1}{x^5}$$

**Power to a Power.** When raising a power to another power, keep the base the same and multiply the exponents: $(a^b)^c = a^{b \cdot c}$. This property is not addressed in the student materials, but it is provided here for instructional purposes should the property arise.

**Examples**

$(5^2)^3 = (5)^{2 \cdot 3} = 5^6 = 15{,}625$

$(x^4)^2 = (x)^{4 \cdot 2} = x^8$

**Exponent Patterns.** Notice the following pattern as the exponent changes from a positive integer to zero and then to a negative integer. Positive integer exponents result in repeated multiplication of $x$, a zero exponent results in 1 and negative integer exponents result in repeated multiplication of $\frac{1}{x}$.

**Examples**

$$x^3 = x \cdot x \cdot x$$
$$x^2 = x \cdot x$$
$$x^1 = x$$
$$x^0 = 1$$
$$x^{-1} = \frac{1}{x^1} = \frac{1}{x}$$
$$x^{-2} = \frac{1}{x^2} = \frac{1}{x \cdot x}$$
$$x^{-3} = \frac{1}{x^3} = \frac{1}{x \cdot x \cdot x}$$

**Order of Operations.** Recall that in the order of operations, evaluating exponents follows evaluating expressions in parentheses (or grouping symbols). We must be cautious about the term that constitutes the base of an exponent especially with regard to negative numbers.

**Examples**

$-2^2 = -(2 \cdot 2) = -4$, but $(-2)^2 = -2 \cdot -2 = 4$

$2 + 3^2 = 2 + 9 = 11$, but $(2 + 3)^2 = 5^2 = 25$

- *Scientific Notation.* Scientific notation uses powers of 10 to describe very large or very small numbers. Numbers written in scientific notation have two parts: the mantissa and a power of ten. The mantissa is the number, $n$, between 1 and 10 ($1 \leq n < 10$) that is multiplied by a power of 10. Multiplying or dividing a number by a positive power of 10 moves the decimal place in the number to the right or left respectively. Using powers of 10 allows for writing large and small numbers efficiently. Using a negative power of 10 is equivalent to dividing by a power of 10.

## Nonlinear Equations with Exponents

As exponents are introduced into equations, we move from examining linear equations to nonlinear equations. The graphs of nonlinear functions are not straight lines. Nonlinear functions do not have constant rates of change. Equations and functions with exponents can either have a constant as an exponent, a variable as an exponent or a combination of constants and variables as an exponent.

$$3x^2 + 5x - 2 = 0 \qquad y = x^2 + 2 \qquad y = 2^x + 3 \qquad y = 4^{(2x+3)} - 1$$

- *Quadratic Equations.* An equation in one variable in which the greatest exponent of that variable is 2 is a quadratic equation. A quadratic equation can be written in the form $0 = ax^2 + bx + c$, where $a \neq 0$.

  This unit examines only simple solutions of quadratic equations of the form $c = ax^2$. To solve a quadratic equation for $x$, we use square roots.

  **Examples**

  $$576 = 4x^2$$
  $$\frac{576}{4} = x^2$$
  $$144 = x^2$$
  $$\pm\sqrt{144} = \sqrt{x^2}$$
  $$\pm 12 = x$$

- *Quadratic Functions.* A quadratic function is a function in which one variable is related to a quadratic expression of another variable. Quadratic functions can be written in the form $y = ax^2 + bx + c$, where $a$, $b$ and $c$ are real numbers with $a \neq 0$. The graphs of quadratic functions are parabolas. We can examine some basic characteristics of parabolas using graphs of the form $y = ax^2$. If the value of $a$ is positive, the parabola opens upward. If the value of $a$ is negative, the parabola opens downward. As $|a|$ gets smaller, the parabola opens wider and as $|a|$ gets larger, the parabola narrows.

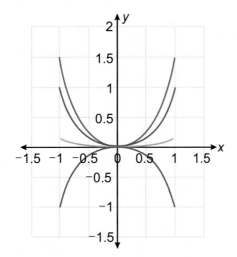

The graphs to the left from top to bottom are:

1: $y = 1.5x^2$
2: $y = x^2$
3: $y = 0.2x^2$
4: $y = -x^2$

The values of $b$ and $a$ in $y = ax^2 + bx + c$ shift the vertex, which will be located at the point where $x = \frac{-b}{2a}$. Notice that in the above graphs, the vertices are all at the point $(0, 0)$ since $b = 0$ in each equation. The value of $c$ in $y = ax^2 + bx + c$ is the $y$-value of the $y$-intercept. Quadratic functions where $b$ and $c$ are not 0 are not addressed in the student materials, but information is provided here should questions arise.

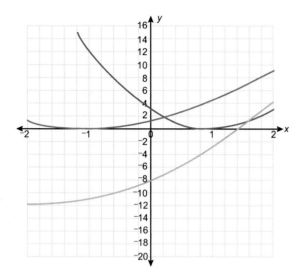

The graphs to the left from top to bottom (on the left side):

1: $y = 3(x - 1)^2$; vertex at $(1, 0)$
2: $y = (x + 1)^2$; vertex at $(-1, 0)$
3. $y = x^2 + 4x - 8$; vertex at $(-2, -12)$

We can evaluate a quadratic function of the form $y = ax^2 + bx + c$ to find $y$ for a given value of $x$.

$y = 3x^2$ \qquad Find $y$ when $x = 5$: \quad $y = 3(5)^2 = 3(25) = 75$

$y = 2x^2 + 4x + 1$ \qquad Find $y$ when $x = 2$: \quad $y = 2(2)^2 + 4(2) + 1 = 17$

- *Exponential Functions.* An exponential function uses a variable as an exponent in its equation. Exponential functions can be written in the form $y = a^x$ where $a > 0$ and $a \neq 1$. Graphs of exponential functions either always increase (growth functions) or always decrease (decay functions). In this unit students informally look at growth and decay using simple functions and associated graphs. The discussion and examples below provide additional material on growth and decay models.

  **Exponential Growth.** Exponential growth functions are of the form $y = a^x$, where $a > 1$. Because growth functions can often model phenomena that are increasing over time, we use the variable $t$ for time, the constant $P$ for the initial amount/value of $y$ (the $y$-value when $t = 0$) and $r$ as the base, which is related to the rate of growth: $y = P \cdot r^t$. For $r > 1$, the $y$-values increase as the $t$-value increases.

**Example**

You deposit $100 in a savings account that earns interest at a rate of 6% annually. What is the balance in your account after 10 years?

Model: $A = P(1 + i)^t$

    $A$ = amount in account after $t$ years

    $P$ = initial deposit in dollars

    $i$ = interest rate (per year)

    $t$ = number of years since opening account

So, $A = 100(1 + 0.06)^t = 100(1.06)^t$.
When $t = 10$, $A = 100(1.06)^{10} = 179.08$.
After 10 years, there is $179.08 in the account.

**Savings Account Balance**

**Exponential Decay.** Exponential decay functions are of the form $y = a^x$, where $0 < a < 1$. Because decay functions can often model phenomena that are decreasing over time, we use the variable $t$ for time, the constant $P$ as the initial amount/value of $y$ (the $y$-value when $t = 0$) and $r$ as the base, which is related to the rate of decay: $y = P \cdot r^t$. With $0 < r < 1$, the $y$-values decrease as the $t$-value increases.

**Example**

You buy a new car for $21,000 and as soon as you leave the car dealer lot, it begins to depreciate at a rate of 15% per year. What is the value of your car after 5 years?

Model: $V = P(1 - d)^t$

    $V$ = the value of car after $t$ years

    $P$ = initial price of the car in dollars

    $d$ = annual depreciation rate

    $t$ = years since buying car

So, $V = 21,000(1 - 0.15)^t = 21,000(0.85)^t$ and when $t = 5$, $V = 21,000(0.85)^5$. After 5 years the vehicle is worth $9,317.81.

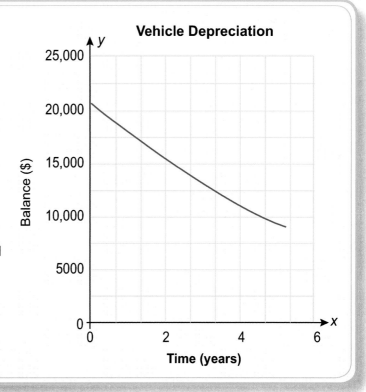

**Vehicle Depreciation**

# Solve It:
## Focusing on Equations, Inequalities and Exponents

## Unit Planner

See Assessment Resources for Unit Test to use as Unit Pretest if desired.

## Section 1: Algebraic Expressions and Equations

**Pacing based on 45-minute classes**

### Lesson 1.1: Mathmagic: Creating Magic Using Algebraic Expressions

In this lesson, students explore a variety of Mathmagic tricks to determine how they work. Students should translate the steps of the tricks to find equivalent algebraic expressions. Students will then learn how to create their own Mathmagic tricks.

| Pacing | Lesson Guides* (need to be duplicated) | Materials* | Essential *On Your Own* Questions | *On Your Own* Extensions | Mathematically Speaking |
|---|---|---|---|---|---|
| DAY 1 | | | On Your Own 2<br>Think Back 11–15 | Think Beyond 9, 10 | ■ algebraic expression<br>■ distributive property of multiplication over addition<br>■ equivalent expressions<br>■ factor an expression<br>■ greatest common factor (GCF) |
| DAY 2 | ■ Lesson Guide 1.1A: *Finding the Greatest Common Factor (GCF)* | | On Your Own 3–5 | | |
| DAY 3 | ■ Lesson Guide 1.1A: *More Mathmagic Tricks*<br>■ Lesson Guide 1.1: *Creating Your Own Mathmagic Trick*<br>■ Lesson Guide 1.1A: *On Your Own Question 2* | | Write About It 1<br>On Your Own 6, 7, 8 | | |

* The Think Like a Mathematician Daily Record Sheet should be used daily

# Lesson 1.2: It's All in the Ordering!

In this lesson students explore the order of operations. They discover that there is a need for an agreed-upon order and set of rules.

| Pacing | Lesson Guides*<br>(need to be duplicated) | Materials* | Essential<br>*On Your Own* Questions | *On Your Own*<br>Extensions | Mathematically<br>Speaking |
|---|---|---|---|---|---|
| DAY 1 | ■ Lesson Guide 1.2: *Please Excuse My Dear Aunt Sally* | ■ Calculators<br>■ Chart paper | Write About It 1<br>On Your Own 2, 4<br>Think Back 11, 12 | Think Beyond 8, 10 | ■ grouping symbols<br>■ order of operations |
| DAY 2 | ■ Lesson Guide 1.2A: *Analyzing the Competition* | ■ Calculators<br>■ Chart paper | On Your Own 3, 5, 6<br>Think Back 13, 14 | | |

\* The Think Like a Mathematician Daily Record Sheet should be used daily

# Lesson 1.3: Looks Can Be Deceiving: Equivalent Expressions

In this lesson, students learn to solve more complex equations with parentheses using a variety of methods. The "bar diagram" strategy introduced in earlier grades is revisited and extended.

| Pacing | Lesson Guides*<br>(need to be duplicated) | Materials* | Essential<br>*On Your Own* Questions | *On Your Own*<br>Extensions | Mathematically<br>Speaking |
|---|---|---|---|---|---|
| DAY 1 | ■ Lesson Guide 1.3: *Practice with Bar Diagrams* | ■ Calculators<br>■ Chart paper (optional) | Questions 2–6, 11,<br>Think Back 12, 13 | Think Beyond 13b, 15b | ■ addition property of equality<br>■ additive identity property<br>■ additive inverse property<br>■ bar diagram<br>■ constant<br>■ equation<br>■ like terms<br>■ multiplication property of equality<br>■ multiplicative identity property<br>■ multiplicative inverse property<br>■ solution (solution set) |
| DAY 2 | ■ Lesson Guide 1.3: *The Equivalence Game* | ■ Calculators<br>■ Chart paper (optional) | Write About It 1<br>On Your Own 7–10<br>Think Back 14–16 | | |

\* The Think Like a Mathematician Daily Record Sheet should be used daily

# Lesson 1.4: Equations with Variables on Both Sides

In this lesson, students explore solving equations with like terms on both sides of the equal sign. Students come to recognize the need to get all terms with the variable on one side of the equal sign and all other terms on the other.

| Pacing | Lesson Guides* (need to be duplicated) | Materials* | Essential *On Your Own* Questions | *On Your Own* Extensions | Mathematically Speaking |
|---|---|---|---|---|---|
| **DAY 1** | | ■ Calculators<br>■ Chart paper (optional) | Write About It 1<br>On Your Own 2, 3<br>Think Back 12–16 | Think Beyond 9, 11 | |
| **DAY 2** | | ■ Calculators<br>■ Chart paper (optional) | On Your Own 4–8, 10 | | |

\* The Think Like a Mathematician Daily Record Sheet should be used daily

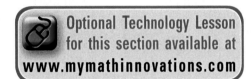

Optional Technology Lesson for this section available at **www.mymathinnovations.com**

# Assessment Opportunities

| | Student Edition | Assessment Resources | Online |
|---|---|---|---|
| **Sum It Up (Student Self-Asessment)** | pp. 45–47 | | |
| **Student Study Guide (Self-Assessment)** | pp. 48–50 | | |
| **Quiz** | | pp. 1–3 | |

# Section 2: Inequalities

**Pacing based on 45-minute classes**

## Lesson 2.1: From Equations to Inequalities

In this lesson, students solve inequalities and compare this to solving equations. Students graph inequalities on a number line and learn how to combine two inequalities into one statement.

| Pacing | Lesson Guides* (need to be duplicated) | Materials* | Essential *On Your Own* Questions | *On Your Own* Extensions | Mathematically Speaking |
|---|---|---|---|---|---|
| **DAY 1** | ■ Lesson Guide 2.1A: *Number Lines* | ■ Calculators | On Your Own 3<br>Think Back 12–16 | Think Beyond 9, 10, 11 | ■ inequality<br>■ replacement set<br>■ solution set<br>■ symbols ">"<br>■ symbols "≥"<br>■ symbols "<"<br>■ symbols "≤"<br>■ symbols "≈" |
| **DAY 2** | | ■ Calculators | Write About It 1<br>On Your Own 2, 4–8 | | |

\* The Think Like a Mathematician Daily Record Sheet should be used daily

# Lesson 2.2: An Interesting Twist

In this lesson, students learn that it is necessary to reverse the direction of the inequality symbol when dividing or multiplying both sides of an inequality by a negative number in order for the resulting inequality to be true.

| Pacing | Lesson Guides*<br>(need to be duplicated) | Materials* | Essential<br>*On Your Own* Questions | *On Your Own*<br>Extensions | Mathematically<br>Speaking |
|---|---|---|---|---|---|
| DAY 1 | ■ Lesson Guide 2.2: *Strange Happenings*<br>■ Lesson Guide 2.2: *Strange Happenings with Your Own Inequality*<br>■ Lesson Guide 2.2A: *Do You See a Pattern?*<br>■ Lesson Guide 2.2A: *Checking the Solution to an Inequality* | ■ Calculators | Write About It 1<br>On Your Own 2<br>Think Back 10–14 | Think Beyond 9 | ■ addition property of inequality<br>■ multiplication property of inequality for multiplication by a positive number<br>■ multiplication property of inequality for multiplication by a negative number |
| DAY 2 | ■ Lesson Guide 2.2: *Make a Match Cards* | ■ Calculators | On Your Own 3–8 | | |

* The Think Like a Mathematician Daily Record Sheet should be used daily

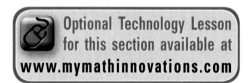

Optional Technology Lesson for this section available at www.mymathinnovations.com

## Assessment Opportunities

| | Student Edition | Assessment Resources | Online |
|---|---|---|---|
| Sum It Up (Student Self-Asessment) | pp. 72–73 | | |
| Student Study Guide (Self-Assessment) | pp. 74–75 | | |
| Quiz | | pp. 4–6 | |

**Pacing based on 45-minute classes**

## Lesson 3.1: Thinking Really Big

In this lesson, students will read, write and compare very large numbers. They will explore the rules for scientific notation and use exponents to express powers of ten. They will solve problems and play card games that involve large numbers written in scientific notation and standard notation. They will learn how a calculator records and displays numbers in scientific notation.

| Pacing | Lesson Guides*<br>(need to be duplicated) | Materials* | Essential<br>*On Your Own* Questions | *On Your Own*<br>Extensions | Mathematically<br>Speaking |
|---|---|---|---|---|---|
| **DAY 1** | ■ Lesson Guide 3.1A: *Do You Know the Powers of 10?* | ■ Calculators | Write About It 1<br>On Your Own 2–4, 6<br>Think Back 14–16 | Think Beyond 5d, 13 | ■ astronomical unit (AU)<br>■ base<br>■ exponent<br>■ mantissa<br>■ scientific notation<br>■ standard notation |
| **DAY 2** | ■ Lesson Guide 3.1: *Big Numbers Rule!* | ■ Calculators<br>■ Scissors<br>■ Internet or newspapers and magazines | On Your Own 5a–c, 7, 8–12<br>Think Back 17, 18 | | |

* The Think Like a Mathematician Daily Record Sheet should be used daily

## Lesson 3.2: Using Big Numbers: Exponents To The Rescue

In this lesson, students discover shortcut rules for operating with exponents. Students discover that the rules for multiplying numbers with exponents work only when the bases of the numbers are the same.

| Pacing | Lesson Guides*<br>(need to be duplicated) | Materials* | Essential<br>*On Your Own* Questions | *On Your Own*<br>Extensions | Mathematically<br>Speaking |
|---|---|---|---|---|---|
| **DAY 1** | ■ Lesson Guide 3.2: *Multiplying Powers of 10* | ■ Calculators | Write About It 1<br>On Your Own 2–4<br>Think Back 10–12 | Think Beyond 9 | ■ light-year<br>■ power |
| **DAY 2** | | ■ Calculators | On Your Own 5–8<br>Think Back 13, 14 | | |

* The Think Like a Mathematician Daily Record Sheet should be used daily

## Lesson 3.3: Dividing with Exponents

In this lesson, by looking at patterns, students form a generalization for dividing numbers written in scientific notation.

| Pacing | Lesson Guides*<br>(need to be duplicated) | Materials* | Essential<br>*On Your Own* Questions | *On Your Own*<br>Extensions | Mathematically<br>Speaking |
|---|---|---|---|---|---|
| **DAY 1** | | ■ Calculators<br>■ Internet access or encyclopedia | Write About It 1<br>On Your Own 2–6<br>Think Back 9–13 | Think Beyond 7, 8 | |

* The Think Like a Mathematician Daily Record Sheet should be used dail

# Lesson 3.4: It's a Very, Very Small World

In this lesson, students learn how to use scientific notation to write and work with small numbers. Students will represent numbers with negative exponents as equivalent fractions and decimals.

| Pacing | Lesson Guides* (need to be duplicated) | Materials* | Essential *On Your Own* Questions | *On Your Own* Extensions | Mathematically Speaking |
|---|---|---|---|---|---|
| DAY 1 | ■ Lesson Guide 3.4: *Patterns with Powers of 10* <br> ■ Lesson Guide 3.4: *Comparing Different Bases: Looking for Patterns with Negative Exponents* | ■ Calculators <br> ■ Internet access (optional) | On Your Own 2, 3 <br> Think Back 10, 11 | Think Beyond 8, 9 | ■ micrometer <br> ■ micron <br> ■ nanometer <br> ■ nanotechnology |
| DAY 2 | ■ Lesson Guide 3.4A: *Dividing by Powers of 10* | ■ Calculators <br> ■ Internet access (optional) | Write About It 1 <br> On Your Own 4, 5, <br> Think Back 12, 13 | | |
| DAY 3 | | ■ Calculators <br> ■ Internet access (optional for Think Beyond questions) | On Your Own 6, 7 <br> Think Back 14 | | |

\* The Think Like a Mathematician Daily Record Sheet should be used daily

Optional Technology Lesson for this section available at www.mymathinnovations.com

## Assessment Opportunities

| | Student Edition | Assessment Resources | Online |
|---|---|---|---|
| **Sum It Up (Student Self-Asessment)** | pp. 115–116 | | |
| **Student Study Guide (Self-Assessment)** | pp. 117–118 | | |
| **Quiz** | | pp. 7–10 | |

# Section 4: Functions with Exponents and the Curves They Make

## Lesson 4.1: Equations With Exponents

Pacing based on 45-minute classes

In this lesson, students explore solving equations by using square roots. Students work with area formulas in real-life situations.

| Pacing | Lesson Guides* (need to be duplicated) | Materials* | Essential *On Your Own* Questions | *On Your Own* Extensions | Mathematically Speaking |
|---|---|---|---|---|---|
| DAY 1 | | ■ Calculators | Write About It 1 <br> On Your Own 2–3, 5–8 <br> Think Back 10–14 | Think Beyond 4, 9 | ■ radical sign <br> ■ square root <br> ■ symbol "$\sqrt{\ }$" |

\* The Think Like a Mathematician Daily Record Sheet should be used daily

## Lesson 4.2: What a Difference an Exponent Makes!

In this lesson, students are introduced to quadratic functions. They will compare these new functions to linear functions.

| Pacing | Lesson Guides* (need to be duplicated) | Materials* | Essential *On Your Own* Questions | *On Your Own* Extensions | Mathematically Speaking |
|---|---|---|---|---|---|
| **DAY 1** | | ■ Graphing calculators<br>■ Graph paper | Think Back 12–16 | Think Beyond 9–11 | ■ function<br>■ line of symmetry<br>■ parabola<br>■ quadratic equation<br>■ quadratic function<br>■ vertex |
| **DAY 2** | ■ Lesson Guide 4.2A: *Tables for Quadratic Functions* | ■ Graphing calculators<br>■ Graph paper | Write About It 1<br>On Your Own 2–8 | | |

\* The Think Like a Mathematician Daily Record Sheet should be used daily

## Lesson 4.3: Variables as Exponents

I In this lesson, students explore exponential functions. They will use the variable $x$ as an exponent in these equations. They will discover that their graphs are curves rather than lines and do not cross the $x$-axis. Students explore real-life situations that represent two types of exponential functions: exponential growth and exponential decay. They play the Function Game, in which they identify and match linear, quadratic and exponential functions using their graphs, equations and tables of values.

| Pacing | Lesson Guides* (need to be duplicated) | Materials* | Essential *On Your Own* Questions | *On Your Own* Extensions | Mathematically Speaking |
|---|---|---|---|---|---|
| **DAY 1** | ■ Lesson Guide 4.3: *Paper Folding* | ■ Graphing calculators<br>■ Graph paper<br>■ Plain copy paper | Write About 1<br>On Your Own 4<br>Think Back 12–16 | Think Beyond 5, 10, 11 | ■ explicit rule<br>■ exponential decay<br>■ exponential function<br>■ exponential growth<br>■ recursive rule |
| **DAY 2** | ■ Lesson Guide 4.3: *Paper Folding*<br>■ Lesson Guide 4.3A: *Heat 'Em Up!*<br>■ Lesson Guide 4.3: *Function Game Cards*<br>■ Lesson Guide 4.3A: *Babysitting Job Earnings* | ■ Food thermometer<br>■ Cup of boiling water<br>■ Graphing calculators<br>■ Graph paper<br>■ Plain copy paper<br>■ Internet | On Your Own 2, 3, 6–9 | | |

\* The Think Like a Mathematician Daily Record Sheet should be used daily

Optional Technology Lesson for this section available at www.mymathinnovations.com

## Assessment Opportunities

| | Student Edition | Assessment Resources | Online |
|---|---|---|---|
| **Sum It Up (Student Self-Asessment)** | pp. 147–149 | | |
| **Student Study Guide (Self-Assessment)** | pp. 150–152 | | |
| **Quiz** | | pp. 11–14 | |
| **Unit Test** | | pp. 16–19 | |
| **Unit Reflection Form** | | p. 20 | |
| **Unit Project** | | pp. 21–22 | |
| **Answers** | | pp. 24–30 | |

# Algebraic Expressions and Equations

**LESSON 1.1**

# Mathmagic: Creating Magic Using Algebraic Expressions

**Suggested Pacing:** 3 Days

In this lesson, students explore a variety of Mathmagic tricks to determine how they work. Students should translate the steps of the tricks to find equivalent algebraic expressions. Students will then learn how to create their own Mathmagic tricks.

---

**LESSON OBJECTIVES**

- Students will use algebraic properties (commutative, additive inverse, additive identity) to write equivalent algebraic expressions.

- Students will use the distributive property of multiplication over addition to factor and write equivalent algebraic expressions.

- Students will create a Mathmagic trick and justify why the trick works by translating the steps in the trick to algebraic expressions and then simplifying the expressions using algebraic properties and operations.

---

| DAY 1 | Materials* | ESSENTIAL *ON YOUR OWN* QUESTIONS |
|---|---|---|
| Magic Tricks ... or Are They?<br><br>What's the *Math* in *Math*magic All About? | | Questions 2, 11–15 |

| DAY 2 | Materials* | ESSENTIAL *ON YOUR OWN* QUESTIONS |
|---|---|---|
| Using the Distributive Property<br><br>The Opposite Process: Factoring Expressions<br><br>Common Factors | **In Class**<br>■ Lesson Guide 1.1A: *Finding the Greatest Common Factor (GCF)* | Questions 3–5 |

| DAY 3 | Materials* | ESSENTIAL *ON YOUR OWN* QUESTIONS |
|---|---|---|
| Using Factoring in Mathmagic Trick 1<br><br>Creating Your Own Tricks | **In Class**<br>■ Lesson Guide 1.1A: *More Mathmagic Tricks*<br>■ Lesson Guide 1.1: *Creating Your Own Mathmagic Trick*<br><br>**On Your Own**<br>■ Lesson Guide 1.1A: *On Your Own Question 2* | Questions 1, 6, 7, 8 |

*The Think Like a Mathematician Daily Record Sheet should be used daily

**MATHEMATICALLY SPEAKING**

▶ algebraic expression

▶ distributive property of multiplication over addition

▶ equivalent expressions

▶ factor an expression

▶ greatest common factor (GCF)

# Algebraic Expressions and Equations

Imagine that you are the Director of the Isaac Newton Discovery Center, a science exploration center for families that includes the Falling Apple Science Museum and the Magellan Aquarium. As Director, your job is to make sure the center runs successfully.

You often use algebra to help you do this. You will revisit many of the algebraic concepts you learned in earlier grades to develop a new and deeper understanding of them and extend them further.

**LESSON 1.1** Mathmagic: Creating Magic Using Algebraic Expressions

 **Start It Off** _____

In Questions 1–8, match the phrase on the left with the correct expression on the right:

1. Three less than seven times a number      **A.** $n^2 - 7$

2. Seven minus three times a number      **B.** $7 - 3n$

3. The quantity "a number minus seven" squared      **C.** $7n - 3n$

4. The square of a number minus seven      **D.** $7n - 3$

5. Three times the quantity of a number minus seven      **E.** $3n - 7$

6. Seven times a number minus three times the number      **F.** $(n - 7)^2$

7. Seven less than three times a number      **G.** $7 + (-3n)$

8. Seven plus negative three times a number      **H.** $3(n - 7)$

9. Are any of these expressions equivalent? Explain.

---

 **Start It Off** _____

1. D
2. B
3. F
4. A
5. H
6. C
7. E
8. G
9. Yes, G and B are equivalent expressions.

**TEACHING THE LESSON**

In this lesson, students explore a variety of Mathmagic tricks to determine how they work. They will translate the steps of the tricks into algebraic expressions. Students then simplify the expressions using appropriate rules and algebraic properties. As a culminating activity, students create their own Mathmagic tricks. The focus on equivalent expressions serves as a precursor to solving more sophisticated equations later in the section.

## Magic Tricks . . . or Are They?

Introduce students to their new role as Director of the Isaac Newton Discovery Center. Read together Mathmagic Trick 1. Encourage students to try the trick and compare their responses with three classmates. Most of the students will get the same answer. A few students may choose a different country such as the Dominican Republic. Note the color of the animal is irrelevant but reinforces the fact that most will have the same answer "a grey elephant." Discuss the notion that this trick is really a carefully created math problem that uses algebraic expressions and operations. Help students recall the meaning of an algebraic expression by asking:

- *What is an algebraic expression?*
- *What are some examples of an algebraic expression?*

1. Students should arrive at the number 4 in Step 6 and the number 5 in Step 8. Most students will choose Denmark as the country and elephant as the animal.

## What's the *Math* in *Mathmagic All About?*

Discuss how to translate the steps from Mathmagic Trick 1 to pictures or diagrams as students review the steps in the table on page 2. For Question 2a, discuss the definition of an algebraic expression as a class. Have students discuss Question 2b with a partner and share their explanations with the class.

---

## Magic Tricks . . . or Are They?

Isaac Newton (1642–1727)

One of the new exhibits at the Isaac Newton Discovery Center is called Mathmagic. In the exhibit, visitors solve and create math tricks. A math trick is one where the creator can predict the answer ahead of time, regardless of the numbers that people use. Here are some math tricks at the Mathmagic exhibit to try out.

### 1. Mathmagic Trick 1

**Step 1.** Choose a counting number between 1 and 10.
**Step 2.** Double it.
**Step 3.** Add 8.
**Step 4.** Divide the answer by 2.
**Step 5.** Subtract your original number.
**Step 6.** Find your answer below and look at the letter below it.

| 1 | 2 | 3 | 4 | 5 | 6 | 7 | 8 | 9 | 10 |
|---|---|---|---|---|---|---|---|---|----|
| A | B | C | D | E | F | G | H | I | J  |

**Step 7.** Think of a country whose name begins with this letter.
**Step 8.** Now add 1 to your number you used in the chart. Think of a big animal whose name begins with the letter corresponding to this new number.
**Step 9.** Think of the color of this animal.

**? Hint**
See page 168

---

Explain to students that they can simplify the steps in a Mathmagic trick using algebra. Have students read Mathmagic Trick 2 and try the trick three times using the given numbers in Part b. Ask students to compare their answers and discuss their results with the class.

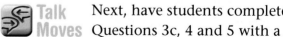 Next, have students complete **Talk Moves** Questions 3c, 4 and 5 with a partner. Circulate as pairs solve the problems. Discuss student responses as a class. Use talk moves, such as agree/disagree and why and repeat/rephrase, to further the discussion. Learn more about the talk moves in the Teaching and Learning Strategies on p. T5.

Check with 3 classmates who sit near you. Did you all get the same answer? Most people get the same answer when they try this trick. How can this be? It is not really magic but rather a carefully created problem that uses algebra.

 **Let's Review** An **algebraic expression** is a mathematical phrase that contains at least one variable. It may also contain numbers and/or operations. Some examples of algebraic expressions are: $-2x$, $3y + 7$, $c$.

## What's the *Math* in *Math*magic All About?

Let $n$ represent your favorite number. Follow the steps in the table to see why everyone got the same animal.

| Step | Words | Diagram |
|---|---|---|
| 1 | Choose your favorite number between 1 and 10. | $n$ |
| 2 | Double it. | $n$ $n$ |
| 3 | Add 8. | $n$ $n$ +1 +1 +1 +1 +1 +1 +1 +1 |
| 4 | Divide the answer by 2. | $n$ +1 +1 +1 +1 |
| 5 | Subtract your original number. | +1 +1 +1 +1 |

**2. a)** You can represent the picture in Step 4 with the algebraic expression $n + 1 + 1 + 1 + 1$. Why is this an algebraic expression?

**b)** Talk to your partner. Why did so many students get the same animal? Be ready to share your explanation with the class.

Making drawings to figure out how a trick works can take a long time. Algebra helps us to translate words and pictures into math symbols. We then simplify problems using the rules and properties of algebra. Let's start with some easy Mathmagic tricks to see how this works.

**2. a)** An algebraic expression is a mathematical phrase that contains at least one variable and may also have numbers and/or operations. This expression contains the variable $n$ with the operation addition.

**b)** Answers may vary. Student responses should indicate that regardless of the starting number chosen, the steps are planned so that some steps are inverses, or undo each other, ensuring that the final number is 4. For example, Step 1 and Step 5 are inverse operations, making it irrelevant which number is the starting number. Step 2 and Step 4 are also inverse operations. After 8 is added to the result in Step 3, dividing by 2 in Step 4 yields the starting number plus 4. After the starting number is subtracted to complete Step 5, the result is always 4. Finally, adding 1 to this number yields a sum of 5. Using the given table, the number 5 matches the letter $E$. Most people automatically think of an elephant as a very large animal that begins with the letter $E$.

**4** Course 3: Solve It: Focusing on Equations, Inequalities and Exponents

3. a) 9

b) The answer is always 9.

c)

| Step | Words | Diagram | Expression |
|---|---|---|---|
| 1 | Think of a number. | $n$ | $n$ |
| 2 | Add 15. | $n$ +1 +1 +1 +1 +1 / +1 +1 +1 +1 +1 +1 / +1 +1 +1 +1 | $n +15$ |
| 3 | Subtract 6. | $n$ +1 +1 +1 +1 / +1 +1 +1 +1 +1 | $n + 15 - 6$ |
| 4 | Subtract your original number. | +1 +1 +1 +1 / +1 +1 +1 | $n + 15 - 6 - n$ |

**b)** Fill in the empty cells in the table below.

| Step | Words | Diagram | Expression |
|------|-------|---------|------------|
| 1 | Start with −5. | (−1)(−1)(−1)(−1)(−1) | −5 |
| 2 | Add $n$. | | −5 + $n$ |
| 3 | Add 7. | [$n$](+1)(+1) | |
| 4 | Subtract 2. | | |

**c)** Explain why this trick always works, no matter what number you choose.

5. Mario made up a Mathmagic trick of his own. He wrote the following algebraic expression to represent his trick:

$$1.7 + n - 2.4 + \frac{1}{2} + 1.2 - n.$$

He said, "Everyone should get an answer of 1." Do you agree with Mario? Talk to you partner and be ready to defend your answer.

## Using the Distributive Property

6. Let's think back to Mathmagic Trick 1. Fill in the empty cells in the table below.

| Step | Words | Diagram | Expression |
|------|-------|---------|------------|
| 1 | Choose your favorite number. | [$n$] | $n$ |
| 2 | Double it. | [$n$][$n$] | |
| 3 | Add 8. | [$n$][$n$] (+1)(+1)(+1)(+1) (+1)(+1)(+1)(+1) | |
| 4 | Divide the answer by 2. | [$n$] (+1)(+1)(+1)(+1) | $\frac{2n+8}{2}$ |
| 5 | Subtract your original number. | (+1)(+1)(+1)(+1) | $\frac{2n+8}{2} - n$ |

**c)** Answers may vary. Student responses should indicate that regardless of the number chosen, the steps are planned so that only the number chosen remains. Adding the number to −5 and then, in Step 3, adding 7, gives the student the chosen number plus 2. Step 4, subtract 2, always results in the chosen number.

5. Students should agree with Mario. When the expression is simplified, the result is 1 regardless of the starting number selected.

$$1.7 + n - 2.4 + \frac{1}{2} + 1.2 - n =$$

$$1.7 - 2.4 + \frac{1}{2} + 1.2 - n + n =$$

$$1.7 - 2.4 + \frac{1}{2} + 1.2 + 0 =$$

$$1.7 + 1.2 + \frac{1}{2} - 2.4 =$$

$$3.4 - 2.4 =$$

$$1$$

 **NOTE** Students may find it easier to place numbers in the same format next to each other (e.g., $1.7 - 2.4 + \frac{1}{2}$). They may also find it easier to convert $\frac{1}{2}$ into decimal form before simplifying the equation.

4. **a)** Answers will vary. Students should end up with the number they chose as their favorite number.

**b)**

| Step | Words | Diagram | Expression |
|------|-------|---------|------------|
| 1 | Start with –5. | (−1)(−1)(−1)(−1)(−1) | −5 |
| 2 | Add $n$. | **(−1)(−1)(−1)(−1)(−1)** **[n]** | −5 + $n$ |
| 3 | Add 7. | [$n$](+1)(+1) | −5 + $n$ + 7 |
| 4 | Subtract 2. | **[n]** | −5 + $n$ + 7 − 2 |

## Summarize Day 1

Use Question 5 as a Wrap It Up discussion for Day 1. Ask students to explain why the answer will always be 1.

The discussion should include the following key ideas:

- Adding the constants results in the number 1.

- This will always happen no matter what the value of $n$ is because $-n + n = 0$.

## TEACHING THE LESSON

### Using the Distributive Property

Have students work independently on Question 6 and have them compare their responses with a partner when finished. Discuss any discrepancies with the class. Discuss factoring as the opposite of the distributive property. Go over the Let's Review to remind students of the distributive property. Next, have students work independently on Question 7 and share their responses with a partner. Discuss any discrepancies with the class.

6. Step 2 Expression: $2n$

   Step 3 Expression: $2n + 8$

   Step 5 Expression: $n + \frac{8}{2} - n = \frac{8}{2} + 0 = 4$

---

When the last expression is simplified, the last number is 4. To simplify we use a process called factoring. You can think of factoring as the opposite of the distributive property.

**MATHEMATICALLY SPEAKING**

- distributive property of multiplication over addition
- equivalent expressions

 **Let's Review** The **distributive property of multiplication over addition** allows you to expand an expression that uses parentheses. It states that for all real numbers $a$, $b$ and $c$, $a(b + c) = a \cdot b + a \cdot c$.

For example, $4(6 + 5) = 4 \cdot 6 + 4 \cdot 5$.

By multiplying both addends inside the parentheses by 4, you are "distributing" the 4 over the addends in the addition expression. The expressions on each side of the equal sign both have a value of 44. Expressions that have the same value are called **equivalent expressions**.

7. Use the distributive property to distribute the term outside the parentheses. Do not simplify further.

   a) $21(3 + 0.3)$       d) $-2(20 + 7y)$

   b) $-6(10 + \frac{1}{2})$       e) $1.5(x - y)$

   c) $14(x + 10)$       f) $-4(c + 6)$

   **? Hint** See page 168

### The Opposite Process: Factoring Expressions

You can also factor an expression to obtain an equivalent expression. For example, you can factor the 5 from each term in $5 \cdot 7 + 5 \cdot 3$ to get the equivalent expression $5(7 + 3)$. These expressions are equivalent because they both have a value of 50.

To factor an expression, you need to find a common factor of both terms. The factor can be a number, a variable or a term that includes both numbers and variables. In the example above, the factor common to both terms is 5.

**6** Course 3: Solve It: Focusing on Equations, Inequalities and Exponents

---

7. a) $63 + 6.3$

   b) $-60 + (-3)$ or $-60 - 3$

   c) $14x + 140$

   d) $-40 + (-14)y$ or $-40 - 14y$

   e) $1.5x - 1.5y$

   f) $-4c + 24$

**Let's Review** To factor completely, you need to find the greatest common factor (GCF). This is the greatest factor that is common to the terms.

**Example**

Find the greatest common factor of 20 and 16.

Find all factors of each number.

• Factors of 20    ①②④ 5, 10, 20
• Factors of 16    ①②④ 8, 16

The common factors are 1, 2 and 4. The greatest common factor is 4.

**8.** Find the greatest common factors of the following:

a)  $-24$ and $64$          d)  $5a$ and $7a$

b)  $30$ and $17$          e)  $9xy$ and $21x$

c)  $-75b$ and $100$

**Example**

To factor $3x + 15$, first find the greatest common factor of the terms.

The greatest common factor of $3x$ and $15$ is $3$.

Next, write the expression in the form $a \cdot b + a \cdot c$, where $a$ is the common factor.

$3x + 15 = 3 \cdot x + 3 \cdot 5$

Finally, factoring 3 from each term, write an equivalent expression.

$3 \cdot x + 3 \cdot 5 = 3(x + 5)$

Use the distributive property to check.

$3(x + 5) = 3x + 15.$

To summarize, here are the steps to factor an expression:

**1)**  Find the greatest common factor (GCF) of the terms in the expression.

**2)**  Use the opposite of the distributive property. Write an equivalent expression that factors the GCF from each term.

**3)**  Check by using the distributive property. If the product is the same as the original expression, then you are correct.

**9.** Factor the following expressions.

a)  $4b - 8$          d)  $14 - 10x$

b)  $24 + 6y$          e)  $81b + 45b$

c)  $125 + 225z$          f)  $2ab - 12b$

 **Differentiation**

**Think Differently:** For students who are unsure of what a factor is, explain that factors are numbers that divide into a given number with no remainder. Ask students to identify all the factors of the number 12: 1, 2, 3, 4, 6 and 12. Remind students that 1 and the number itself are always factors of a given number. For additional practice with identifying factors and finding the greatest common factor, offer students Lesson Guide 1.1A: *Finding the Greatest Common Factor* (GCF). *Accommodation Guides* (Lesson Guides which contain an A after the number) are designed to provide additional support for those students experiencing difficulty with a lesson activity.

---

## The Opposite Process: Factoring Expressions

Explain to students that they need to find a common factor in both terms when factoring an expression. Make sure students are comfortable identifying the factors of a given number or term. Ask:

• *What is a factor of a number?*

Guide students to recognize that when factoring an expression, they need to find the greatest common factor of both terms. Discuss the examples as a class. Have students complete Question 8 and compare their answers with a partner. Encourage students to share their strategies for finding the greatest common factor.

**8.  a)**  8

  **b)**  1

  **c)**  25

  **d)**  $a$

  **e)**  $3x$

Review how to factor expressions with students, discussing the example given. Have students complete Question 9 independently. Have them check their work by multiplying the factored expression to make sure it equals the original expression. Discuss student responses as a class.

9. **a)** $4(b - 2)$

   **b)** $6(4 + y)$

   **c)** $25(5 + 9z)$

   **d)** $2(7 - 5x)$

   **e)** $9b(9 + 5)$

   **f)** $2b(a - 6)$

## Summarize Day 2

As a Wrap It Up discussion for Day 2, have students share their responses to Question 9 with the class. Ask students:

- *How did you find the greatest common factor in each expression?*

- *How did you use the distributive property to check your answers?*

**TEACHING THE LESSON**

## Using Factoring in Mathmagic Trick 1

Discuss the factoring example in Mathmagic Trick 1. Have students complete Questions 10 and 11 independently. Encourage students to share their responses and solution strategies when finished. Emphasize that when factoring an expression, students must find the greatest common factor of both terms in the expression.

---

### Using Factoring in Mathmagic Trick 1

Look back at the expression in Mathmagic Trick 1: $\frac{2n + 8}{2} - n$.

- Factor $2n + 8$ to get the equivalent expression $2(n + 4)$.
$$\frac{2n + 8}{2} - n = \frac{2(n + 4)}{2} - n$$

- Divide the numerator and denominator by 2 to get $n + 4$.
$$\frac{2n + 8}{2} - n = \frac{2(n + 4)}{2} - n = n + 4$$

- Subtract $n$ to get 4.
$$\frac{2n + 8}{2} - n = n + 4 - n = 4$$

10. **a)** Simplify the following expressions.

   i) $\frac{2c - 16}{2}$

   ii) $\frac{2x + 100}{25}$

   iii) $\frac{14 - 7b}{7}$

   **b)** Talk to your partner about Mathmagic Trick 1. Why does it work?

---
**Mathmagic Trick 4**

11) **a)** Think of a number.
    Triple it and subtract 9.
    What number do you end up with?

---

   **b)** Write the steps for this trick using words, diagrams and algebraic expressions.

   **c)** Simplify the expression in the last step. Is this the same number you ended with?

   **d)** Will this trick always end up with the same number? Why or why not?

For students who need more practice working with Mathmagic tricks, offer Lesson Guide 1.1A: *More Mathmagic Tricks*.

10. **a)** i) $c - 8$

   ii) $x + 4$

   iii) $2 - b$

   **b)** Answers will vary. Students should indicate that the trick works because the steps involve inverse operations that undo each other. This ensures the answer will always be 4.

**11. a)** The number you end up with is $-3$.

**b)**

| Steps in Words | Diagrams | Algebraic Expressions |
|---|---|---|
| Step 1: Think of a number. | [n] | $n$ |
| Step 2: Triple the number. | [n] [n] [n] | $3n$ |
| Step 3: Subtract 9. | [n] [n] [n] (−1) <br> (−1)(−1)(−1)(−1) <br> (−1)(−1)(−1)(−1) | $3n - 9$ |
| Step 4: Divide the result by 3. | [n] (−1)(−1)(−1) | $\dfrac{3n - 9}{3}$ |
| Step 5: Subtract your original number. | (−1)(−1)(−1) | $\dfrac{3n - 9}{3} - n$ |

**c)** $\dfrac{3n - 9}{3} - n$

$\dfrac{3(n - 3)}{3} - n$

$n - 3 - n = -3$

Yes, $-3$ is the same number students ended up with in Question 11a.

**d)** Yes. Part c showed that the algebraic expression representing the steps of the trick is always equivalent to $-3$. The trick will work for any number.

## Creating Your Own Tricks

Have students create their own Mathmagic tricks. Emphasize that when designing their tricks, students must use multiplication and division as part of their steps. Distribute two copies of Lesson Guide 1.1: *Creating Your Own Mathmagic Trick* to each student. One copy may be used to guide students as they create their own tricks and complete Question 12. When finished, have students trade their Mathmagic tricks with a partner and use the second copy of the lesson guide to solve their partner's trick. In Question 13, students analyze each other's tricks to determine whether they will get the same result for any number by writing algebraic expressions that describe each step.

 **Differentiation**

**Think Differently:** For students needing additional support in creating a Mathmagic trick, allow them to work with a partner.

12. Answers will vary. Students should **a)** write down steps, **b)** create a table using words, diagrams and expressions and **c)** find the answer to the trick.

13. Answers will vary. Students should **a)** trade and solve a partner's trick, **b)** write an expression for each step and **c)** determine if the answer to the trick will always be the same.

 **Talk Moves** Have students share a few Mathmagic tricks with the class. Discuss any discrepancies that arise when partners did not arrive at the same number. In analyzing the tricks, ask students to verify whether the trick works by creating algebraic expressions for each step. Use talk moves, such as adding on and agree/disagree and why, to clarify misconceptions and further understanding.

You may wish to display the Mathmagic tricks in the classroom or have them available at a learning center for other math classes to solve. The tricks are great to have on hand at Parents' Open House or Family Math Night. They can be used to showcase student thinking and reasoning about algebraic properties and demonstrate how students are connecting algebra to interesting applications.

## Creating Your Own Tricks

**12.** Make up a Mathmagic trick using multiplication and division.

    **a)** Write down the steps.

    **b)** Create a table that shows the steps using words, diagrams and expressions.

    **c)** Find the answer to your trick. Will you always get the same answer? Why or why not?

**13. a)** Have your partner perform your Mathmagic trick, and solve your partner's trick.

    **b)** Write an expression that describes each step of your partner's Mathmagic trick.

### ⬆W rap It Up

Where is the "Math" in Mathmagic? Talk to your partner and discuss how you would tell someone how to create a Mathmagic trick.

**MATHEMATICALLY SPEAKING**

▸ algebraic expression
▸ distributive property of multiplication over addition
▸ equivalent expressions
▸ factor an expression
▸ greatest common factor (GCF)

### ⬆W rap It Up

Answers will vary. The discussion should include the following key ideas:

- The steps in the Mathmagic trick should be carefully planned. Somewhere in the trick, steps that undo each other, or are the inverse of each other, need to be included.

- The inverse steps should not follow one another. This would make the trick seem obvious.

- To make sure the trick works, write an algebraic expression that models the steps of the trick. When simplified, the resulting number should always be the same number, regardless of which starting number is used.

- To create the trick, include several algebraic properties such as the following: additive identity property, multiplicative identity property, additive inverse property, distributive property of multiplication over addition, commutative property of addition and commutative property of multiplication.

## Reflect

Use these questions to help you reflect on the lesson and plan for future instruction.

- What are some strategies students used to identify the greatest common factor of several terms?

- How successful are students in justifying the steps used to create equivalent algebraic expressions?

- How skillful are students in translating the steps of a Mathmagic trick to equivalent algebraic expressions and then simplifying those expressions?

## On Your Own

1. 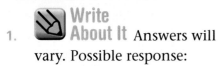 **Write About It** Answers will vary. Possible response:

A Mathmagic trick is a math trick where the creator can predict the answer to the trick ahead of time, regardless of the numbers people use at the start. The trick uses algebra to predict the number.

For example, here is a Magic Trick.

Think of a number.
Multiply it by 3. Add 15.
Divide your answer by 3. Then subtract 5. Did you end up with your original number?

The distributive property can be used to simplify algebraic expressions by allowing you to factor the expression. To do this, you must find the greatest common factor of both terms and then use the opposite of the distributive property.

Here is how this trick works.

| | |
|---|---|
| $3x + 15$ | The greatest common factor of both terms is 3. |
| $3 \cdot x + 3 \cdot 5$ | Write the terms as the product of the GCF and another number. |
| $3(x + 5)$ | Using the opposite of the distributive property, write an equivalent expression. |
| $x + 5$ | If we divide by 3, we get $x + 5$. |
| $x$ | When we subtract 5, we get our original number. |

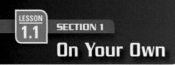
 **Write About It**

1. Create a poster for the Mathmagic exhibit at the Newton Discovery Center. On the poster, describe what a Mathmagic trick is. Use the expression $3x + 15$ to create a Magic Trick. Show how to use factoring and the distributive property to create your trick. Make sure your explanation will be easy for visitors to understand.

2. Try the following Mathmagic trick.

   **Step 1.** Think of a number between 1 and 20.

   **Step 2.** Add 3.

   **Step 3.** Multiply your answer by 4.

   **Step 4.** Subtract 8.

   **Step 5.** Divide your answer by 2.

   **Step 6.** Subtract twice your original number.

   Create a table to show why everyone always ends up with the same number.

3. Jessica created a Mathmagic trick and made a chart to show the steps.

   **a)** Fill in the missing parts.

| Step | Words | Diagram | Expression |
|---|---|---|---|
| 1 | Choose your favorite number | $n$ | |
| 2 | | $n$ $-1$ $-1$ $-1$ $-1$ | |
| 3 | | $n$ $n$ $-1$ $-1$ $-1$ / $-1$ $-1$ $-1$ $-1$ $-1$ | |
| 4 | | $n$ $n$ $-1$ $-1$ | |
| 5 | Divide by 2. | | |
| 6 | Subtract your original number. | | |

   **b)** What is the final answer?

   **c)** Show how to get the final answer by simplifying the expression in Step 6.

**2.**

| Step | Words | Diagram | Expression |
|---|---|---|---|
| 1 | Think of a number between 1 and 20. | $\boxed{n}$ | $n$ |
| 2 | Add 3. | $\boxed{n}$ $(+1)(+1)(+1)$ | $n + 3$ |
| 3 | Multiply your answer by 4. | $\boxed{n}$ $(+1)(+1)(+1)$ <br> $\boxed{n}$ $(+1)(+1)(+1)$ <br> $\boxed{n}$ $(+1)(+1)(+1)$ <br> $\boxed{n}$ $(+1)(+1)(+1)$ | $4(n + 3)$ |
| 4 | Subtract 8. | $\boxed{n}$ $(+1)$ $\boxed{n}$ $(+1)$ <br> $\boxed{n}$ $(+1)$ $\boxed{n}$ $(+1)$ | $4(n + 3) - 8$ |
| 5 | Divide your answer by 2. | $\boxed{n}$ $(+1)$ $\boxed{n}$ $(+1)$ | $\dfrac{4(n + 3) - 8}{2}$ |
| 6 | Subtract twice your original number. | $(+1)(+1)$ | $\dfrac{4(n + 3) - 8}{2} - 2n$ |

## 🔎 Differentiation

**Think Differently:** For students who need support organizing their explanations in a table, offer Lesson Guide 1.1A: *On Your Own Question 2.*

**3. a)**

| Step | Words | Diagram | Expression |
|---|---|---|---|
| 1 | Choose your favorite number between 1 and 10. | $\boxed{n}$ | $n$ |
| 2 | **Subtract 4 from your number.** | $\boxed{n}$ $(-1)(-1)(-1)(-1)$ | $n - 4$ |
| 3 | **Double the result or multiply the result by 2.** | $\boxed{n}$ $\boxed{n}$ $(-1)(-1)(-1)$ <br> $(-1)(-1)(-1)(-1)(-1)$ | $2(n - 4)$ |
| 4 | **Add 6.** | $(-1)(-1)(-1)(-1)$ | $2(n - 4) + 6$ |
| 5 | Divide by 2. | $\boxed{n}$ $(-1)$ | $\dfrac{2(n - 4) + 6}{2}$ |
| 6 | Subtract your original number. | $(-1)$ | $\dfrac{2(n - 4) + 6}{2} - n$ |

**b)** The final answer is $-1$.

**c)** $\dfrac{2(n-4)+6}{2} - n$

$\dfrac{2(n-4)+2 \cdot 3}{2} - n$

$n - 4 + 3 - n =$

$n - n - 4 + 3 =$

$0 - 4 + 3 = -1$

**4. a)** $5x + 20$

**b)** $7(b - 2)$

**c)** $6 - \dfrac{a}{2}$

**d)** $3c - 5$

**e)** $174.4$

**f)** $-16a + 24b$

**g)** $9(d - 2)$

**h)** $-76$

**i)** $7$

**j)** $18 - 3x$

**k)** $0$

**l)** $27x(2y + 1)$

**m)** $-3a - 2$

**n)** $15(3 - a)$

**o)** $156x$

**p)** $75b(-a + 2)$

**5. a)** Numbers selected at the start will vary. The answer should be 4 regardless of the number chosen at the beginning of the trick.

**b)** Jade did not factor the numerator of the fraction correctly. She forgot to factor 4 from 16 in the numerator. $\dfrac{4(n+4)}{4}$

This expression will now simplify to $n + 4$. After the last step in the trick is completed (subtracting the original number), the final result is 4, since $n + 4 - n = 4$.

**4.** Write an equivalent expression for each of the following by factoring, using the distributive property or simplifying the expression.

a) $5(x + 4)$

b) $7b - 14$

c) $\frac{1}{2}(12 - a)$

d) $\frac{15c - 25}{5}$

e) $a + 103.4 - a + 71$

f) $-8(2a - 3b)$

g) $9d - 18$

h) $-2(46 - 8)$

i) $3b - 17 + 24 - 3b$

j) $(6 - x)3$

k) $-35d + 35d$

l) $54xy + 27x$

m) $\frac{-12a - 8}{4}$

n) $45 - 15a$

o) $12x + 144x$

p) $-75ab + 150b$

---

**Mathmagic Trick 5**

**5.** Jade was figuring out Bronson's Mathmagic trick.

Choose a number and multiply it by 4.

Add 16 to the product and divide by 4.

Subtract your original number.

---

a) She chose 2 to start and ended with 4 as her answer. Try two other numbers and see if you get the same answer.

b) Jade wrote the expressions below for Bronson's trick. She wanted to show that 4 would always be the answer no matter what number you started with. But she got 16 instead of 4. Explain what she did wrong.

$$\frac{4n + 16}{4} - n = \frac{4(n + 16)}{4} - n = n + 16 - n$$

But $n + 16 - n = 16$! It is not 4.

**6.**

| Step | Words | Jerilyn's Answer | Sean's Answer | Carlos's Answer | Expression |
|---|---|---|---|---|---|
| 1 | Choose a number. | 6 | 2.5 | −8 | $n$ |
| 2 | Add 15. | 21 | 17.5 | 7 | $n + 15$ |
| 3 | Multiply the sum by 3. | 63 | 52.5 | 21 | $3(n + 15)$ |
| 4 | Subtract 30. | 33 | 22.5 | −9 | $3(n + 15) - 30$ |
| 5 | Divide by 3. | 11 | 7.5 | −3 | $\frac{3(n + 15) - 30}{3}$ |
| 6 | Subtract your original number. | 5 | 5 | 5 | $\frac{3(n + 15) - 30}{3} - n$ |

**7. a)** Pick a number.

Multiply the number by 6.

Add 6.9.

Subtract 14 from the resulting sum.

Add 7.1 to the difference.

**b)** Pick a number.

Multiply the number by 2.

Subtract 10 from the result.

Divide the result by 2.

Add 5 to the quotient.

**c)** Pick a number.

Multiply that number by 3.

Add 6 to the result.

Subtract 1 from the resulting sum.

Subtract twice your number from the difference.

**8.** Expression 7b will simplify so that the result is the original number. Let $n$ represent the starting number.

$\dfrac{2n - 10}{2} + 5 =$

$\dfrac{2(n-5)}{2} + 5 =$

$n - 5 + 5 = n$

---

**6.** Jerilyn, Sean and Carlos tried a Mathmagic trick that their teacher invented. Some of their answers for each step are in the chart below. Fill in the blank boxes.

| Step | Words | Jerilyn's Answer | Sean's Answer | Carlos's Answer | Expression |
|---|---|---|---|---|---|
| 1 | Choose a number. | 6 | 2.5 | -8 | |
| 2 | | | 21 | | $n + 15$ |
| 3 | | | 63 | 21 | |
| 4 | Subtract 30. | | 22.5 | | |
| 5 | | 11 | | -3 | |
| 6 | | 5 | 5 | 5 | |

**7.** Use the following expressions to write a Mathmagic trick in steps that starts with "Choose a number."

**a)** $6n + 6.9 - 14 + 7.1$

**b)** $\dfrac{2n - 10}{2} + 5$

**c)** $3n + 6 - 1 - 2n$

**8.** Which expression in Question 7 simplifies to $n$? Explain your answer.

 **Think Beyond**

**9. a)** Make a Mathmagic trick that has an answer that is the same as the starting number. Use at least five steps. Use all four operations (addition, subtraction, multiplication and division).

**b)** Write an expression for your trick. Simplify the expression to prove that the final number will always be the starting number.

**Think Beyond**

**10.** Factor the following expressions:

**a)** $3x - 9y + 18z$

**b)** $17a + 54d - 68a$

**c)** $75x^2 - 1.87x^2 + x^2$

---

**9.**  **Think Beyond** Answers will vary. The trick must have 5 steps and use all four basic operations, addition, subtraction, multiplication and division.

**10.** **Think Beyond**

**a)** $3(x - 3y + 6z)$

**b)** $54d - 51a = 3(18d - 17a)$

**c)** $x^2(75 - 1.87 + 1) = 74.13x^2$

11. Monica had $40 to spend on a dress. She found a dress that was originally $50 but is marked 25% off. She took 25% of $40. She knew that 25% is $\frac{1}{4}$, and $\frac{1}{4}$ of 40 is 10. If she added that to her $40, she would have $50. She thought this meant she had just enough to buy the dress. She was surprised to get change back. Where did she go wrong and how much change did she get?

12. $5\frac{1}{3} \div \frac{4}{9} \cdot \frac{1}{6} =$

13. 0.3% of 200 =

   A. 60

   B. 0.6

   C. $0.\overline{6}$

   D. 6

14. Janine's younger twin brothers were trading baseball cards. Eren promised Erol he would give him 5 Yankee players for every 2 Red Sox players Erol gave him. If Erol gave Eren 10 cards with Red Sox players, how many Yankee cards did he get in return? Write a proportion and solve it.

15. The marketing office for the Newton Discovery Center needs new carpeting. The office is 10 ft. by 12 ft. How many square yards of carpet are needed?

Think
Back

11. Monica should have taken 25% of $50. The amount off the dress was 25% of $50, or $12.50. The sale price of the dress is $50 − $12.50 = $37.50. Monica should have gotten $40 − $37.50 = $2.50 in change.

12. 2

13. **B.** 0.6

14. 5 : 2 = ___ : 10
    He got 25 cards with Yankee players.

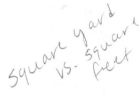

15. 13.3 square yards

> **NOTE** Depending on how carpet is sold, students may have to round up to the nearest full square yard. In this case, 14 square yards of carpet would have to be purchased.

**Example 1**

Find the greatest common factor of 16 and 40. Find all factors of each number.

- Factors of 16       ①②④⑧16
- Factors of 40       ①②④5,⑧10, 20, 40

They have four common factors, 1, 2, 4 and 8. The greatest common factor is 8.

**Example 2**

Find the greatest common factor in this expression: $3c + 12c$

- Factors of $3c$       ①③©
- Factors of $12c$       ①2,③4, 6, 12,©

They have common factors 1, 3 and $c$. The greatest common factor is $3c$.

## Find the greatest common factors in the following expressions:

**1.** 21 and 18

**2.** −36 and 42

**3.** 13 and $24x$

**4.** $45a$ and $30a$

**5.** $12xy$ and $16y$

**6.** $6a − 3$

**7.** $16 + 4z$

**8.** $36 − 27y$

**9.** $14c + 35c$

**10.** $5ab + 25b$

# Lesson Guide 1.1A  *Finding the Greatest Common Factor (GCF)*
## (Answer Key)

1. 3

2. 6

3. 1

4. $15a$

5. $4y$

6. 3

7. 4

8. 9

9. $7c$

10. $5b$

**1.** **a)** Start with –6 and add your favorite number.
Now add 10 to the sum.
Finally, subtract 4.

What number did you end up with?

**b)** Use the table below to show why this works.

| Step | Words | Diagram | Expression |
|------|-------|---------|------------|
| 1 | Start with $^-6$. | | $^-6$ |
| 2 | Add $n$. | $\boxed{-1}\ \boxed{-1}\ \boxed{-1}\ \boxed{-1}\ \boxed{-1}\ \boxed{-1}\ \boxed{+n}$ | |
| 3 | Add 10. | | $^-6 + n + 10$ |
| 4 | Subtract 4. | | |

**c)** Explain why this trick will always work no matter what number you choose.

**2.** **a)** Start with your favorite number and subtract 8.
Add 13 to the difference.
Finally, subtract 5 from the sum.

What number did you end up with?

**b)** Use the table below to show why this works.

| Step | Words | Diagram | Expression |
|------|-------|---------|------------|
| 1 | Start with $n$. | | $n$ |
| 2 | Subtract 8. | | |
| 3 | Add 13. | | |
| 4 | Subtract 5. | | |

**c)** Explain why this trick will always work no matter what number you choose.

Accommodation Guide

**3.** **a)** Think of a number between 1 and 20.

Triple your number.

Add 12 to the product.

Divide the sum by 3.

Subtract your original number.

What number did you end up with?

**b)** Use the table below to show why this works.

| Step | Words | Diagram | Expression |
|------|-------|---------|------------|
| 1 | Think of a number between 1 and 20. | | $n$ |
| 2 | Triple your number. | $\boxed{n}\ \boxed{n}\ \boxed{n}$ | |
| 3 | Add 12. | | |
| 4 | Divide by 3. | | $\dfrac{3n + 12}{3} = \dfrac{3(n + 4)}{3}$ |
| 5 | Subtract your original number. | | |

**c)** Explain why this trick will always work no matter what number you choose for your favorite number.

**1.** **a)** Answers will vary. Students should end up with the number they chose to add in Step 2.

**b)**

| Step | Words | Diagram | Expression |
|---|---|---|---|
| 1 | Start with ⁻6. | ⊖⊖⊖⊖⊖⊖ | $^-6$ |
| 2 | Add $n$. | ⊖⊖⊖⊖⊖⊖ ▢$n$ | $^-6 + n$ |
| 3 | Add 10. | ▢$n$ ⊕⊕⊕⊕ | $^-6 + n + 10$ |
| 4 | Subtract 4. | ▢$n$ | $^-6 + n + 10 - 4$ |

**c)** Answers may vary. Responses should indicate that regardless of the number chosen, the steps are planned so that the number chosen remains. In Step 3, adding 10 to the sum of the chosen number and ⁻6, results in the chosen number plus 4. Step 4 subtracts 4, resulting in the chosen number.

**2.** **a)** Answers will vary. Students should end up with the number they chose to start with.

**b)** Use the table below to show why this works.

| Step | Words | Diagram | Expression |
|---|---|---|---|
| 1 | Start with $n$. | ▢$n$ | $n$ |
| 2 | Subtract 8. | ▢$n$ ⊖⊖⊖⊖ ⊖⊖⊖⊖ | $n - 8$ |
| 3 | Add 13. | ▢$n$ ⊕⊕⊕⊕⊕ | $n - 8 + 13$ |
| 4 | Subtract 5. | ▢$n$ | $n - 8 + 13 - 5$ |

**c)** Answers may vary. Responses should indicate that regardless of the number chosen, the steps are planned so that only the number chosen remains. In Step 3, adding 13 to the difference of the original number and 8 results in the chosen number plus 5. Step 4 subtracts 5, always resulting in the chosen number.

**3.  a)  4**

**b)**

| Step | Words | Diagram | Expression |
|------|-------|---------|------------|
| 1 | Think of a number between 1 and 20. | $n$ | $n$ |
| 2 | Triple your number. | $n$ $n$ $n$ | $3n$ |
| 3 | Add 12. | $n$ $n$ $n$ $+1$ $+1$ $+1$ $+1$ $+1$ $+1$ $+1$ $+1$ $+1$ $+1$ $+1$ $+1$ | $3n + 12$ |
| 4 | Divide by 3. | $n$ $+1$ $+1$ $+1$ $+1$ | $\dfrac{3n + 12}{3} = \dfrac{3(n + 4)}{3}$ |
| 5 | Subtract your original number. | $+1$ $+1$ $+1$ $+1$ | $\dfrac{3(n + 4)}{3} - n$ |

**c)  Answers may vary. Responses should indicate that regardless of the starting number, the steps are planned so that some steps are inverses, or undo each other, ensuring that the final number is 4.**

## _____ 's Mathmagic Trick
### (name)

| Step | Words | Diagram | Expression |
|------|-------|---------|------------|
|      |       |         |            |
|      |       |         |            |
|      |       |         |            |
|      |       |         |            |
|      |       |         |            |
|      |       |         |            |

| Step | Words | Diagram | Expression |
|------|-------|---------|------------|
|      |       |         |            |
|      |       |         |            |
|      |       |         |            |
|      |       |         |            |
|      |       |         |            |
|      |       |         |            |

# It's All in the Ordering!

**Suggested Pacing:** $2\frac{1}{2}$ Days

In this lesson students explore the order of operations. They discover that there is a need for an agreed-upon order and set of rules.

---

**LESSON OBJECTIVES**

- Students will use the rules for the order of operations to simplify algebraic expressions.
- Students will use the order of operations to solve equations.

---

| DAY 1 | Materials* | ESSENTIAL *ON YOUR OWN* QUESTIONS |
|---|---|---|
| One Equation— Three Solution? | **In Class**<br>■ Calculators<br>■ Chart paper<br>■ Lesson Guide 1.2: *Please Excuse My Dear Aunt Sally* | Questions 1, 2, 4, 10–12 |
| **DAY 2** | **Materials*** | **ESSENTIAL *ON YOUR OWN* QUESTIONS** |
| Analyzing the Competition<br><br>Admission Costs for Newton Discovery Center | **In Class**<br>■ Calculators<br>■ Chart paper<br>■ Lesson Guide 1.2A: *Analyzing the Competition*<br>**On Your Own**<br>■ Calculators | Questions 3, 5, 6, 8, 13, 14 |

*The Think Like a Mathematician Daily Record Sheet should be used daily

---

## MATHEMATICALLY SPEAKING

▶ grouping symbols ▶ order of operations

# It's All in The Ordering!

 Start It Off

Enter each expression on your calculator. Write the answer in the table. Write down the order in which the calculator performed the operations. The first one is done for you. Just like reading a book, most calculators read a problem from left to right. But, the calculator does not always perform the operations in this order.

| Expression | Answer | Order of Operations Performed |
|---|---|---|
| 6 · 3 + 8 · 4 | 50 | multiply 6 · 3, multiply 8 · 4, add 18 + 32 |
| 6 + 3 · 8 − 4 | | |
| 6 ÷ 3 − 8 ÷ 4 | | |
| 6 + 3 − 8 + 4 | | |
| 6 · 3 ÷ 2 · 4 | | |
| 6 ÷ 3 ÷ 2 · 4 | | |
| 6 − 3 · 2 − 4 | | |
| 6 · 3 − 2 ÷ 4 | | |

Attendance at the Isaac Newton Discovery Center has been down the last three years. You suspect that one reason might be that your admission prices are higher than other nearby attractions. As Director, you need to adjust admission prices. You will be using algebraic expressions, equations and formulas to help you.

 Start It Off

**NOTE** Some calculators carry out operations in the order in which they were entered. Please check students' calculators to be sure they perform operations in the correct order before having students complete this lesson.

| Expression | Answer | Order of Operations Performed |
|---|---|---|
| 6 • 3 + 8 • 4 | 50 | multiply 6 • 3, multiply 8 • 4, add 18 + 32 |
| 6 + 3 • 8 − 4 | 26 | multiply 3 • 8, add 24 + 6, subtract 30 − 4 |
| 6 ÷ 3 − 8 ÷ 4 | 0 | divide 6 ÷ 3, divide 8 ÷ 4, subtract 2 − 2 |
| 6 + 3 − 8 + 4 | 5 | add 6 + 3, subtract 9 − 8, add 1 + 4 |
| 6 • 3 ÷ 2 • 4 | 36 | multiply 6 • 3, divide 18 ÷ 2, multiply 9 • 4 |
| 6 ÷ 3 ÷ 2 • 4 | 4 | divide 6 ÷ 3, divide 2 ÷ 2, multiply 1 • 4 |
| 6 − 3 • 2 − 4 | −4 | multiply 3 • 2, subtract 6 − 6, subtract 0 − 4 |
| 6 • 3 − 2 ÷ 4 | 17.5 | multiply 6 • 3, divide 2 ÷ 4, subtract 18 − 0.5 |

## One Equation—Three Solutions?

A competitor, the Northeast Aquarium, offers a special discount for school groups with two or more adult chaperones. This rate is determined using the following equation:

$$p = 20 + 7.95s + 15.95(a - 2), \text{ where}$$

- *p* stands for the price of admission,
- 20 is a fixed amount of $20 that must be paid no matter how many students or adults attend,
- *s* represents the number of students, and
- *a* represents the number of adults.

**1.** **a)** The first two adults are free. How is this represented in the formula?

   **b)** What does the 7.95 represent?

   **c)** What does the 15.95 represent?

Three student volunteers, Jeremy, Ann and Naomi, work in the ticket office at Northeast Aquarium. A group of 22 students and 5 adults visited the aquarium. The volunteers had to find the cost of their admission. Jeremy came up with $692.65. Ann figured the cost to be $242.75. Naomi found the total cost to be $662.75.

**2.** They wrote down their methods in the notebook below.

   **a)** Who got the correct answer?

   **b)** Discuss with your partner where the other two students made mistakes.

**? Hint**
See page 168

*(handwritten notes, left margin:)* added before multiply · ignored parentheses · correct · added before multiplied

**Jeremy** $p =$
$20 + 7.95s + 15.95(a - 2)$
$27.95(22) + 15.95(5 - 2)$
$614.90 + 15.95 \cdot 5 - 2$
$614.90 + 79.75 - 2 = 692.65$

**Ann** $p =$
$20 + 7.95(22) + 15.95(3)$
$20 + 17.90 + 47.85 = 242.75$

**Naomi** $p =$
$27.95(22) + 15.95(5) - 15.95(2)$
$614.90 + 79.75 - 31.90 = 662.75$

Section 1: Algebraic Expressions and Equations • Lesson 1.2   **15**

explore other grouping symbols (brackets and the division bar) and learn how these are used when evaluating expressions and solving equations.

## One Equation—Three Solutions?

Read together about the Northeast Aquarium's special discount for school groups. Ask students:

- *Why do you think the Northeast Aquarium offers a special discount rate to school groups?*

 **Talk Moves** Complete Question 1 as a class. After discussing the given equation for the discount rate, have students work with a partner to complete Question 2. Discuss student responses as a class. Emphasize that the student errors were a result of performing operations in the wrong order and not due to mistakes in calculations. Use talk moves, such as revoicing and repeat/rephrase, to clarify student ideas and build understanding.

**1.** **a)** $(a - 2)$

   **b)** The cost per student ticket is $7.95.

   **c)** The cost per adult ticket is $15.95.

**2.** **a)** Ann is correct. The cost is $242.75.

   **b)** Naomi's mistake is that she added $20 + 7.95$ first rather than multiplying $7.95 \cdot 22$ and then adding 20 to that result. Since she added before multiplying, she did not follow the order of operations.

## DAY 1 TEACHING THE LESSON

In this lesson, students explore the order of operations that is used to evaluate expressions and solve equations. To set the stage for the need to have an order of operations, the lesson begins by challenging students to analyze different solutions of a given situation. As students evaluate each situation, they should come to appreciate the importance of having the order of operations. The mnemonic *Please Excuse My Dear Aunt Sally* (PEMDAS) is presented to help students remember this order. Students will also

Jeremy made two mistakes. Like Naomi, he added 20 + 7.95 first rather than multiplying 7.95 • 22. His second mistake was that he did not simplify the parentheses first (5 − 2). Instead, he multiplied 15.95 • 5, ignoring the parentheses. Jeremy should have subtracted 5 − 2 to get a difference of 3, then multiplied by 15.95. Like Naomi, Jeremy did not follow the order of operations.

Review the phrase students learned in previous grades to help remember the order of operations, *Please Excuse My Dear Aunt Sally*.

Have students complete Question 3 independently and have them compare their responses with a partner. Discuss any discrepancies with the class to clarify understanding.

Emphasize that the *P* in the mnemonic device represents the grouping symbol parentheses. Brackets and the division bar are also grouping symbols. Allow time to discuss how these grouping symbols affect the order of operations. Students often overlook these symbols, and as a result, make careless errors.

Distribute a copy of Lesson Guide 1.2: *Please Excuse My Dear Aunt Sally* to each student. Then have the class compete Question 4 independently.

You should have found that all the students did each operation correctly. But, it was the *order* in which they performed the operations that gave such different results.

**Let's Review**

**Please Excuse (My Dear) (Aunt Sally)**

**P** refers to parentheses.

**E** refers to exponents.

**M** and **D** refer to multiplication and division.

**A** and **S** refer to addition and subtraction.

In earlier grades you learned this phrase to help you remember the order of operations, the consistent order in which operations are performed. Remember that for multiplication and division, you perform these operations in order from left to right. It doesn't matter which comes first, so we have put parentheses around (My Dear). The same holds true for addition and subtraction. But remember that all multiplication and division should be done before you start any addition or subtraction that are not within a set of parentheses.

**MATHEMATICALLY SPEAKING**

▸ order of operations
▸ grouping symbols

**3.** Without using a calculator, find the value of each expression.

**a)** $3 - 5 \cdot 2$

**b)** $6 \div 2 + 7 \cdot 5$

**c)** $28 - 4 \cdot 1.5 \cdot 5$

**d)** $100 \cdot 0.5 \div 2 \cdot 4$ (This is an interesting answer!)

**4.** Explain how the operations are related in Part d.

The **P** in **Please** stands for *parentheses*. Parentheses are a type of grouping symbol. Brackets [ ] are grouping symbols too. The division bar is also a grouping symbol. It separates the numerator from the denominator. All operations inside any of these grouping symbols should be performed first.

**3. a)** $3 - 10 = ^-7$

   **b)** $3 + 35 = 38$

   **c)** $28 - 30 = ^-2$

   **d)** $25 \cdot 4 = 100$

**4.** Using PEMDAS: $100 \cdot 0.5 = 50$ and $50 \div 2 = 25$ and $25 \cdot 4 = 100$. Since multiplication and division are inverse operations, we can rewrite Part d using only multiplication: $100 \cdot 0.5 \cdot (\frac{1}{2}) \cdot 4$ or $100 \cdot (\frac{1}{2}) \cdot (\frac{1}{2}) \cdot 4$.

Using the associative property of multiplication, we can write $100 \cdot (\frac{1}{4}) \cdot (4) = 100 \cdot 1 = 100$.

**Example**

Evaluate $\dfrac{12 + 3(-40 - 6)}{(2 - 4) \cdot 3}$.

**Step 1.** Do what is inside parentheses first.

$$\frac{12 + 3(-40 - 6)}{(2 - 4) \cdot 3} = \frac{12 + 3(-46)}{(-2) \cdot 3}$$

**Step 2.** The division bar separates the numerator from the denominator. Simplify the numerator and denominator first, before dividing.

$$\frac{12 + 3(-46)}{(-2) \cdot 3} = \frac{12 + {}^-138}{-6} = \frac{-126}{-6}$$

 **NOTE** Remember to simplify the numerator, you need to multiply 3(−46) before adding 12. Multiplication is done before addition.

**Step 3.** Divide the numerator by the denominator.

$$\frac{-126}{-6} = 21$$

Note: If there is more than one grouping symbol in the expression, work from the inside out. For example,
$[6 + (12 - 4)] \cdot 2 = [6 + 8] \cdot 2 = 14 \cdot 2 = 28$.

**5.** Fill in the table below.

| Expression | Answer | How Did We Do This? |
|---|---|---|
| $12(8 - 3) + 3$ | 63 | First subtract $8 - 3 = 5$. Then multiply $12 \cdot 5 = 60$. Then add $60 + 3$. |
| $\dfrac{60 - 26}{15 + 2}$ | | First subtract $60 - 26$. Then add $15 + 2$. Finally divide 34 by 17. |
| $2 + (300 - 6) \cdot 0.10$ | 31.4 | |
| $[2 + (300 - 6)] \cdot 0.10$ | 29.6 | |
| $[80 \div (6.3 + 3.7)] \cdot 3$ | 24 | |
| $12 - 4(62 - 5)$ | −216 | |
| $50 - (40 - 60)$ | | First subtract $40 - 60 = {}^-20$. Then subtract $50 - ({}^-20)$. |
| $^-6 - (3 - 5) + (^-5.4)$ | −9.4 | |
| $\dfrac{4 - 0.5(100 + 52)}{3 \cdot 12}$ | | |
| $\dfrac{15 + 3(^-40 - 0.6)}{2 - 4(3)}$ | | |

Handwritten work:

$12 + 3(-40 - 6)$
$12 + 3(-46)$
$12 + (-138)$
$= -126$

$(2 - 4) \cdot 3$
$-2 \cdot 3$
$= -6$

$\dfrac{-126}{-6} = 21$

**5.**

| Expression | Answer | How Did We Do This? |
|---|---|---|
| $12(8 - 3) + 3$ | 63 | First do $8 - 3 = 5$. Then multiply $12 \cdot 5 = 60$. Then add $60 + 3$. |
| $\dfrac{60 - 26}{15 + 2}$ | **2** | First subtract $60 - 26$. Then add $15 + 2$. Finally divide 34 by 17. |
| $2 + (300 - 6) \cdot 0.10$ | 31.4 | **First, subtract $300 - 6$. Then multiply $294 \cdot 0.10$. Then add $29.4 + 2$ to get a sum of 31.4.** |
| $[2 + (300 - 6)] \cdot 0.10$ | 29.6 | **First, subtract $300 - 6$. Then add $2 + 294$. Then multiply $296 \cdot 0.10$ to get a product of 29.6.** |
| $[80 \div (6.3 + 3.7)] \cdot 3$ | 24 | **First, add $6.3 + 3.7$. Then divide $80 \div 10$. Then multiply $8 \cdot 3$ to get a product of 24.** |
| $12 - 4(62 - 5)$ | −216 | **First subtract $62 - 5$. Then multiply $4 \cdot 57$. Then subtract $12 - 228$ to get a difference of −216.** |
| $50 - (40 - 60)$ | **70** | First subtract $40 - 60$. Then subtract $50 - (-20)$. |
| $^-6 - (3 - 5) + {}^-5.4$ | −9.4 | **First subtract $3 - 5$. Then subtract $^-6 - (^-2)$. Then add $^-4 + {}^-5.4$ to get a sum of −9.4.** |
| $\dfrac{4 - 0.5(100 + 52)}{3 \cdot 12}$ | **−2** | **First add $100 + 52$. Then multiply $0.5 \cdot 152$. Then subtract $4 - 76$. Next, multiply $3 \cdot 12$. Then divide $^-72 \div 36$ to get a quotient of −2.** |
| $\dfrac{15 + 3(^-40 - 0.60)}{2 - 4(3)}$ | **10.68** | **First subtract $^-40 - 0.6$. Then multiply $3 \cdot {}^-40.6$. Then add $15 + {}^-121.8$. Next, multiply $4 \cdot 3$. Then subtract $2 - 12$. Then divide $2106.8 \div {}^-10$ to get a quotient of 10.68.** |

## Summarize Day 1

 **Talk Moves** As a Wrap It Up discussion for Day 1, have students share their responses to Question 5 in a class discussion. Use the talk move agree/disagree and why to clarify any discrepancies or misconceptions.

Guide the discussion to emphasize the following:

- Discuss the differences between the third and fourth example. Ask students:

- *How do the brackets change the order of operations? Does changing the order affect the final answer?*

- Remind students that the division bar is also a grouping symbol. It indicates that you perform any operations in the numerator and in the denominator first before dividing.

- Discuss how even if all the operations are the same, parentheses can change the final answer. Have students solve $50 - 40 - 60$ and compare with their answer to $50 - (40 - 60)$.

---

## Analyzing the Competition

6. The New England Museum of Science offers a different pricing scheme. Their regular ticket prices are $17 for adults and $14 for students. For school groups of 20 or more with at least 3 adult chaperones, they offer a group discount of $4 per adult and $4 per student with 3 free adults.

    a) Write an equation that finds the cost for a school group of 20 or more to visit the New England Museum of Science.

    b) Talk to your partner and predict who offers the better deal—Northeast Aquarium or the New England Museum of Science.

    c) Fill in the table below. Was your prediction correct?

| Name of School | Number of Students | Number of Adults | Northeast Aquarium Admission | New England Museum of Science Admission |
|---|---|---|---|---|
| Oak Hill School | 20 | 6 | | |
| Avon Middle School | 60 | 10 | | |
| King Junior High | 80 | 12 | | |

    d) **What went wrong?** Naomi wrote the equation $p = (14 - 4)s + (17 - 3)a$ for admission costs to the New England Museum of Science. Help Naomi understand why her equation is incorrect.

## Admission Costs for Newton Discovery Center

One of your duties as the Director is to offer competitive prices. Come up with a school group discount equation so that each school above will find your rate the least expensive. Remember, you can't make it too cheap, or you will go broke!

7. Work with a partner to create a formula for student group discounts for the Newton Discovery Center. Include at least one set of grouping symbols in your formula.

8. Write a proposal, including your equation, with charts showing the cost of admission using the schools above. Justify why your proposed price will be more attractive than the two other nearby competitors. Present your argument to the Board of Directors (the class) for approval.

**18** Course 3: Solve It: Focusing on Equations, Inequalities and Exponents

---

# DAY 2 TEACHING THE LESSON

## Analyzing the Competition

In their role as Director of the Isaac Newton Discovery Center, students need to be aware of the pricing strategies of other educational centers. Students will analyze the group discount rate for the New England Museum and compare it to the Northeast Aquarium to determine which center is offering a better deal. Have students complete Question 6 with a partner.

Circulate among pairs as students solve this problem. Use the *Student Snapshot* observation tool to informally assess student understanding and record observations. Discuss student responses as a class.

 **Differentiation**

**Think Differently:** Lesson Guide 1.2A: *Analyzing the Competition* is available for those students who may need additional support in organizing information as they work on Question 6.

6. **a)** Let *s* represent the number of students, *a* the number of adults and *p* the total price.

   When the group size is 20 or more, $(s + a) > 20$, then $p = (14 - 4)s + (17 - 4) \cdot (a - 3)$ or $p = 10s + 13(a - 3)$.

   **b)** Predictions will vary. The Northeast Aquarium is actually a little less expensive.

   **c)**

| Name of School | Number of Students | Number of Adults | Northeast Aquarium Admission | New England Museum of Science Admission |
|---|---|---|---|---|
| Oak Hill School | 20 | 6 | $242.80 | $239 |
| Avon Middle School | 60 | 10 | $624.60 | $691 |
| King Junior High | 80 | 12 | $815.50 | $917 |

   **d)** Naomi's equation is incorrect because she subtracted 3 from the adult ticket price of $17, rather than subtracting 3 from the number of adults. Naomi should have subtracted $4 from the adult ticket price, and then multiplied that result by the number of adults minus three, since 3 adult tickets are free with groups of 20 or more.

   To further demonstrate that this equation is incorrect, students could calculate the cost of admission to the New England Museum of Science using Naomi's equation:

   Oak Hill School            $284
   Avon Middle School     $740
   King Junior High          $968

   Since the costs don't match up, Naomi's equation is incorrect.

## Admission Costs for Newton Discovery Center

Explain to students that they will create a proposal, including an equation, for student group discounts for the Isaac Newton Discovery Center. As director, each needs to make sure the discount is competitive to attract groups, but lucrative enough to make a profit for the center. Emphasize that the rate must be less expensive than the Northeast Aquarium and the New England Science Museum.

Have students work with a partner to develop their proposals by completing Question 7. Then have pairs present their proposals to the class. Encourage students to justify why their pricing scheme will be competitive.

 **NOTE** For math classes with 45 minutes of instruction, continue with the presentation of proposals on another day.

7. Answers will vary. The equation student pairs create must have a least one set of grouping symbols, and the school group admission discount rate must be less expensive than the Northeast Aquarium and the New England Museum of Science.

8. Have pairs of students present their proposals to the class. Encourage students to justify why their pricing scheme will be competitive.

 **W**rap It Up

Answers will vary. The discussion should include the following key ideas:

- Having a specific order to perform operations ensures that the same answer will be found consistently when simplifying.

- The rules for order of operations eliminate confusion when doing a string of calculations.

- Grouping symbols, such as parentheses and brackets, change the order of some operations.

- The division bar is also a symbol that groups calculations. The calculations in the numerator and denominator are done separately, and then the numerator is divided by the denominator.

Examples will vary. Possible example:

$3(-2 + 7) + 12$

According to the order of operations, first add $-2 + 7$. Then multiply $3 \cdot 5$. Next, add $15 + 17$ to get a sum of 32.

Without using the order of operations, one might first multiply $3 \cdot -2$. Then add 7 to $-6$. Next, add 1 to 12 to get a sum of 13.

The order of operations ensures that calculations are done in a consistent manner so as to arrive at the same answer each time the calculations are carried out.

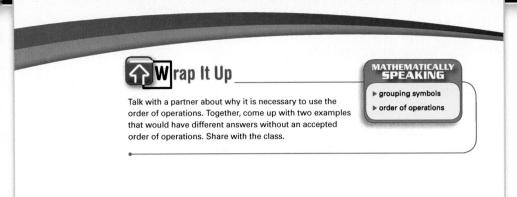

## Wrap It Up

Talk with a partner about why it is necessary to use the order of operations. Together, come up with two examples that would have different answers without an accepted order of operations. Share with the class.

**MATHEMATICALLY SPEAKING**

▶ grouping symbols
▶ order of operations

## Reflect

Use these questions to help you reflect on the lesson and plan for future instruction.

- How effectively do students apply the rules for the order of operations?

- What lingering misconceptions about the order of operations need to be addressed in future instruction?

**1.** Answers will vary.
Possible response using parentheses:

| | |
|---|---|
| $-2(2.5 - 4) + 6$ | First do calculations inside the parentheses. Subtract $2.5 - 4$. |
| $-2(-1.5) + 6$ | Next, multiply $-2 \cdot -1.5$. |
| $3 + 6$ | Then add $3 + 6$. |
| 9 | |

Possible response using division bar: Perform the calculations in the numerator, perform the calculations in the denominator, then divide the result in the numerator by the result in the denominator.

| | |
|---|---|
| $\dfrac{3 + -7 \cdot 5}{0.5 - 2.5}$ | Multiply $-7 \cdot 5$. |
| $\dfrac{3 + -35}{0.5 - 2.5}$ | Add $3 + -35$. |
| $\dfrac{-32}{0.5 - 2.5}$ | Subtract $0.5 - 2.5$. |
| $\dfrac{-32}{-2}$ | Divide $-32 \div -2$. |
| 16 | |

Possible response using brackets: Perform the calculations within the brackets first.

| | |
|---|---|
| $3[4(-1 + 7) + 3] - 3$ | Add $-1 + 7$. |
| $3[4 \cdot 6 + 3] - 3$ | Multiply $4 \cdot 6$. |
| $3[24 + 3] - 3$ | Add $24 + 3$. |
| $3[27] - 3$ | Multiply $3 \cdot 27$. |
| $81 - 3$ | Subtract $81 - 3$. |
| 78 | |

---

**Write About It**

1. Make up three expressions that each contain at least two operations. Each expression should use a different kind of grouping symbol. Evaluate each expression and explain how you evaluated it, step by step.

2. Evaluate the following expressions without using a calculator.

    a) $34 \div 2 + 2$

    b) $3 + 8 \div 4 - 2$

    c) $5 + 6 - 7 + 9 - 1.5$

    d) $7 + 7 \cdot 2 \div 2 \cdot 3$

    e) $20 - 2(3 + 8) \cdot \frac{1}{2}$

    f) $\dfrac{1.8}{3} - \dfrac{7 - 11.2}{2}$

    g) $\dfrac{-4[7 + (-6)]}{8}$

    h) $12 - 8 \div 2 \cdot 3$

3. Jeff's Cookie Corner is in the food court at the Newton Discovery Center. Jeff gets a good price for cookie dough from his wholesale supplier. He can buy a container of dough, which makes 1,000 cookies, for only $55. However, he must pay an additional $7.50 per container to ship the dough.

    a) Write an equation for the total cost, $c$, of $d$ containers of dough.

    b) Find the total cost for 4,000 cookies.

    c) Find the total cost for 7,500 cookies.

    **? Hint**
    See page 168

    d) Is the price per cookie for 4,000 cookies the same as the price per cookie for 7,500 cookies? Explain why or why not.

4. In 2009, the cost of admission to the San Francisco Exploratorium was $14 for adults, $11 for teens 13–17, $9 for children ages 4–12 and free for children 3 and under.

    a) Write an equation for the cost of admission for the general public. Let $C$ = cost of admission, $a$ = number of adults, $t$ = number of teens and $c$ = number of children ages 4–12.

**2. a)** 19   **e)** 9

**b)** 3   **f)** 1.5

**c)** 11.5   **g)** $-\dfrac{1}{2}$

**d)** 28   **h)** 0

**3. a)** $c = (55 + 7.50)d$ or $c = 55d + 7.50d$ or $c = 62.50d$

**b)** $4{,}000 \div 1{,}000 = 4$. Jeff needs 4 containers of dough to make 4,000 cookies.

$c = (55 + 7.50)4$
$c = 62.5 \cdot 4$
$c = 250$

It will cost Jeff $250 to purchase the dough to make 4,000 cookies.

**b)** The Martin family is planning a trip to the San Francisco Exploratorium. Mr. and Mrs. Martin are adults, Jen is 16, Dave is 9 and Jonas is $2\frac{1}{2}$. They have a coupon for $25 off the price of admission. Dave wrote the following equation to find their admission cost: $p = 2 \cdot 14 + 11 + 9 - 25$.

   **i)** What does the 2 represent?

   **ii)** What does the −25 represent?

**c)** Jen said he needed to group the (14 + 11 + 9) first with parentheses. Is she correct? Explain.

**5.** The Martins sometimes take one or more grandparents with them when they visit the Exploratorium. In the equation below, $g$ represents the number of grandparents they take and $C$ represents the Martin family's cost of admission.

$$C = 2 \cdot 14 + g \cdot 14 + 11 + 9 - 25$$

**a)** Find the total cost of admission if Grandma and Grandpa Martin join them.

**b)** Use factoring to find an equivalent expression for $2 \cdot 14 + g \cdot 14$. Write the equation for $C$ using your expression.

**c)** Find the total cost of admission using the equation you wrote in Part b. Did you get the same answer as you did using the original equation? Why or why not?

**4. a)** $C = 14a + 11t + 9c$, where $C$ represents the total cost, $a$ represents the number of adults, $t$ represents the number of teens and $c$ represents the number of children ages 4–12.

**b) i)** 2 represents the number of adults.

   **ii)** −25 represents the reduction in price from the coupon.

**c)** Dave is correct. Jen should not put 14 + 11 + 9 in parentheses because the price of adult tickets ($14) should be multiplied by 2 to determine the cost of two adult tickets. Since the family does not need to purchase two teen tickets or two children's tickets, it doesn't make sense to group the numbers in parentheses.

---

**c)** $7,500 \div 1,000 = 7.5$. Jeff needs 8 containers of dough to make 7,500 cookies since he cannot order 7.5 containers.

$c = (55 + 7.50)8$

$c = 62.5 \cdot 8$

$c = 500$

It will cost Jeff $500 to purchase the dough to make 7,500 cookies.

**d)** The price per cookie for 4,000 cookies is $0.0625 or 6.25 cents per cookie ($\frac{250}{4,000} = 0.0625$), while the price for 7,500 cookies is $0.0667 or 6.67 cents per cookie ($\frac{500}{7,500}$). Since Jeff must buy full containers, he pays more per cookie if he doesn't use all the 8 containers of dough and make 8,000 cookies.

**5. a)** $51

**b)** $14(2 + g)$

$C = 14(2 + g) + 11 + 9 - 25$

**c)** $p = 14(2 + g) + 11 + 9 - 25$

$p = 14(2 + 2) + 11 + 9 - 25$

$p = 14 \cdot 4 + 11 + 9 - 25$

$p = 56 + 11 + 9 - 25$

$p = 67 + 9 - 25$

$p = 76 - 25$

$p = 51$

The answer is the same. The new equation is equivalent to the original equation.

**6. a)** multiplication and subtraction. Multiplication should be performed before subtraction according to the rules for the order of operations.

**b)** $n = 2{,}550 - 2{,}550 \cdot 2\% \cdot d$

$n = 2{,}550 - 2{,}550 \cdot 2\% \cdot 1$

$n = 2{,}550 - 2{,}550 \cdot 0.02$

$n = 2{,}550 - 51$

$n = 2{,}499$

**c)** $n = 2{,}550 - 2{,}550 \cdot 2\% \cdot d$

$n = 2{,}550 - 2{,}550 \cdot 2\% \cdot 6$

$n = 2{,}550 - 2{,}550 \cdot 0.12$

$n = 2{,}550 - 306$

$n = 2{,}244$

**d)** Use the equation $1{,}785 = 2{,}550 - 2{,}550 \cdot 2\%(d)$

$1{,}785 - 2{,}550 = {}^-2{,}550 \cdot 2\%(d)$

$^-765 = {}^-51d$

$15 = d$

The temperature was $85 + 15 = 100°F$.

**7. a)** $n = 2{,}550 - 2{,}550 \cdot 5\%$ $\cdot d$, where $n$ represents the number of people attending the Aquatic Animal Show and $d$ represents the number of degrees the temperature drops below 60°F.
$n = 2{,}550 - 2{,}550 \cdot 5\% \cdot d$

**b)** $n = 2{,}550 - 2{,}550 \cdot 5\% \cdot 2$

$n = 2{,}550 - 2{,}550 \cdot 0.1$

$n = 2{,}550 - 255$

$n = 2{,}295$

The predicted attendance when the temperature is 58°F is 2,295 patrons.

---

**6.** Attendance at the Aquatic Animal Show in the Magellan Aquarium at the Newton Discovery Center is dependent on the weather. The temperature that brings in the greatest attendance is between 70 and 80 degrees Fahrenheit. For every degree that is above 85, attendance drops by 2%.

Your chief financial officer (CFO) created the following equation to help predict attendance.

$n = 2{,}550 - 2{,}550 \cdot 2\% \cdot d$, where $n$ represents the number of people attending the Aquatic Animal Show, and $d$ represents the number of degrees the temperature is above 85°F.

**a)** What operations do you need to use to find the attendance? In what order should you do them?

**b)** Find the predicted attendance if the temperature is 86°F.

**c)** Find the predicted attendance if the temperature is 91°F.

**d)** What was the temperature outside if the attendance was 1,785 people?

**7.** This equation changes as the weather gets cooler. Below 60°F, the attendance drops an estimated 5% for every degree below 60°F.

**a)** Write a new equation for the predicted attendance for cooler weather.

**b)** Find the predicted attendance if the temperature is 58°F.

**c)** Find the predicted attendance if the temperature is 50°F.

 **Think Beyond**

**8.** Jen wrote the equation for attendance on a hot day at the Aquatic Animal Show this way: $n = 2{,}550[1 - (2\% \cdot d)]$. She said her answers were the same as above.

**a)** Explain to Jen why her answer is the same.

**b)** Write the equation for cool days the same way Jen wrote her equation for the hot days. Use your equation to estimate the numbers of attendees on days that are 58° and 50°, and check that the results match the answers you calculated in Question 7.

---

**c)** $n = 2{,}550 - 2{,}550 \cdot 5\% \cdot d$

$n = 2{,}550 - 2{,}550 \cdot 5\% \cdot 10$

$n = 2{,}550 - 2{,}550 \cdot 0.5$

$n = 2{,}550 - 1{,}275$

$n = 1{,}275$

The predicted attendance when the temperature is 50°F is 1,275 patrons.

 **Think Beyond**

**8.**

**a)** The expression on the right side of the equal sign is equivalent to the original expression. Both terms in the original expression have a greatest common factor of 2,550. The original expression was simplified by factoring.

9. The equation for the profit at the Silky Smoothie snack bar is $p = 2.50 \cdot b - 400$, where $p$ represents the daily profit and $b$ represents the number of customers. All the Silky Smoothie fruit drinks are the same price.

a) What do you think the number 2.50 represents?

b) What do you think the number 400 represents? Why do you subtract this number?

c) Find the daily profit if 150 visitors buy a smoothie. Why is your answer negative? What does this means? *mean*

d) Find the daily profit if 450 visitors buy a smoothie.

e) If the profit for April 12 was $225, how many visitors bought a smoothie that day?

**Think Beyond**

10. Write a new equation to show what the profit at the Silky Smoothie snack bar would be *per buyer*.

a) Find the profit per buyer if 450 visitors buy a Silky Smoothie.

b) Find the profit per buyer if 800 visitors buy a Silky Smoothie.

c) Why might you want to know the profit per buyer?

9. a) The number 2.50 represents the cost of a smoothie fruit drink.

b) Possible response: The number 400 represents the operating costs of the snack bar. Since these are expenses, the 400 is subtracted from the revenues to determine the profit.

c) $-$25 The negative profit means that the amount of money collected from the fruit drink sales is less than the operating/supply costs. This means that the snack bar is not making a profit, since the costs are more than the money collected from sales. The Silky Smoothie snack bar is operating at a loss.

d) $725

e) 250 visitors. Use the equation $225 = 2.50 \cdot b - 400$ and solve for $b$.

**Think Beyond**

10. 
$$p = \frac{(2.50(b) - 400)}{b}$$

where $p$ now represents the per buyer profit and $b$ represents the number of buyers.

a) $1.6\overline{1}$ or approximately $1.61

b) $2.00

c) This might help you determine if the snack bar is worth keeping open. For example, is it worth keeping it open if only 200 people visit per day for a daily profit of $0.50 per person?

b) $n = 2,550[1 - (5\% \cdot d)]$, where $n$ represents the number of people attending the Aquatic Animal Show and $d$ represents the number of degrees the temperature is below 60°F.

$n = 2,550[1 - (5\% \cdot d)]$      $n = 2,550[1 - (5\% \cdot d)]$

$n = 2,550[1 - (5\% \cdot 2)]$      $n = 2,550[1 - (5\% \cdot 10)]$

$n = 2,550[1 - 0.1]$      $n = 2,550[1 - 0.5]$

$n = 2,550 \cdot 0.9$      $n = 2,550 \cdot 0.5$

$n = 2,295$      $n = 1,275$

Same result as Question 6d for 58°F      Same result as Question 6d for 50°F

**Think Back**

11. What is the distance on the number line between 4 and three times $-7$?

12. A ladder has steps that are 1.5" thick with 8" between steps. What is the distance between the top of the second step and the bottom of the seventh step?

**Hint**
See page 168

13. Matt is driving 420 miles from Maine to Pennsylvania. He knows that his car's tank holds 15 gallons. His car averages 21 miles per gallon on the highway.

a) If he fills his tank, can he make it all the way without stopping for gas?

b) If so, how much gas is still left? If not, how many more gallons does he need?

14. Alexa said she got 11 out of 15 problems correct on a math test and Emile said he had done better by getting 18 out of 24 problems correct on a science quiz. Was Emile right? Defend your answer using fractions rather than using percents for comparison.

**Think Back**

11. The distance is 25 units. $|4 - 3 \cdot -7| = 25$

12. 46 inches

13. a) He would run out of gas with 105 miles left.

b) He needs 5 more gallons to make it to Pennsylvania.

15. Vicki knows that her walkie-talkie can be heard up to 150 feet away. If Vicki stands still, how much area could Alexandra cover and still be able to hear Vicki?

**? Hint**
See page 168

14. Using common denominators: $\frac{11}{15} = \frac{88}{120}$ and $\frac{18}{24} = \frac{90}{120}$ so Emile did better. Emile was correct.

15. 70,650 ft.$^2$

| Expression | Answer | How Did We Do This? |
|---|---|---|
| $12(8 - 3) + 3$ | 63 | First subtract $8 - 3 = 5$. Then multiply $12 \cdot 5 = 60$. Then add $60 + 3$. |
| $\dfrac{60 - 26}{15 + 2}$ | | First subtract $60 - 26$. Then add $15 + 2$. Finally, divide 34 by 17. |
| $2 + (300 - 6) \cdot 0.10$ | 31.4 | |
| $[2 + (300 - 6)] \cdot 0.10$ | 29.6 | |
| $[80 \div (6.3 + 3.7)] \cdot 3$ | 24 | |
| $12 - 4(62 - 5)$ | $-216$ | |
| $50 - (40 - 60)$ | | First subtract $40 - 60 = -20$. Then subtract |
| $50 - (-20)$. | | |
| $-6 - (3 - 5) + (-5.4)$ | $-9.4$ | |
| $\dfrac{4 - 0.5(100 + 52)}{3 \cdot 12}$ | | |
| $\dfrac{15 + 3(-40 - 0.6)}{2 - 4(3)}$ | | |

| Name of School | Number of Students | Number of Adults | Northeast Aquarium Admission | New England Museum of Science Admission |
|---|---|---|---|---|
| Oak Hill School | 20 | 6 | | |
| Avon Middle School | 60 | 10 | | |
| King Junior High | 80 | 12 | | |

**LESSON 1.3**

# Looks Can Be Deceiving: Equivalent Expressions

**Suggested Pacing:** 2 Days

In this lesson, students learn to solve more complex equations with parentheses using a variety of methods. The "bar diagram" strategy introduced in earlier grades is revisited and extended.

---

**LESSON OBJECTIVES**

- Students will simplify and solve complex equations with parentheses using the bar diagram method.
- Students will use the distributive property along with the inverse properties and properties of equality to solve equations.
- Students will combine like terms to simplify expressions and solve equations.

---

| DAY 1 | Materials* | ESSENTIAL *ON YOUR OWN* QUESTIONS |
|---|---|---|
| Using Bar Diagrams<br><br>Using Properties to Solve Equations | **In Class**<br>■ Calculators<br>■ Chart paper (optional)<br>■ Lesson Guide 1.3: *Practice with Bar Diagrams*<br><br>**On Your Own**<br>■ Calculators | Questions 2–6, 11–13 |
| **DAY 2** | **Materials*** | **ESSENTIAL *ON YOUR OWN* QUESTIONS** |
| Combining Like Terms with Variables<br><br>Solving Equations by Combining Like Terms<br><br>Ordering Supplies at Jeff's Cookie Corne | **In Class**<br>■ Calculators<br>■ Chart paper (optional)<br>■ Lesson Guide 1.3: *The Equivalence Game*<br><br>**On Your Own**<br>■ Calculators | Questions 1, 7–10, 14–16 |

\*The Think Like a Mathematician Daily Record Sheet should be used daily

---

## MATHEMATICALLY SPEAKING

- ▶ addition property of equality
- ▶ additive identity property
- ▶ additive inverse property
- ▶ bar diagram

- ▶ constant
- ▶ equation
- ▶ like terms
- ▶ multiplication property of equality

- ▶ multiplicative identity property
- ▶ multiplicative inverse property
- ▶ solution (solution set)

## LESSON 1.3 Looks Can Be Deceiving: Equivalent Expressions

### ➡ Start It Off

At the Newton Discovery Center gift shop, you are going to sell t-shirts for $10 each. The sales tax is 7%. Josh, a student volunteer in the gift shop, is creating an equation to calculate the Center's revenue.

| Number of T-Shirts | 1 | 2 | 3 | 4 | 5 | 6 | 10 | 21 | n |
|---|---|---|---|---|---|---|---|---|---|
| Center Revenue (sales price plus sales tax) | 10 + 0.70 | 20 + 1.40 | | | 50 + 3.50 | | | | |

1. List the variables you need to find an equation for the Discovery Center's revenue for the shirts.

2. Write an explicit rule as an equation for the revenue ($r$) of $n$ T-shirts in three different ways:

   with two terms on one side of the equation, with parentheses on one side of the equation, and with one term on each side of the equation.

3. Use one of your equations to fill in the rest of the table.

**MATHEMATICALLY SPEAKING**
- ▶ equation
- ▶ solution (solution set)

**Let's Review** Remember that an equation states that two expressions are equal. To solve an equation, you find the value or values that make the equation true. These values are called the solution(s). In this section, you will learn how to solve equations where the variable is found in more than one term and sometimes on both sides of the equal sign. In some cases, parentheses are used.

### ➡ Start It Off

1. The independent variable, $n$, is the number of T-shirts. The dependent variable, $r$, is the Center's revenue (price of the shirt plus the sales tax).

2. $r = 10n + 0.70n$ or $r = n(10 + 0.70)$ or $r = 10.70n$

3.

| Number of T-Shirts Sold | 1 | 2 | 3 | 4 | 5 | 6 | 10 | 21 | n |
|---|---|---|---|---|---|---|---|---|---|
| Center Revenue (Sale price plus sales tax) | 10 + 0.70 = 10.70 | 20 + 1.40 = 21.40 | 30 + 2.10 = 32.10 | 40 + 2.80 = 42.80 | 50 + 3.50 = 53.50 | 60 + 4.20 = 64.20 | 100 + 7.00 = 107 | 210 + 14.70 = 224.70 | $10n + 0.70n$ = $10.70n$ |

## Using Bar Diagrams

 **Let's Review** In earlier grades, you learned how to use bar diagrams to solve equations.

**Example 1**

At the Discovery Center gift shop, four baseball caps and two travel mugs cost $58 before tax. The baseball caps are $8.50 each. How much does a travel mug cost?

Below is a bar diagram representing this situation.

| $58 | | | | | |
|---|---|---|---|---|---|
| $8.50 | $8.50 | $8.50 | $8.50 | Mug $ | Mug $ |
| $34 | | | | $24 | |
| $34 | | | | $12 | $12 |

From the diagram, you can see that each travel mug costs $12.

**MATHEMATICALLY SPEAKING**
▶ bar diagram

Bar diagrams also work for more complicated equations.

**Example 2**

Use a bar diagram to solve $3(x + 2) + 5 = 32$.

We can create the following bar diagram.

| 32 | | | |
|---|---|---|---|
| $x + 2$ | + 2 | $x + 2$ | 5 |
| 27 | | | 5 |
| 9 | 9 | 9 | 5 |

So, $x + 2 = 9$, and $x$ must equal 7. Check this solution by substituting 7 into the original equation.

**1.** Fill in the bar diagram and then solve the equation.

**a)** $4(x - 2) + 6 = 50$

| 50 | | | | |
|---|---|---|---|---|
| | | | | 6 |
| | 11 | | | |

**b)** So, $x - 2 =$ _____ and $x =$ _____.

**2.** Use bar diagrams to help you solve the following equations.

**a)** $2(x + 8) + 7 = 43$

**b)** $14 + 5(2a + 3) = 59$

**c)** $35 = 6(c - \frac{1}{3}) + 5$

---

Guide the discussion to focus on the idea that an equation is a mathematical statement where two expressions are equal to each other. Explain to students that there are many different ways to solve equations. Focus on the idea that the solution to the equation makes it a true statement. Emphasize to students that they will learn a number of strategies to solve complex equations with parentheses as they continue to explore real-life situations at the Isaac Newton Discovery Center.

## Using Bar Diagrams

Review the bar diagram strategy students used with *Math Innovations* in Courses 1 and 2 to solve equations and discuss the given example.

 **Differentiation**

**Think Differently:** For students who need more practice with bar diagrams, offer Lesson Guide 1.3A: *Practice with Bar Diagrams*.

---

## DAY 1 TEACHING THE LESSON

In this lesson, students learn to solve equations with parentheses using a variety of methods. The "bar diagram" strategy introduced in earlier grades is revisited and extended. Also, students explore how combining like terms with variables, factoring and the distributive property are useful when creating equivalent expressions to solve equations.

Begin the lesson by asking:

- *What is an equation?*

Explain that this strategy can also be used to solve more complex equations. Have students explore and discuss the given example and then complete Question 1 as a class.

Have students work independently on Question 2 and discuss their solution strategies as a class. Encourage a few students to share their bar diagrams on chart paper. You may wish to post these in the classroom for students to refer to when solving future equations.

**1. a)**

| 50 | | | | |
|---|---|---|---|---|
| $x - 2$ | $x - 2$ | $x - 2$ | $x - 2$ | 6 |
| 44 | | | | 6 |
| 11 | 11 | 11 | 11 | 6 |

**b)** So, $x - 2 = 11$ and $x = 13$.

## Using Properties to Solve Equations

Another way to solve equations is to use properties. In Grade 7, you learned how to solve equations using properties of equality and inverse operations.

Let's Review

**MATHEMATICALLY SPEAKING**

► addition property of equality
► additive identity property
► additive inverse property
► multiplication property of equality
► multiplicative identity property
► multiplicative inverse property

| Property | Description | Example |
|---|---|---|
| addition property of equality | When the same number is added to both sides of an equation, the sides remain equal. | If $x + 8 = 12$, then $x + 8 + (-8) = 12 + (-8)$ |
| additive identity property | Adding 0 to a number or expression does not change the value of the number or expression. | $-4 + 0 = -4$ |
| additive inverse property | The sum of a number and its additive inverse or opposite is 0. | $350 + (-350) = 0$ |
| multiplication property of equality | When both sides of an equation are multiplied by the same number, the sides remain equal. | If $2x = 16.5$, then $\frac{1}{2}(2x) = \frac{1}{2}(16.5)$ |
| multiplicative identity property | Multiplying a number or expression by 1 does not change the value of the number or expression. | $-54.26 \cdot 1 = -54.26$ |
| multiplicative inverse property | The product of a number and its reciprocal or inverse is 1. | $45 \cdot \frac{1}{45} = 1$ |

2. **a)** $2(x + 8) + 7 = 43$

| 43 | | |
|---|---|---|
| $x + 8$ | $x + 8$ | 7 |
| 36 | | 7 |
| 18 | 18 | 7 |

So, $x + 8 = 18$, and $x = 10$.

**b)**

| 59 | | | | |
|---|---|---|---|---|
| 14 | $2a + 3$ | $2a + 3$ | $2a + 3$ | $2a + 3$ | $2a + 3$ |
| 14 | 45 | | | |
| 14 | 9 | 9 | 9 | 9 | 9 |

So, $2a + 3 = 9$, and $x = 3$.

**c)** $35 = 6(c - \frac{1}{3}) + 5$

| 35 | | | | | | |
|---|---|---|---|---|---|---|
| $c - \frac{1}{3}$ | $c - \frac{1}{3}$ | $c - \frac{1}{3}$ | $c - \frac{1}{3}$ | $c - \frac{1}{3}$ | $c - \frac{1}{3}$ | 5 |
| 30 | | | | | | 5 |
| 5 | 5 | 5 | 5 | 5 | 5 | 5 |

So, $c - \frac{1}{3} = 5$ and $c = 5\frac{1}{3}$.

3. Using properties, fill in the empty cells in the table below to show how to solve the equation $3(x + 2) + 5 = 32$ for $x$.

| Equation | Justification |
|---|---|
| $3(x + 2) + 5 = 32$ | starting equation |
| $3x + 6 + 5 = 32$ | |
| $3x + 11 = 32$ | combining like terms (The like terms here are the numbers 6 and 5.) |
| $3x + 11 + (^-11) = 32 + (^-11)$ | |
| $3x + 0 = 21$ | additive inverse property |
| $3x = 21$ | |
| $\frac{1}{3}(3x) = \frac{1}{3} \cdot 21$ | multiplication property of equality |
| $x = \underline{\hspace{1cm}}$ | |

4. Solve the following equations. List each step and give a justification. Check to make sure your answer is correct.

a) $4(x - 10) = 68$

b) $10(7 - x) - 4 = 16$

c) $74 = 6 - 4(2a + 7)$

**Hint**
See page 168

# Combining Like Terms with Variables

**MATHEMATICALLY SPEAKING**

▸ constant
▸ like terms

Besides numbers that we refer to as constants, terms with the same variable(s) raised to the same power(s) are called like terms. For example, $2a$ and $3a$ are like terms, and $6x^2$ and $-15x^2$ are like terms.

We can combine like terms in an expression using factoring.

**Example**

$2a + 3a = (2 + 3)a = 5a$
By factoring the $a$ from each term, we can add the 2 and 3 inside the parentheses.

$6x^2 - (-15x^2) = (6 - (-15))x^2 = 21x^2$
By factoring the $x^2$ from each term, we can subtract the 6 and $-15$ inside the parentheses.

# Using Properties to Solve Equations

Remind students to always check their work by substituting their solution for the value of the variable to make sure their answer is correct.

**Talk Moves** Review the inverse properties, identity properties and properties of equality as a class. Have student pairs complete Question 3 and then discuss responses as a class. Assign Question 4 to be completed independently. Afterwards, have students share their solutions with the class. Use the talk move agree/disagree and why to promote critical thinking and deepen understanding as students present their solution steps and justifications.

3.

| Equation | Justification |
|---|---|
| $3x + 6 + 5 = 32$ | distributive property of multiplication over addition |
| $3x + 11 + (^-11) = 32 + (^-11)$ | addition property of equality |
| $3x = 21$ | additive identity property |
| $x = 7$ | multiplicative inverse property |

**4.** Order of some steps may vary. Possible responses:

**a)** $4(x - 10) = 68$

| | |
|---|---|
| $4x - 40 = 68$ | distributive property of multiplication over subtraction |
| $4x - 40 + 40 = 68 + 40$ | addition property of equality |
| $4x + 0 = 108$ | additive inverse property |
| $4x = 108$ | additive identity property |
| $\frac{1}{4}(4x) = \frac{1}{4}(108)$ | multiplication property of equality |
| $x = 27$ | multiplicative inverse property, multiplication |

**b)** $10(7 - x) - 4 = 16$

| | |
|---|---|
| $70 - 10x - 4 = 16$ | distributive property of multiplication over subtraction |
| $70 - 10x - 4 + 4 = 16 + 4$ | addition property of equality |
| $70 - 10x + 0 = 20$ | additive inverse property |
| $70 + 10x = 20$ | additive identity property |
| $70 + (^-70) - 10x = 20 + (^-70)$ | additive property of equality |
| $0 - 10x = ^-50$ | additive inverse property |
| $^-10x = ^-50$ | additive identity property |
| $-\frac{1}{10}(^-10x) = -\frac{1}{10}(^-50)$ | multiplication property of equality |
| $x = 5$ | multiplicative inverse property, multiplication |

**c)** $74 = 6 - 4(2a + 7)$

| | |
|---|---|
| $74 = 6 + (^-8a) + (^-28)$ | distributive property of multiplication over addition |
| $74 + 28 = 6 + (^-8a) + (^-28) + 28$ | addition property of equality |
| $102 = 6 + (^-8a) + 0$ | additive inverse property |
| $102 = 6 + (^-8a)$ | additive identity property |
| $102 + (^-6) = 6 + (^-6) + (^-8a)$ | addition property of equality |
| $96 = 0 + (^-8a)$ | additive inverse property |
| $96 = ^-8a$ | additive identity property |
| $-\frac{1}{8}(96) = -\frac{1}{8}(^-8a)$ | multiplication property of equality |
| $^-12 = a$ | multiplicative inverse property, multiplication |

## Summarize Day 1

As a Wrap It Up discussion for Day 1, discuss the advantages and disadvantages of solving equations using bar diagrams versus using properties.

The discussion should include the following key ideas:

- Bar diagrams represent solutions visually, which is helpful for visual-spatial learners. For more complex equations, the diagrams can use a great deal of space and take time to create.

- Identifying which properties students use to simplify expressions will help students in the future. This assists students to think in a logical, deductive manner. This process can take time because students are asked to justify each step.

## Combining Like Terms with Variables

Review like terms and discuss the given example. Have students complete Question 5 with a partner. Discuss student responses as a class. Then review the rules for **The Equivalence Game** in Question 6. Have pairs play the game using Lesson Guide 1.3: *The Equivalence Game*. Circulate as students are working to informally assess understanding. You may wish to record anecdotal notes in the *Student Snapshot* observation tool to document student progress.

**5. a)** $(14 + 71)x = 85x$

   **b)** $(25 - 17)a = 8a$

   **c)** $54x + 27y$; Terms cannot be combined.

   **d)** $(32 - 1)y = 31y$

   **e)** $16c - 16$; Terms cannot be combined.

   **f)** $(-7.83 + 8.24)b = 0.41b$

**6.** Students play **The Equivalence Game**.

## Solving Equations by Combining Like Terms

Discuss the given example and solve Question 7a as a class. Have students work on Question 7b independently and then share responses in a class discussion.

5. When possible, write equivalent expressions by combining like terms.

   **a)** $14x + 71x$

   **b)** $25a - 17a$

   **c)** $54x + 27y$

   **d)** $32y - y$

 **Hint**
See page 168

   **e)** $16c - 16$

   **f)** $-7.83b + 8.24b$

6. Play the equivalence card game with your partner.

**GAME** ····· The Equivalence Game ·····

Players: **2**

Materials: **Equivalence Game cards**

Directions: **The rules are similar to the card game, "Go Fish."**

1. Each player is dealt 7 cards. The remainder of the cards are put face down between the players.

2. The goal is to make pairs of equivalent expressions.

3. The player whose last name comes first in the alphabet is Player 1. Player 1 shows Player 2 a card with an expression. Player 1 asks the Player 2 if he or she has an equivalent expression.

4. If Player 2 does have an equivalent expression, it must be handed over to make a pair. The pair is put down on the table in front of Player 1.

5. If Player 2 does not have an equivalent expression, then Player 1 picks up a card from the deck. If this card has an equivalent expression, Player 1 continues and selects a new expression. If not, Player 2 gets a turn.

6. Play ends when one player has no cards in his or her hand. The winner is the person with the most pairs.

30    Course 3: Solve It: Focusing on Equations, Inequalities and Exponents

**7. a)**

| Equation | Justification |
|---|---|
| $(8 + 25)z - 17 = 148$ | starting equation |
| $33z - 17 = 148$ | combining like terms |
| $33z - 17 + 17 = 148 + 17$ | **addition property of equality** |
| $33z + 0 = 148 + 17$ | **additive inverse property** |
| $33z = 165$ | additive identity property and addition |
| $(\frac{1}{33})\, 33z = (\frac{1}{33})165$ | multiplication property of equality |
| $z = 5$ | **multiplicative inverse property, multiplication.** |

## Solving Equations by Combining Like Terms

Sometimes you need to combine like terms in order to solve an equation.

**7.** Fill in the empty cells in the solutions below.

**a)**

| Equation | Justification |
|---|---|
| $8z + 25z - 17 = 148$ | starting equation |
| $33z - 17 = 148$ | combining like terms |
| $33z - 17 + 17 = 148 + 1$ | |
| $33z + \underline{\quad\quad} = 148 + 17$ | |
| $33z = 165$ | additive identity property, addition |
| | multiplication property of equality |
| $z = \underline{\quad\quad}$ | |

**b)**

| Equation | Justification |
|---|---|
| $45 - 6x + 12x - 9 = 0$ | starting equation |
| $45 + 6x - 9 = 0$ | |
| $6x + \underline{\quad\quad} = 0$ | combining like terms |
| | addition property of equality |
| $6x + \underline{\quad\quad} = 0 - 36$ | |
| $6x = {}^-36$ | |
| | multiplication property of equality |
| | |

## Ordering Supplies at Jeff's Cookie Corner

Jeff at Jeff's Cookie Corner at the Newton Discovery Center is offered a new price for dough from his supplier. If Jeff buys his cookie dough from the supplier at $55 per case, there will be no shipping charge. Each case of dough makes 1,000 cookies. For every case of dough, he can also buy a case of 1,000 cookie bags for $15. If he places an order in the next 10 days, he will receive a $20 discount on the total order.

**b)**

| Equation | Justification |
|---|---|
| $45 - 6x + 12x - 9 = 0$ | starting equation |
| $45 + 6x - 9 = 0$ | **combining like terms** |
| $6x + \mathbf{36} = 0$ | combining like terms |
| $\mathbf{6x + 36 + (-36) = 0 + (-36)}$ | addition property of equality |
| $6x + \mathbf{0} = 0 - 36$ | **additive inverse property** |
| $6x = {}^-36$ | **additive identity property** |
| $(\frac{1}{6})6x = -36(\frac{1}{6})$ | multiplication property of equality |
| $x = {}^-6$ | **multiplicative inverse property, multiplication.** |

## Ordering Supplies at Jeff's Cookie Corner

Have students complete Questions 8 and 9 independently and compare their responses with a partner. Discuss any discrepancies in a class discussion.

**8. a)** $n$ represents the number of cases of cookie dough and cookie bags.

   **b)** $c = 70n - 20$

   **c)** $1,730

8. Jeff writes an equation to determine his total cost, $c$. He plans on ordering the same number of dough and cookie bag cases.

$$c = 55n + 15n - 20$$

a) What does $n$ represent in this equation?

b) Write an equivalent equation by combining like terms.

c) Find the cost of purchasing 25 cases of both dough and cookie bags.

9. Solve the following equations. First combine like terms and then solve for the variable.

a) $9x + 27 - 2x = 55$

b) $9.1 = 1.5 + x - 6x$

c) $17 = 24a - (2a - 6)$

d) $\frac{3}{4}(12c - 16c) = 6.9$

e) $\frac{1}{3}(6c - 3) + c = 2(6c - 0.5)$

 **W rap It Up**

Kalid and Katherine were solving $7x - 5 = 17 + 13$. Kalid solved it this way: $2x = 30$, so $x = 15$. Katherine said you can't combine $7x$ and $^-5$. Explain why Katherine is right. Show Kalid how to solve the equation.

▶ addition property of equality

▶ additive identity property

▶ additive inverse property

▶ bar diagram

▶ constant

▶ equation

▶ like terms

▶ multiplication property of equality

▶ multiplicative identity property

▶ multiplicative inverse property

▶ solution (solution set)

---

9. **a)** $9x - 2x = 55 - 27$; $x = 4$

**b)** $9.1 - 1.5 = x - 6x$; $x = {}^-1.52$

**c)** $17 - 6 = 24a - 2a$; $a = \frac{1}{2}$

**d)** $\frac{3}{4}(-4c) = 6.9$; $c = {}^-2.3$

**e)** $2c - 1 + c = 12c - 1$
$-1 + 1 = 12c - 3c$, $c = 0$

**W rap It Up**

Student responses should include the following key ideas:

• Kalid cannot combine $7x$ and $-5$ because they are not like terms.

• Kalid should have solved the problem in the following way:

| Equation | Justification |
|---|---|
| $7x - 5 = 17 + 13$ | starting equation |
| $7x - 5 = 30$ | addition of like terms |
| $7x - 5 + 5 = 30 + 5$ | addition property of equality |
| $7x + 0 = 35$ | additive inverse property, addition |
| $7x = 35$ | additive identity property |
| $\frac{1}{7}(7x) = \frac{1}{7} \cdot 35$ | multiplication property of equality |
| $x = 5$ | multiplicative inverse property, multiplication |

**Reflect**

Use these questions to help you reflect on the lesson and plan for future instruction.

• To what extent are students able to justify the steps used in solving equations?

• How efficiently do students apply algebraic properties to solve equations?

• What strategies are students confident using when solving complex equations?

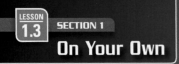

**On Your Own**

Write About It

1. Explain how combining like terms can help you solve equations. Use an example to help you explain.

2. Solve the following equations by creating bar diagrams.

   a) $3(m - 4) = 21$

   b) $70 = 10 + 5(3 - x)$

   c) $2(3x + 6) + 7 = 100$

3. Fill in the empty cells.

| Equation | Justification |
|---|---|
| $3(2x + 9) = 30$ | starting equation Solve for $x$. |
| $6x + 27 = 30$ | |
| | addition property of equality |
| $6x + 0 = 3$ | |
| | additive identity property |
| | |
| | multiplicative inverse property |

4. Solve the following equations. Give a justification for each step.

   a) $6(3n - 1) = 12$

   b) $42 = -3(y + 8)$

5. Solve the following equations.

   a) $31 = 6 - (x + 4)$

   b) $2 - 2(-5n - 10) = 30$

   c) $4(x + \frac{1}{2}) - 2.5 = 7.25$

6. Miranda is thinking of a number. She says, "If I multiply it by 5 and then subtract 3 and then multiply the result by 2, my answer is 34." Write an equation for her number. Solve the equation to find Miranda's number.

**On Your Own**

Write About It

1. Answers will vary. Possible response:

Combining like terms can simplify the steps when solving equations.

Example:    $12 + 4a - 2a - 4 = 2$

One way to solve this equation:

$$12 + (4 - 2)a - 4 = 2$$
$$12 + (2)a - 4 = 2$$
$$12 + 2a - 4 = 2$$
$$12 + 2a - 4 + 4 = 2 + 4$$
$$12 + 2a + 0 = 6$$
$$12 + 2a = 6$$
$$12 + (-12) + 2a = 6 + (-12)$$
$$0 + 2a = -6$$
$$2a = -6$$
$$\frac{1}{2}(2a) = \frac{1}{2} \cdot -6$$
$$a = -3$$

By combining like terms, there are fewer steps.

$$12 + 2a - 4 = 2$$
$$12 - 4 + 2a + (-2a) = 2 + (-2a)$$
$$8 + 0 = 2 + (-2a)$$
$$8 = 2 + (-2a)$$
$$8 + -2 = 2 + (-2) + (-2a)$$
$$6 = 0 + (-2a)$$
$$6 = -2a$$
$$-\frac{1}{2} \cdot 6 = -\frac{1}{2}(-2a)$$
$$-3 = a$$

**2. a)** $3(m - 4) = 21$

| 21 | | |
|---|---|---|
| $m - 4$ | $m - 4$ | $m - 4$ |
| 21 | | |
| 7 | 7 | 7 |

So, $m - 4 = 7$ and $m = 11$.

**b)** $70 = 10 + 5(3 - x)$

| 70 | | | | | |
|---|---|---|---|---|---|
| 10 | $3 - x$ | $3 - x$ | $3 - x$ | $3 - x$ | $3 - x$ |
| 10 | 60 | | | | |
| 10 | 12 | 12 | 12 | 12 | 12 |

So, $3 - x = 12$ and $x = {}^-9$.

**c)** $2(3x + 6) + 7 = 100$

| 100 | | | | | | | | |
|---|---|---|---|---|---|---|---|---|
| $3x + 6$ | | | | $3x + 6$ | | | | 7 |
| 93 | | | | | | | | 7 |
| 46.5 | | | | 46.5 | | | | 7 |
| $x$ | $x$ | $x$ | 6 | $x$ | $x$ | $x$ | 6 | 7 |
| 40.5 | | | 6 | 40.5 | | | 6 | 7 |
| 13.5 | 13.5 | 13.5 | 6 | 13.5 | 13.5 | 13.5 | 6 | 7 |

So, $x = 13.5$.

**3.**

| Equation | Justification |
|---|---|
| $3(2x + 9) = 30$ | starting equation |
| $6x + 27 = 30$ | **distributive property of multiplication over addition** |
| $6x + 27 + ({}^-27) = 30 + ({}^-27)$ | addition property of equality |
| $6x + 0 = 3$ | **additive inverse property** |
| $6x = 3$ | additive identity property |
| $\left(\frac{1}{6}\right)6x = 3\left(\frac{1}{6}\right)$ | **multiplication property of equality** |
| $x = \frac{1}{2}$ | multiplicative inverse property |

**4. a)**

| Equation | Justification |
|---|---|
| $6(3n - 1) = 12$ | starting equation |
| $18n - 6 = 12$ | distributive property of multiplication over subtraction |
| $18n - 6 + 6 = 12 + 6$ | addition property of equality |
| $18n + 0 = 18$ | additive inverse property |
| $18n = 18$ | additive identity property |
| $\left(\frac{1}{18}\right)18n = 18\left(\frac{1}{18}\right)$ | multiplication property of equality |
| $n = 1$ | multiplicative inverse property |

**b)**

| Equation | Justification |
|---|---|
| $42 = -3(y + 8)$ | starting equation |
| $42 = -3y + (-24)$ | distributive property of multiplication over addition |
| $42 + 24 = -3y + (-24) + 24$ | addition property of equality |
| $66 = -3y + 0$ | additive inverse property |
| $66 = -3y$ | additive identity property |
| $\left(-\frac{1}{3}\right)66 = -3y\left(-\frac{1}{3}\right)$ | multiplication property of equality |
| $-22 = y$ | multiplicative inverse property |

**5. a)** $x = {}^-29$

   **b)** $n = 0.8$

   **c)** $x = 1.9375$

**6.** $2(5n - 3) = 34$    Miranda's number is 4.

**7. a)** always; they are equivalent expressions, since when combining like terms, $2a + 4a = 6a$.

**b)** always; they are equivalent expressions, since when combing like terms, $x - 8x = -7x$.

**c)** sometimes; they are equivalent only when $b = 0$.

**d)** sometimes; they are equivalent only when $x = 0$.

**e)** always; they are equivalent expressions, since $4 + 7 = 11$ and $-2y \cdot 11 = -22y$.

**f)** always; they are equivalent expressions, since when multiplying $2(l + w)$ using the distributive property, the product equals $2l + 2w$.

**g)** sometimes; they are equivalent only when $x = 1$.

**h)** never; they are not equivalent expressions, since when multiplying $2(2t + 8)$ using the distributive property of multiplication over addition, the product equals $4t + 16$, which is not equivalent to $8 + 4t$.

**i)** never; they are not equivalent expressions, since when combining like terms, $40x - 4.8x$ equals $35.2x$.

**j)** always; they are equivalent expressions, since when multiplying $3(x + 3)$ using the distributive property of multiplication over addition, the product is $3x + 9$. When $2x$ is added to $3x$, the simplified expression is $5x + 9$.

---

**7.** Decide if each set of expressions are *sometimes*, *always* or *never* equivalent. Explain your reasoning.

**a)** $2a + 4a,\ 6a$      **g)** $7x + 30x,\ 30 + 7x$

**b)** $6(x - 8x),\ 6(-7x)$      **h)** $8 + 4t,\ 2(2t + 8)$

**c)** $5b - 75,\ -5(b + 15)$      **i)** $40x - 4.8x,\ -4.8x - 40$

**d)** $(x + 9)5,\ x + 45$      **j)** $3(x + 3) + 2x,\ 5x + 9$

**e)** $-2y(4 + 7),\ -22y$      **k)** $4x + 5,\ 4x - 5$

**f)** $2(l + w),\ 2l + 2w$      **l)** $3(x - 6),\ 2(x - 9) + x$

**8.** Match each equation on the left with its corresponding property.

**a)** $-15x + (15x) = 0$

**b)** $21z + 4.5 + 0 = 21z + 4.5$

**c)** If $\frac{3}{2x} = 16$, then $\frac{2}{3}\left(\frac{3}{2x}\right) = \frac{2}{3}(16)$.  *(x in wrong place)*

**d)** $\frac{1}{2}(2x) = 1 \cdot x$

**e)** $6(-x + 7) = -6x + 42$

     **i)** multiplication property of equality

     **ii)** addition property of equality

     **iii)** additive inverse property

     **iv)** multiplicative inverse property

     **v)** associative property of addition

     **vi)** distributive property of multiplication over addition

     **vii)** additive identity property

**9.** Solve the following equations. Give a justification for each step.

**a)** $4b - 21b + 102 = 34$      **b)** $15 - 2a + 5 - 3a = 100$

**10.** Solve the following equations.

**a)** $3z - 2(3 + 4z) = 5$

**b)** $7 - 2(1 - x) + 3x = -5$

**c)** $\frac{1}{2}(12 + x) + 1.5x = 20$

---

**k)** never; they are not equivalent expressions.

**l)** always; they are equivalent expressions, since the product of $3(x - 6)$ is $3x - 18$. When simplifying $2(x - 9) + x$, the result is the same, $3x - 18$.

**8. a)** iii; additive inverse property

**b)** vii; additive identity property

**c)** i; multiplication property of equality

**d)** iv; multiplicative inverse property

**e)** vii; distributive property of multiplication over addition

11. Jeff at the Cookie Corner has found a new supplier. His new supplier charges $50 per case of cookie dough, plus a $2.95 shipping charge per case. A case makes 1,000 cookies. Jeff can also buy a case of 500 cookie bags for $8.00, and there is always free shipping on cases of cookie bags. She doesn't offer any discount. Recall that his current supplier charges $55 per case and $15 per 1,000 cookie bags with a $20 discount.

a) Write an equation for Jeff's costs if he buys from the new supplier. Make sure to include the cost (c) of buying n cases of cookies and the appropriate number of cookie bags. There should be a cookie bag for each cookie.

b) Find the cost for buying 25 cases of cookie dough and enough cookie bags for each cookie.

c) Which supplier offers the better deal?

## 9. a)

| Equation | Justification |
|---|---|
| $4b - 21b + 102 = 34$ | starting equation |
| $-17b + 102 = 34$ | combining like terms |
| $-17b + 102 + (-102) 5 34 + (-102)$ | addition property of equality |
| $-17b + 0 5 -68$ | additive inverse property |
| $-17b = -68$ | additive identity property |
| $-\left(\frac{1}{17}\right) -17b = -68\left(-\frac{1}{17}\right)$ | multiplication property of equality |
| $b = 4$ | multiplicative inverse property |

## 9. b)

| Equation | Justification |
|---|---|
| $15 - 2a + 5 - 3a = 100$ | starting equation |
| $20 - 5a = 10$ | combining like terms |
| $20 - 5a + (-20) = 100 + (-20)$ | addition property of equality |
| $-5a + 0 = 80$ | additive inverse property |
| $-5a = 80$ | additive identity property |
| $\left(-\frac{1}{5}\right) -5a = 80 \left(-\frac{1}{5}\right)$ | multiplication property of equality |
| $a = 8$  −16 | multiplicative inverse property |

**10. a)** $3z - 2(3 + 4z) = 5$

$3z - 6 - 8z = 5$

$-5z - 6 = 5$

$-5z = 11$

$z = -2.2$

**b)** $7 - 2(1 - x) + 3x = -5$

$7 - 2 + 2x + 3x = -5$

$5 + 5x = -5$

$5x = -10$

$x = -2$

**c)** $\frac{1}{2}(12 + x) + 1.5x = 20$

$6 + (\frac{1}{2})x + 1.5x = 20$

$6 + 2x = 20$

$2x = 14$

$x = 7$

**11. a)** $c = (50 + 2.95)n + 8 \cdot 2n$, where $c$ represents the total cost and $n$ represents the number of cases of cookie dough purchased. Since this supplier sells bags in cases of 500, the number of cases of bags must be twice the number of cases of cookie dough in order to bag all the cookies.

**b)** $c = (50 + 2.95)25 + 8(2 \cdot 25)$

$c = 52.95 \cdot 25 + 8 \cdot 50$

$c = 1{,}323.75 + 400$

$c = \$1{,}723.75$

**c)** This new supplier is offering a better deal; it is $6.25 cheaper than the original supplier.

---

🔲 **Think Back**

**12.** The price of a sweater was increased from $50 to $60. What was the percent increase of the sweater?

A. 10%

B. 20%

C. 25%

D. 80%

**13.** Rose rows her boat gently down the stream, rowing at a rate of 2 miles per hour (mph). The current of the river is 1 mile per hour.

**a)** She rows 1 mile downstream *with* the current and then rows back at the same rate of 2 mph *against* the current. How long does it take her to make the round trip?

❖ **Think Beyond**

b) What was the average rate in miles per hour for her complete trip?

**14.** In 1910, 1 pound of flour cost $0.18. By 1975, a pound of flour cost $0.98. By what multiple did the price increase? Do you think the price went up the same amount every year?

---

🔲 **Think Back**

**12.** **B.** 20%

**13. a)** It took her 20 minutes to go downstream and 1 hour to go back upstream for a total time of 1 hour 20 minutes.

**b)** $\dfrac{2 \text{ miles}}{80 \text{ minutes}} = \dfrac{1 \text{ mile}}{40 \text{ minutes}}$; therefore $1:40$ which is equivalent to $1.5:60$.

Rose's average rate was 1.5 miles per hour.

15. **What went wrong?** Sierra has taken four math tests, scoring 91%, 84%, 95% and 82%. She has one more test left before the marking period ends. She wants to have at least a 90% average on all her tests.

    • She adds the four scores and gets 352.

    • She divides 352 by 4 and gets 88% as her average.

    • Because the average of 88 and 92 is 90, Sierra decides that if she gets 92% on the final test, she will have a final average of 90%.

    Her teacher tells her 92% will not be enough.

    **a)** What score would she have to get on her last test to get an average of 90%?

    **b)** Write an equation to find what her last test score should be, and solve for the score.

16. Without graphing, identify which two lines are parallel. Explain.

    **A.** $y = -x + 6$ and $y = x + 6$

    **B.** $y = -x - 6$ and $y = -x + 6$

    **C.** $y = x + 2$ and $y = -x + \frac{1}{2}$

14. The price for flour in 1975 was approximately 5.4 times as much as the price in 1910. The price most likely did not increase the same amount each year. There would have been many factors, including the economy, war, technology, etc., that could have affected the manner in which the price of flour changed each year.

15. **a)** She averaged four tests, instead of the total of five tests that she will take. Sierra would need a total of 5 • 90 or 450 points to average 90%. Since she now has a total of 352 points, she needs 450 − 352 or 98% on the final test to bring her average up to a 90%.

b)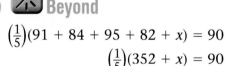

$$\left(\tfrac{1}{5}\right)(91 + 84 + 95 + 82 + x) = 90$$
$$\left(\tfrac{1}{5}\right)(352 + x) = 90$$
$$70.4 + \left(\tfrac{1}{5}\right)x = 90$$
$$\left(\tfrac{1}{5}\right)x = 19.6$$
$$x = 98$$

16. **B.** $y = -x - 6$ and $y = -x + 6$

Lines that are parallel have the same slope. When equations are written in the slope-intercept form, $y = mx + b$, the slope is $m$, the value of the coefficient of the $x$-variable. In both equations the slope is the same; the value of $m$ is $-1$. Therefore, the lines are parallel.

**1.** Kayla bought three pairs of pants and a sweater. Each pair of pants cost $45. She spent a total of $174 before tax. What was the price of the sweater?

Kayla drew the following bar diagram to help her find the price.

| $45 | $45 | $45 | s |
|:---:|:---:|:---:|:---:|
| $174 | | | |

**a)** Write an equation for the diagram. Use *s* to represent the cost of the sweater.

**b)** Solve your equation for *s*. What was the cost of the sweater?

**2.** Caden bought a CD and a DVD. The DVD cost $6 more than the CD. She spent a total of $34 before tax.

**a)** Complete the bar diagram below. *c* represents the cost of the CD

| c | |
|:---:|:---:|
| $34 | |

**b)** Write and solve an equation for the diagram.

**c)** What was the cost of the CD? The DVD?

## Lesson Guide 1.3A *Practice with Bar Diagrams [2 of 2]*

**3.** There are a total of 20 students in a class. There are three times as many girls as boys.

**a)** Complete the bar diagram below.

| | |
|---|---|
| | $3b$ |
| 20 | |

**b)** Write and solve an equation for the diagram. Use $b$ to represent the number of boys in the class.

**c)** How many girls and boys are in the class?

**4.** Fill in the bar diagram and then solve the equation.

**a)** $3(x + 4) + 6 = 27$

| | | | |
|---|---|---|---|
| 27 | | | |
| $x + 4$ | $x + 4$ | | 6 |
| 21 | | | 6 |
| | | | |

**b)** So, $x + 4 =$ __________ and $x =$ __________.

# Lesson Guide 1.3A *Practice with Bar Diagrams [Answer key]*

**1. a)** $45 + $45 + $45 + s = $174

**b)** $s = 39$. The sweater cost $39.

**2. a)**

| $c$ | $c + 6$ |
|---|---|
| $34 | |

**b)** $c + (c + 6) = $34
$$2c + 6 = $34$$
$$2c = $28$$
$$c = $14$$

**c)** The CD cost $14 and the DVD cost $20.

**3. a)** Complete the bar diagram below.

| $b$ | $3b$ |
|---|---|
| 20 | |

**b)** $b + 3b = 20$
$$4b = 20$$
$$b = 5$$

**c)** There are 5 boys and 15 girls in the class.

**4.** Fill in the bar diagram and then solve the equation.

**a)** $3(x + 4) + 6 = 27$

| 27 | | | |
|---|---|---|---|
| $x + 4$ | $x + 4$ | $x + 4$ | 6 |
| 21 | | | 6 |
| 7 | 7 | 7 | 6 |

**b)** So, $x + 4 = 7$ $x = 3$

| | | | |
|---|---|---|---|
| $16 - (4 - 9)$ | $-2x \cdot \frac{1}{2}$ | $-12x + 4x + 6x$ | $\frac{15}{15} \cdot 0$ |
| $3a - a$ | $\frac{1}{4}(b \cdot 20)$ | $(-6) \cdot (-\frac{1}{6})$ | $6a - 4a + 2$ |
| $\frac{2}{3}(15a - 3)$ | $-21x + 22 + (-22)$ | $12 + 9 \div 3$ | $18 + 0$ |
| $\frac{1}{7}(7x)$ | $55 + 2x + (-55)$ | $(5a - 3)2$ | $-8b - 1 + 8b$ |
| $21$ | $-x$ | $-2x$ | $0$ |
| $2a$ | $\frac{1}{4}b - 5$ | $1$ | $2a + 2$ |
| $10a - 2$ | $-21x$ | $15$ | $18$ |

© Kendall Hunt Publishing Company

| The Equivalence Game | The Equivalence Game | The Equivalence Game | The Equivalence Game |
|---|---|---|---|
| The Equivalence Game | The Equivalence Game | The Equivalence Game | The Equivalence Game |
| The Equivalence Game | The Equivalence Game | The Equivalence Game | The Equivalence Game |
| The Equivalence Game | The Equivalence Game | The Equivalence Game | The Equivalence Game |
| The Equivalence Game | The Equivalence Game | The Equivalence Game | The Equivalence Game |
| The Equivalence Game | The Equivalence Game | The Equivalence Game | The Equivalence Game |
| The Equivalence Game | The Equivalence Game | The Equivalence Game | The Equivalence Game |

| | | | |
|---|---|---|---|
| $x$ | $2x$ | $10a - 6$ | $-1$ |
| $\frac{1}{5} \cdot 5x - 7$ | $x - 7$ | $0 - 18$ | $0 + (-18)$ |
| $\frac{2a + 8}{2}$ | $a + 4$ | $10 - 4(a - 1)$ | $14 - 4a$ |
| $16 \div 2 + 2$ | $10$ | $16 \div (2 + 2)$ | $4$ |
| $\frac{-3(6 + (-6))}{8}$ | $1$ | $0$ | $5 - 7 + 6 - 3$ |
| $-15 + x + 5(3 - x)$ | $-4x$ | $\frac{64x}{16}$ | $4x$ |
| $3(a - 1) - 3a + 2$ | $-1$ | $-19a + 20a + 8$ | $a + 8$ |

| | | | |
|---|---|---|---|
| **The Equivalence Game** | **The Equivalence Game** | **The Equivalence Game** | **The Equivalence Game** |
| **The Equivalence Game** | **The Equivalence Game** | **The Equivalence Game** | **The Equivalence Game** |
| **The Equivalence Game** | **The Equivalence Game** | **The Equivalence Game** | **The Equivalence Game** |
| **The Equivalence Game** | **The Equivalence Game** | **The Equivalence Game** | **The Equivalence Game** |
| **The Equivalence Game** | **The Equivalence Game** | **The Equivalence Game** | **The Equivalence Game** |
| **The Equivalence Game** | **The Equivalence Game** | **The Equivalence Game** | **The Equivalence Game** |
| **The Equivalence Game** | **The Equivalence Game** | **The Equivalence Game** | **The Equivalence Game** |

# LESSON 1.4 Equations with Variables on Both Sides

**Suggested Pacing:** 2 Days

In this lesson, students explore solving equations with like terms on both sides of the equal sign. Students come to recognize the need to get all terms with the variable on one side of the equal sign and all other terms on the other.

---

**LESSON OBJECTIVES**

■ Students will combine like terms to solve complex equations.

■ Students will justify steps for combining like terms using appropriate algebraic properties.

---

| DAY 1 | Materials* | | ESSENTIAL *ON YOUR OWN* QUESTIONS |
|---|---|---|---|
| Solving Equations with Variables on Both Sides of the Equal Sign | **In Class**<br>■ Calculators<br>■ Chart paper (optional)<br><br>**On Your Own**<br>■ Calculators | | Questions 1–3, 12–16 |
| **DAY 2** | **Materials*** | | ESSENTIAL *ON YOUR OWN* QUESTIONS |
| **Using Equivalent Expressions at the Discovery Center** | **In Class**<br>■ Calculators<br>■ Chart paper (optional)<br><br>**On Your Own**<br>■ Calculators | | Questions 4–8, 10, 11 |

\* The Think Like a Mathematician Daily Record Sheet should be used daily

 **Start It Off** _____

| Number of Tables | 1 | 2 | 3 | 4 | 10 | 15 | $n$ | 50 |
|---|---|---|---|---|---|---|---|---|
| Number of People | 4 | 6 | 8 | 10 | 22 | 32 | $2n + 2$ | 102 |

1. **B.** Perimeter of the table(s)

2. $p = 2n + 2$ or $p = 2(n + 1)$

 **DAY 1 TEACHING THE LESSON**

In this lesson, students continue to explore solving complex equations that involve terms with the same variable on both sides of the equal sign. Students come to recognize the need to get all terms with the same variable on one side of the equal sign and all other terms on the other.

## Solving Equations with Variables on Both Sides of the Equal Sign

Discuss with students that when solving equations, it is sometimes necessary to get all terms with the same variable on one side of the equation. Together as a class, explore the steps used to solve the sample equation.

 **NOTE**

Students may wonder where to begin when solving equations with variables on both sides of the equal sign. Rather than moving like variable terms to one side first, as shown in the example, it is also acceptable to move the numerical values to one side first. Furthermore, it is also appropriate to combine like terms with variables on the right side of the equal sign first, rather than always starting on the left side. It is important for students to recognize that it doesn't matter how they begin to combine like terms. Also note that it is very common for students to make errors solving equations when the coefficients of variables are negative. Encourage students to combine like terms with variables so the result is a positive value for the coefficient to reduce the likelihood of these errors.

---

 **LESSON 1.4**

# Equations with Variables on Both Sides

 **Start It Off**

At the Blast Off Café near the solar system exhibit at the Newton Discovery Center, Phoebe, the manager, is setting up tables. Each table seats 4 people, one on each side. Phoebe is trying different table arrangements, by putting tables together as shown below.

Fill in the table.

| Number of Tables | 1 | 2 | 3 | 4 | 10 | 15 | $n$ | 50 |
|---|---|---|---|---|---|---|---|---|
| Number of People | 4 | 6 | 8 | | | | | |

1. Finding the number of people is like finding the

   A. area of the table(s).

   B. perimeter of the table(s).

   C. total number of tables.

2. Write an equation to find the number of people, $p$, that can be seated at $n$ tables in two different ways.

 **Talk Moves** Have students work with a partner to complete Questions 1 and 2 and share their solution strategies as a class. Encourage a few students who combined like terms differently for Question 2 to record their steps on chart paper and post their work in the classroom for others to examine. Since students should arrive at the same solution, these different methods demonstrate that there are many ways to solve equations. Use talk moves, such as repeat/rephrase and adding on, to extend the discussion and solidify student understanding.

Next, have students work independently to complete Question 3. Encourage students to compare their responses with a partner.

## Solving Equations with Variables on Both Sides of the Equal Sign

Sometimes, terms with a variable are on both sides of an equation. To solve such an equation, you must first get all variable terms on one side of the equation and all constant terms on the other. Then, you can combine like terms and solve for the variable.

**Example**

Solve for $x$: $4x + 8 = 2x$.

First, to get the variable terms on one side, use the addition property of equality to add $-2x$ to both sides.

| | |
|---|---|
| $4x + 8 + (-2x) = 2x + (-2x)$ | addition property of equality |
| $2x + 8 = 2x + (-2x)$ | combining like terms |
| $2x + 8 = 0$ | additive inverse property |

Now we use the addition property of equality again by adding $-8$ to both sides.

| | |
|---|---|
| $2x + 8 + (-8) = 0 + (-8)$ | addition property of equality |
| $2x + 0 = 0 + (-8)$ | additive inverse property |
| $2x = -8$ | additive identity property |
| $x = -4$ | multiplication property of equality |

1. Fill in the empty cells in the table below to solve $9(x + 7) = -2 + 4x$. You may use more than one property on some lines.

| Equation | Justification |
|---|---|
| $9x + 63 = -2 + 4x$ | |
| $9x + 63 + (-4x) = -2 + 4x + (-4x)$ | |
| $5x + 63 = -2 + 4x + (-4x)$ | |
| $5x + 63 = -2 + 0$ | |
| $5x + 63 = -2$ | |
| $5x + 63 + (-63) = -2 + (-63)$ | |
| $5x = -65$ | |
| $\frac{1}{5}(5x) = \frac{1}{5}(-65)$ | |
| $x =$ | |

2. Work with a partner to solve the equation $4x + 8 = 2x - 7$ in two different ways. One of you should start by adding 7 to both sides. The other should start by adding $-4x$ to both sides. Compare your answers.

 It is sometimes difficult to justify each step with one reason, since there may be two or three things we do simultaneously.

2. Possible two solutions:

$$4x + 8 = 2x - 7$$
$$4x + 8 + 7 = 2x - 7 + 7$$
$$4x + 15 = 2x + 0$$
$$4x + 15 = 2x$$
$$4x + (-4x) + 15 = 2x + (-4x)$$
$$15 = -2x$$
$$-\frac{1}{2} \cdot 15 = -\frac{1}{2}(-2x)$$
$$-7\frac{1}{2} = x$$

$$4x + 8 = 2x - 7$$
$$4x + (-4x) + 8 = 2x + (-4x) - 7$$
$$0 + 8 = -2x - 7$$
$$8 = -2x - 7$$
$$8 + 7 = -2x - 7 + 7$$
$$15 = -2x + 0$$
$$15 = -2x$$
$$-\frac{1}{2} \cdot 15 = -\frac{1}{2}(-2x)$$
$$-7\frac{1}{2} = x$$

| Equation | Justification |
|---|---|
| $9x + 63 = -2 + 4x$ | distributive property of multiplication over addition |
| $9x + 63 + (-4x) = -2 + 4x + (-4x)$ | addition property of equality |
| $5x + 63 = -2 + 4x + (-4x)$ | commutative property of addition, combining like terms |
| $5x + 63 = -2 + 0$ | additive inverse property, combining like terms |
| $5x + 63 = -2$ | additive identity property |
| $5x + 63 + (-63) = -2 + (-63)$ | addition property of equality |
| $5x = -65$ | additive inverse property, additive identity property, combining like terms |
| $\frac{1}{5}(5x) = \frac{1}{5}(-65)$ | multiplication property of equality |
| $x = -13$ | multiplicative inverse property, multiplicative identity property |

3. Solve each equation. Justify each step for Part a and b.

a) $22x + 4x = 130$

b) $3z + 5 = z - 13$

**Hint**
See page 168

c) $-28 - 3x = -31x$

d) $(x - 12)5 = 7.5 + 2.3x$

**Hint**
See page 168

e) $5(4 - x) = 6x + 21$

f) $7(b + 3) = 5 - b$

## Using Equivalent Expressions at the Discovery Center

4. At the dolphin pool at the Magellan Aquarium, there is going to be a new rectangular pool with a shallow section for staff trainers. The dimensions are shown below.

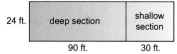

| 24 ft. | deep section | shallow section |

90 ft.          30 ft.

a) Write as many equivalent expressions for the area of the pool as you can. Show that they are equivalent.

b) The aquarium staff would like to change the length of the shallow section. The current ratio between the area of the shallow section and the area of the deep section is 1 : 3. They would like to make this ratio 1 : 5 and still have a total pool length of 120 feet. How would you divide the total length of the pool to make the two sections? Write as many equivalent expressions as you can for the area with this new ratio.

c) In the future, the staff would like the option of varying the width of the pool. Write an equation to find the area ($A$) of the pool with width ($x$) and the lengths as shown in the diagram. Use parentheses in your equation.

d) Write the equation without parentheses.

---

3. Steps will vary. Possible solutions:

a)

| Equation | Justification |
|---|---|
| $22x + 4x = 130$ | |
| $26x = 130$ | combining like terms |
| $\frac{1}{26}(26x) = \frac{1}{26} \cdot 130$ | multiplication property of equality |
| $x = 5$ | multiplicative inverse property, multiplication |

b)

| Equation | Justification |
|---|---|
| $3z + 5 = z - 13$ | |
| $3z + (-z) + 5 = z + (-z) - 13$ | addition property of equality |
| $2z + 5 = 0 - 13$ | additive inverse property |
| $2z + 5 = -13$ | additive identity property |
| $2z + 5 + (-5) = -13 + (-5)$ | addition property of equality |
| $2z + 0 = -18$ | additive inverse property, combining like terms |
| $2z = -18$ | additive identity property |
| $\frac{1}{2}(2z) = \frac{1}{2} \cdot -18$ | multiplication property of equality |
| $z = -9$ | multiplicative inverse property, multiplication |

**c)** $x = 1$

**d)** $x = 25$

**e)** $x = -\frac{1}{11}$

**f)** $b = -2$

## Summarize Day 1

 **Talk Moves** After students compare their answers to Question 3 with a partner, discuss any discrepancies as a class. Use the talk move agree/disagree and why to clarify misconceptions.

The discussion should include the following key ideas:

- Students may have difficulty in Question 3b, combining $3z + (-z)$. From the hint given, they should understand that $-z = -1z$.

- In some equations (e.g., Question 3d), it is necessary to use the distributive property before combining like terms.

- Remind students to combine like terms so that the coefficient of the variable is positive to reduce the likelihood of these errors.

## Using Equivalent Expressions at the Discovery Center

Introduce the scenario of the dolphin pool to students. Have students complete Question 4 with a partner. Circulate among pairs as students solve the problem to informally assess understanding of key ideas from the lesson. Use the *Student Snapshot* observation tool to record anecdotal notes from observations.

 **Differentiation**

**Think Differently:** For students having difficulty writing equations for the new pool dimensions, encourage them to draw and label diagrams of the pool.

 **Talk Moves** Discuss student responses as a class. Encourage students to share their solution strategies on the board or on the interactive white board. Use talk moves, such as agree/disagree and why, to clarify student understanding.

**4. a)** Answers will vary. Possible solutions:

| | | |
|---|---|---|
| 24(90 + 30) | (90 • 24) + (30 • 24) | 24 • 120 |
| 24(120) | 2,160 + 720 | 2,880 ft.² |
| 2,880 ft.² | 2,880 ft.² | |
| | | |
| (90 + 30)24 | (30 • 24) + (90 • 24) | 120 • 24 |
| (120)24 | 720 + 2,160 | 2,880 ft.² |
| 2,880 ft.² | 2,880 ft.² | |
| (30 + 90)24 | (24 • 30) + (24 • 90) | |
| (120)24 | 720 + 2,160 | |
| 2,880 ft.² | 2,880 ft.² | |
| | | |
| 24(30 + 90) | (24 • 90) + (24 • 30) | |
| 24(120) | 2,160 + 720 | |
| 2,880 ft.² | 2,880 ft.² | |

**b)** For a $1:5$ ratio, the shallow end would have a length of 20 feet and the deeper end would have a length of 100 feet. Possible expressions for area:

| | | |
|---|---|---|
| 24(100 + 20) | (100 • 24) + (20 • 24) | 24 • 120 |
| 24(120) | 2,400 + 480 | 2,880 ft.² |
| 2,880 ft.² | 2,880 ft.² | |
| (100 + 20)24 | (20 • 24) + (100 • 24) | 120 • 24 |
| (120)24 | 480 + 2,400 | 2,880 ft.² |
| 2,880 ft.² | 2,880 ft.² | |
| (20 + 100)24 | (24 • 20) + (24 • 100) | |
| (120)24 | 480 + 2,400 | |
| 2,880 ft.² | 2,880 ft.² | |
| | | |
| 24(20 + 100) | (24 • 100) + (24 • 20) | |
| 24(120) | 2,400 + 480 | |
| 2,880 ft.² | 2,880 ft.² | |

deep section | shallow section

100 ft.     20 ft.

**c)** $A = (90 + 30)x$, where $A$ represents the area of the pool in square feet and $x$ represents the width in feet.

**d)** $A = 90x + 30x$, where A represents the area of the pool in square feet and $x$ represents the width in feet.

**e)** $3,600 = 120x$; The width is 30 ft.

**e)** If you are able to increase the area of the pool to 3,600 square feet but still want the pool to have a total length of 120 feet, what will the width of the pool be?

**f)** Let the area of the pool be 3,600 square feet. You want to vary the length of the shallow end. Write an equation to help you find the area of the pool with length of the shallow end ($y$) and other measures as shown in the original diagram above. Use parentheses in your equation.

**g)** Solve the equation to find the length of the shallow end.

Larry, Leona and Leigh were discussing how to solve the following problem:

$2x + 16 = 5x - 20$.

Talk to your neighbor and decide who is correct. Be ready to defend your answer.

**f)** $3,600 = 24(90 + y)$

**g)** The length of the shallow end would have to be 60 feet.

$$3,600 = 24(90 + y)$$
$$3,600 = 2,160 + 24y$$
$$3,600 + (-2,160) = 2,160 + (-2,160) + 24y$$
$$1,440 = 0 + 24y$$
$$\frac{1}{24} \cdot 1,440 = \frac{1}{24}(24y)$$
$$60 = y$$

| deep section | shallow section |
|---|---|
| 90 ft. | $y$ |

**Wrap It Up**

Answers will vary. Student responses should include the following key ideas:

- There are multiple methods to begin to solve equations.

- Larry's and Leona's methods combine like terms with the same variables first. However, Larry's method results in a positive coefficient for the variable and is the one that will most likely produce fewer computation errors.

- Leigh's method combines numerical values first.

- $x = 12$ is the solution to the equation.

## Reflect

Use these questions to help you reflect on the lesson and plan for future instruction.

- Are students flexible in selecting different ways to solve equations?

- Do students prefer to combine terms with the same variables first, or numerical terms first, when beginning to solve an equation?

See corresponding assessments in Assessment Resources.

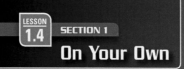

 Write About It

1. Explain how combining like terms can help you solve equations. Use an example along with a description.

2. Solve each equation. Show your steps.

   a) $3x - 4 = 6.2 + 5.1x$

   b) $15 - 3x = 12x + 5$

   c) $7 - 4a = 2(a + 2)$

   d) $\frac{1}{2}(24 + 2v) = 5v - 33$

   e) $\frac{1}{4}x + 7 + 2\frac{1}{2}x = -9.5$

   f) $c = 35 - 16(c - 1)$

   g) $3 - y = 4(y + 2)$

3. Check your solutions for each equation in Question 2.

4. The staff at the Magellan Aquarium now would like to change the length of the shallow section of the dolphin pool. However, they want to keep the total length the same.

   Instead of the $1:3$ ratio between the shallow section and the deep section, the aquarium staff would like to make the ratio $1:7$.

   a) How would you divide the total length of the pool now?

   b) Write at least three different equivalent expressions for the area of this new pool setup.

24 ft. | deep section | shallow section

90 ft.   30 ft.

5. The Falling Apple Science Museum needs a new circular safety rail that people stand behind as they view the solar system exhibit. The rail should be 8 feet away from the exhibit. The radius of the solar system exhibit is $r$ ft. Write four different equations for the length of the railing, $n$.

8 ft.
$r$ ft.

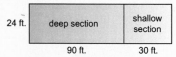 Hint
See page 168

---

## On Your Own

1.  **Write About It** Answers will vary. Student responses should include the following key ideas:

   - Combining like terms makes it easier to isolate the variable on one side of the equation to solve for the variable.

   - When combining like terms with the same variable, try to combine the terms so the coefficient of the variable has a positive value.

   Example:

   | | |
   |---|---|
   | $10 - 3c = 5c - 6$ | |
   | $10 - 3c + 3c = 5c + 3c - 6$ | addition property of equality |
   | $10 + 0 = 8c - 6$ | additive inverse property |
   | $10 = 8c - 6$ | additive identity property |
   | $10 + 6 = 8c - 6 + 6$ | addition property of equality |
   | $16 = 8c + 0$ | additive inverse property |
   | $\frac{1}{8} \cdot 16 = \frac{1}{8}(8c)$ | multiplication property of equality |
   | $2 = c$ | multiplicative inverse property, multiplicative identity property |

2. Steps may vary. Possible responses:

   a)
   $$3x - 4 = 6.2 + 5.1x$$
   $$3x + (-3x) - 4 = 6.2 + 5.1x + (-3x)$$
   $$0 - 4 = 6.2 + 2.1x$$
   $$-4 = 6.2 + 2.1x$$
   $$-4 + (-6.2) = 6.2 + (-6.2) + 2.1x$$
   $$-10.2 = 0 + 2.1x$$
   $$\frac{1}{2.1} \cdot -10.2 = \frac{1}{2.1}(2.1x)$$
   $$-\frac{10.2}{2.1} = -\frac{102}{21} = x \ (x \approx -4.857)$$

**b)**

$$15 - 3x = 12x + 5$$
$$15 - 3x + 3x = 12x + 3x + 5$$
$$15 + 0 = 15x + 5$$
$$15 = 15x + 5$$
$$15 + (-5) = 15x + 5 + (-5)$$
$$10 = 15x$$
$$\tfrac{1}{15} \cdot 10 = \tfrac{1}{15}(15x)$$
$$\tfrac{2}{3} = x$$

**c)**

$$7 - 4a = 2(a + 2)$$
$$7 - 4a = 2a + 4$$
$$7 - 4a + 4a = 2a + 4a + 4$$
$$7 + 0 = 6a + 4$$
$$7 = 6a + 4$$
$$7 + (-4) = 6a + 4 + (-4)$$
$$3 = 6a + 0$$
$$3 = 6a$$
$$\tfrac{1}{6} \cdot 3 = \tfrac{1}{6}(6a)$$
$$\tfrac{1}{2} = a$$

**d)**

$$\tfrac{1}{2}(24 + 2v) = 5v - 33$$
$$12 + v = 5v - 33$$
$$12 + v + (-v) = 5v + (-v) - 33$$
$$12 + 0 = 4v - 33$$
$$12 = 4v - 33$$
$$12 + 33 = 4v - 33 + 33$$
$$45 = 4v + 0$$
$$45 = 4v$$
$$\tfrac{1}{4} \cdot 45 = \tfrac{1}{4}(4v)$$
$$11.25 = v$$

**e)**

$$\tfrac{1}{4}x + 7 + 2\tfrac{1}{2}x = -9.5$$
$$\tfrac{1}{4}x + 7 + (-7) + 2\tfrac{1}{2}x = -9.5 + (-7)$$
$$\tfrac{1}{4}x + 0 + 2\tfrac{1}{2}x = -16.5$$
$$2\tfrac{3}{4}x = -16.5$$
$$2.75x = -16.5$$
$$\tfrac{1}{2.75}(2.75x) = \tfrac{1}{2.75} \cdot -16.5$$
$$x = -6$$

**f)**

$$c = 35 - 16(c - 1)$$
$$c = 35 + {}^-16(c - 1)$$
$$c = 35 + {}^-16c + 16$$
$$c + 16c = 35 - 16c + 16c + 16$$
$$17c = 51$$
$$\tfrac{1}{17}(17c) = \tfrac{1}{17}(51)$$
$$c = 3$$

**g)**

$$3 - y = 4(y + 2)$$
$$3 - y = 4y + 8$$
$$3 - y + y = 4y + y + 8$$
$$3 + 0 = 5y + 8$$
$$3 = 5y + 8$$
$$3 + (-8) = 5y + 8 + (-8)$$
$$-5 = 5y + 0$$
$$-5 = 5y$$
$$\tfrac{1}{5} \cdot -5 = \tfrac{1}{5}(5y)$$
$$-1 = y$$

**3. a)**

$$3x - 4 = 6.2 + 5.1x$$
$$3 \cdot -\tfrac{102}{21} - 4 = 6.2 + 5.1 \cdot -\tfrac{102}{21}$$
$$-\tfrac{102}{7} - 4 = 6.2 + -\tfrac{173.4}{7}$$
$$-\tfrac{130}{7} = -\tfrac{130}{7}$$

**b)**

$$15 - 3x = 12x + 5$$
$$15 - 3(\tfrac{2}{3}) = 12(\tfrac{2}{3}) + 5$$
$$15 - 2 = 8 + 5$$
$$13 = 13$$

**c)**

$$7 - 4a = 2(a + 2)$$
$$7 - 4(\tfrac{1}{2}) = 2(\tfrac{1}{2} + 2)$$
$$7 - 2 = 2(2\tfrac{1}{2})$$
$$5 = 5$$

**d)**

$$\tfrac{1}{2}(24 + 2v) = 5v - 33$$
$$\tfrac{1}{2}(24 + 2 \cdot 11.25) = 5 \cdot 11.25 - 33$$
$$\tfrac{1}{2}(24 + 22.50) = 56.25 - 33$$
$$\tfrac{1}{2}(46.20) = 23.25$$
$$23.25 = 23.25$$

**e)**    $\frac{1}{4}x + 7 + 2\frac{1}{2}x = -9.5$

$\frac{1}{4}(-6) + 7 + 2\frac{1}{2}(-6) = -9.5$

$-1.5 + 7 + (-15) = -9.5$

$-16.5 + 7 = -9.5$

$-9.5 = -9.5$

**f)** $3 = 35 - 16(x - 1)$

$3 = 35 - 16(3 - 1)$

$3 = 35 - 16(2)$

$3 = 35 - 32$

$3 = 3$

**g)**    $3 - y = 4(y + 2)$

$3 - (-1) = 4(-1 + 2)$

$4 = 4(1)$

$4 = 4$

**4. a)** For a 1 : 7 ratio, the shallow end would be 15 feet and the deeper end would be 105 feet.

**b)** Possible expressions for the area (width is 24 feet):

| | | |
|---|---|---|
| 24(105 + 15) | (105 • 24) + (15 • 24) | 24 • 120 |
| (105 + 15)24 | (15 • 24) + (105 • 24) | 120 • 24 |
| (15 + 105)24 | (24 • 15) + (24 • 105) | |
| 24(15 + 105) | (24 • 105) + (24 • 15) | |

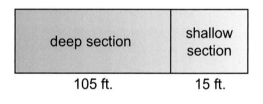

deep section / shallow section

105 ft.          15 ft.

**5.** Selected sample of possible equations:

**NOTE**    In the equations listed below, $n$ represents the number of feet of railing and $r$ represents the radius of the Solar System Exhibit. Although all the equations shown below are acceptable, encourage students to put the coefficient in front of the variable when writing equations, such as $n = 2\pi(r + 8)$, in that order.

$n = \pi2(r + 8)$ $\qquad$ $n = 2\pi(r + 8)$ $\qquad$ $n = \pi2(8 + r)$ $\qquad$ $n = 2\pi(8 + r)$

$= \pi2r + \pi16$ $\qquad\quad$ $= 2r\pi + \pi16$ $\qquad\quad$ $= 2\pi r + \pi16$

$= \pi2r + 16\pi$ $\qquad\quad$ $= 2r\pi + 16\pi$ $\qquad\quad$ $= 2\pi r + 16\pi$

$= \pi16 + 2r\pi$ $\qquad\quad$ $= \pi16 + 2r\pi$ $\qquad\quad$ $= \pi16 + 2\pi r$

$= \pi(r + r + 8 + 8)$ $\quad$ $= (r + r + 8 + 8)\pi$

$= \pi(8 + 8 + r + r)$ $\quad$ $= (8 + 8 + r + r)\pi$

$= \pi(2r + 16)$ $\qquad\;$ $= \pi(16 + 2r)$ $\qquad\qquad\quad\;$ $= (2r + 16)\pi$ $\qquad$ $= (16 + 2r)\pi$

6. The number of feet of railing in Question 5 is the same as the:

   A. area of the circular region.

   B. circumference of the circular region.

   C. diameter of the circular region.

7. Using one of your equations in Question 5, find the length of the railing you will need if the radius of the solar system exhibit is 20.5 feet.

8. Refer to Question 6. Find the length of the railing you will need if the safety rail is 10 feet away from the exhibit and the radius of the exhibit is 20.5 feet.

**Think Beyond**

9. Another plan for the solar system exhibit from Question 6 includes the construction of a circular platform to occupy the space between the exhibit and the safety rail. Write an equation for the area of this platform.

10. Sales at the food court of the Newton Discovery Center are going so well that you need to expand the size of the food stands. Your safety engineer has recommended that you install nonslip tiles around the food stands.

   Here is one design for a new stand:

   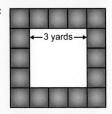
   ←—3 yards—→

   The stand is surrounded by nonslip tiles. Each tile is 1 yard by 1 yard.

   a) What is the number of tiles needed to surround the stand?

   b) To double the length and width of the stand, how many tiles would we need to surround the new stand?

   c) To make the stand a square with sides that are $x$ yards long, how many tiles would we need to surround the stand?

   d) Write as many different equivalent expressions as you can to show the number of tiles that would be needed.

   e) Write two different equations that represent the number of tiles ($n$) you would need for any given length ($x$) of a square stand.

   f) If you had 48 tiles, what would the dimensions of the stand have to be?

**Think Beyond**

9. $A = \pi(r + 8)^2 - \pi r^2$, where $A$ represents the area of the platform between the exhibit and the safety rail and $r$ represents the radius of the Solar System Exhibit.

10. a) 16

    b) 28

    c) Answers will vary. Possible response:

       $4x + 4$

---

**NOTE** See answers for Part d for other possibilities.

---

6. **B.** circumference of the circular region.

7. Equations students select will vary. Possible response:

   $n = \pi 2(r + 8)$

   $= \pi 2(20.5 + 8)$

   $= \pi 2(28.5)$

   $= \pi \cdot 57$

   $\approx 178.98$ feet of railing

8. $n = \pi 2(r + 10)$

   $= \pi 2(20.5 + 10)$

   $= \pi 2(30.5)$

   $= \pi \cdot 61$

   $\approx 191.54$ feet of railing

d) Some selected possible expressions:

| | |
|---|---|
| $2(x + 2) + 2x$ | $2x + 2(x + 2)$ |
| $2x + 2x + 4$ | $4 + 2x + 2x$ |

   $(x + 2) + (x + 2) + x + x$

   $x + x + x + x + 4$

   $2x + (x + 2) + (x + 2)$

| | |
|---|---|
| $4(x + 1)$ | $(1 + x)4$ |
| $(x + 2)^2 - x^2$ | $(x + 2)(x + 2) - x \cdot x$ |

e) Answers may vary. Possible response:

$n = 4x + 4$, where $n$ represents the number of tiles needed and $x$ represents the given length of a square stand.

$n = 2(x + 2) + 2x$, where $n$ represents the number of tiles needed and $x$ represents the given length of a square stand. (See expressions above in Part d for other possibilities.)

f) The square stand would have a side length of 11 yards.

**11. Think Beyond**

a)
$$n = 4x + 4$$
$$100 = 4x + 4$$
$$100 + (-4) = 4x + 4 + (-4)$$
$$96 = 4x$$
$$\tfrac{1}{4} \cdot 96 = \tfrac{1}{4}(4x)$$
$$24 = x$$

The length of a side of the square stand is 24 yards.

The area of a square is $s^2$; therefore the area of the square stand is $24^2$ or 576 square yards.

b) The area of the stand with the tile surround is $(s + 2)^2$; therefore the area of the entire space is $26^2$ or 676 square yards.

**Think Back**

12. John should have calculated $\tfrac{1}{2}$ of 7, not 28. Therefore, $28 + 3.50 = \$31.50$ for his payment.

13. 303.75

---

**Think Beyond**

11. a) If there are 100 tiles, find the area of the stand. Use one of the equations from Question 10.

   b) Find the area of the stand with the surrounding tiles.

**Think Back**

12. **What went wrong?** John babysat his cousin Samara for $4\tfrac{1}{2}$ hours. His aunt had agreed to pay him \$7 per hour. John knew that multiplying a number by $4\tfrac{1}{2}$ was the same as multiplying it by 4 and then multiplying by $\tfrac{1}{2}$, and then adding the products. He found $4 \cdot 7 = 28$. Then he said $\tfrac{1}{2}$ of 28 is 14. Then he added the products, $28 + 14 = \$42$. His aunt said this was not correct and paid him less. What did John do wrong? How much did he actually get paid?

13. Divide 24.3 by 0.08. Show your work.

14. The measure of an interior angle of a regular polygon of $n$ sides is given by $\frac{(n-2)180}{n}$. What is the measure of an interior angle of a regular dodecahedron? (A dodecahedron has 12 sides.)

15. Which of the following statements are true?

   I. The absolute value of a number can be more than the number itself.

   II. The absolute value of a number is never equal to the number.

   III. The absolute value of the number can sometimes be less than the number itself.

   A. I only          D. all three

   B. II only         E. none of the above

   C. III only

16. These two figures have congruent sides. The height of the figure on the left is 4 cm. Name both shapes. Which has a greater perimeter? Which has a greater area? How much greater?

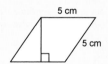
Optional Technology Lesson for this section available at www.mymathinnovations.com

---

14. A dodecahedron has 12 sides; the measure of an interior angle of a regular dodecahedron is 150°.

15. **A.** I only

16. The shape on the left is a rhombus. The shape on the right is a square.

   The perimeter of both shapes is the same, 20 cm.

   The square has a greater area, 25 cm². The rhombus has an area of 20 cm².

   The square's area is greater by 5 cm².

Optional Technology Lesson for this section available at www.mymathinnovations.com

# Sum It Up

In this section, you reviewed and extended some algebra concepts, properties and skills. You can now solve complex equations with parentheses, variables on both sides and terms that need to be combined. The following are the important mathematical ideas covered in this section.

## Factoring

■ To factor an expression, first find the greatest common factor of the terms. Then use the reverse of the distributive property to write an equivalent expression.

For example: $36 - 12x = 12(3 - x)$.

## Order of Operations

■ To evaluate expressions, use the order of operations. Make sure to perform the operations within grouping symbols first.

For example: $[4 + (15 - 3)] \cdot 2 = [4 + 12] \cdot 2 = 16 \cdot 2 = 32$

Evaluate $10 + 8n + 6(c - 1)$ when $n = 4$ and $c = 7$.

$10 + 8 \cdot 4 + 6(7 - 1) = 10 + 32 + 6(6) = 78$

■ The fraction bar is also a grouping symbol. First perform operations in the numerator and denominator separately. Then divide the final answer in the numerator by the final answer in the denominator.

For example: $\frac{17 - 9}{4 \cdot 2} = \frac{8}{8} = 1$

The Sum It Up summarizes the important mathematics students should have learned in this section. Encourage students to use this Sum It Up as they complete the Study Guide and prepare for quizzes and tests.

## Solving Equations

- Bar diagrams are a useful way to solve equations.

    For example: $3(x - 4) + 5 = 20$

| 20 | | | |
|---|---|---|---|
| $x - 4$ | $x - 4$ | $x - 4$ | 5 |
| 15 | | | 5 |
| 5 | 5 | 5 | 5 |

    So $x - 4 = 5$ and $x = 9$.

- You can also solve equations by using the properties of algebra.

    For example: $3(x - 4) + 5 = 20$

| Equation | Justification |
|---|---|
| $3x - 12 + 5 = 20$ | distributive property |
| $3x - 7 = 20$ | combining like terms |
| $3x - 7 + 7 = 20 + 7$ | addition property of equality |
| $3x + 0 = 27$ | additive inverse property |
| $3x = 27$ | additive identity property |
| $\frac{1}{3}(3x) = \frac{1}{3}(27)$ | multiplication property of equality |
| $x = 9$ | multiplicative inverse property and combining like terms |

- Solving some equations requires getting all terms with the variable on one side of the equation, then getting all other terms on the other, combining like terms and then solving for the variable.

    For example: $9x - 8 = 4x + 2.1$

$$9x - 8 + (^-4x) = (^-4x) + 4x + 2.1$$
$$5x - 8 = 0 + 2.1$$
$$5x - 8 = 2.1$$
$$5x - 8 + 8 = 2.1 + 8$$
$$5x + 0 = 10.1$$
$$5x = 10.1$$
$$\frac{1}{5}(5)x = \frac{1}{5}(10.1)$$
$$x = 2.02$$

## MATHEMATICALLY SPEAKING

Do you know what these mathematical terms mean?

- addition property of equality
- additive identity property
- additive inverse property
- algebraic expression
- bar diagram
- constant

- distributive property of multiplication over addition
- equation
- equivalent expressions
- factor an expression
- greatest common factor (GCF)
- grouping symbols

- like terms
- multiplication property of equality
- multiplicative identity property
- multiplicative inverse property
- order of operations
- solution (solution set)

# Study Guide

Solve It: Focusing on Equations, Inequalities and Exponents

## Part 1. What did you learn?

1. The Huntsville Zoo charges $7 for a child ticket and $8 for an adult ticket. The rare snake exhibit costs an extra $3 for children and an extra $4 for adults.

   a. Without simplifying, write an expression for the cost of tickets to the zoo and rare snake exhibit for any number of children, $c$, and any number of adults, $a$.

   b. Simplify the expression you wrote in Part a.

   c. Show or explain how you know your two expressions are equivalent.

   d. Five children and some adults went to the zoo and the snake exhibit. They paid a total of $170. How many adults went with the children? Explain.

2. Match the expression in Column A with its equivalent expression in Column B.

| Column A | Column B |
|---|---|
| a. $\frac{3x - 6}{3}$ | i. $x - 2$ |
| b. $\frac{2x + 2}{2}$ | ii. $x + 2$ |
| c. $-7x - 21$ | iii. $-7(x - 3)$ |
| d. $\frac{4x + 8}{4}$ | iv. $-7(x + 3)$ |
| e. $-7x + 21$ | v. $x + 1$ |

3. Match the examples in Column A to the correct property in Column B. Then, find the simplified expression in Column C.

| Column A | Column B | Column C |
|---|---|---|
| a. $6.25(12x)$ and $6(12x) + 0.25(12x)$ | d. Additive Inverses and the Identity Property of Addition | g. $-420x$ |
| b. If $3x = 22.5$, then $\frac{1}{3} \cdot 3x = 22.5 \cdot \frac{1}{3}$ | e. Distributive Property of Multiplication Over Addition | h. $x = 7.5$ |
| c. $-23x + -397x$ and $-23x + (3x) + -397x + (-3x)$ | f. Multiplicative Inverses and Identity Property of Multiplication | i. $75x$ |

# Study Guide

1.  a. $7c + 8a + 3c + 4a$

    b. $10c + 12a$

    c. Answers will vary. Possible answer: I know my expressions are equivalent because I used the commutative property of addition and combined like terms. $7c + 8a + 3c + 4a = 7c + 3c + 8a + 4a = 10c + 12a$

    d. 10 adults

    $5(10) + 12a = 170$

    $50 + 12a = 170$

    $12a = 120$

    $a = 10$

2.  a, i

    b, v

    c, iv

    d, ii

    e, iii

3.  a, e, i

    b, f, h

    c, d, g

4. Evaluate each of the expressions below.

   **a.** $24 - 12 \div 4$

   **b.** $80 + 20 \cdot 4 - 16$

   **c.** $\dfrac{-5(4 - 12)}{4}$

   **d.** $12 - 2(4 \cdot 3)$

5. Copy and complete the bar diagram and then solve the equation $3(x - 4) + 17 = 101$.

| 101 | | | |
|---|---|---|---|
| | | | 17 |
| | | | 17 |
| | | | 17 |

6. Solve each equation below. Show your work.

   **a.** $4(3a - 8) = 40$

   **b.** $2(b + \frac{2}{5}) + 1\frac{1}{5} = {}^-12$

   **c.** $7c - 5 + 7 - 2c = c$

7. Factor $3x + 15$ by following the steps below.

   **a.** Find the GCF of $3x$ and 15.

   **b.** Distribute the GCF over both terms. Write the equivalent expression.

   **c.** Use multiplication to show that the expression you wrote in Part b is equivalent to $3x + 15$.

4. **a.** 21

   **b.** 144

   **c.** 10

   **d.** $^-12$

5. $x = 32$

| 101 | | | |
|---|---|---|---|
| $x - 4$ | $x - 4$ | $x - 4$ | 17 |
| 84 | | | 17 |
| $32 - 4$ | $32 - 4$ | $32 - 4$ | 17 |

8. Sharon wanted to solve the equation $2(x - 3) = 12$. Sharon said, "I'm stuck! By the order of operations, I need to find $x - 3$ first because the expression is in parentheses. But I can't subtract 3 from $x$ because $x$ is unknown." What is Sharon confused about? What could you say or do to help her solve the equation?

9. Junze solved the equation using the steps below.

| | |
|---|---|
| $3(2x - 6) = 24$ | Original equation |
| $6x - 6 = 24$ | Simplify the equation using the distributive property of multiplication over addition. |
| $6x - 6 + 6 = 24 + 6$ | Add 6 to both sides. |
| $\frac{6x}{6} = \frac{30}{6}$ | Divide both sides by 6. |
| $x = 5$ | Write the solution. |

Then, Junze checked her solution and found that $3(2 \cdot 5 - 6) = 12 \neq 24$. What did Junze do wrong?

10. Sebastian tried to solve the equation $3m - 3 - 4m = 15$. Here is what Sebastian did:

$$3m - 3 - 4m = 15$$
$$^-3 - m = 15$$
$$^-3 - m + 3 = 15 + 3$$
$$m = 18$$

What error(s) did Sebastian make? How can you help him find and fix his errors?

6. **a.** $a = 6$

   **b.** $b = ^-7$

   **c.** $c = -\frac{1}{2}$

7. **a.** 3

   **b.** $3(x + 5)$

   **c.** $3(x + 5) = 3x + 15$

8. Answers will vary. Possible answer: Sharon doesn't understand that she can use the distributive property of multiplication over addition to solve the equation. The expression $2(x - 3)$ can be rewritten as $2x - 6$. Then, the equation reads as follows: $2x - 6 = 12$. If she adds $^-6$ to both sides and then divides both sides by 2, she will find that $x = 9$.

9. Answers will vary. Possible answer: Junze did not apply the distributive property of multiplication over addition correctly in step 2. Step 2 should read $6x - 18$ because Junze needs to multiply 3 by $2x$ and 6. The correct solution is $x = 7$.

10. Answers will vary. Possible answer: Sebastian made his error when he simplified $-3 - m + 3 = 15 + 3$ to $m = 18$. When Sebastian combines like terms, he should get $-m = 18$, not $m = 18$. So, $m = -18$. Sebastian can check this by plugging $-18$ into the original equation for $x$: $3(-18) - 3 - 4(-18) = -54 - 3 + 72 = 15$.

# Inequalities

## LESSON 2.1 From Equations to Inequalities

**Suggested Pacing:** 2 Days

In this lesson, students solve inequalities and compare this to solving equations. Students graph inequalities on a number line and learn how to combine two inequalities into one statement.

---

**LESSON OBJECTIVES**

■ Students will compare equations and inequalities.

■ Students will represent real-life situations as inequalities.

■ Students will determine the solution set of an inequality and graph the solution on a number line.

---

| DAY 1 | Materials* | ESSENTIAL *ON YOUR OWN* QUESTIONS |
|---|---|---|
| The Space Explorer Ride<br><br>The Replacement Set | **In Class**<br>■ Lesson Guide 2.1A: *Number Lines*<br>**On Your Own**<br>■ Calculators | Questions 3, 12–16 |

| DAY 2 | Materials* | ESSENTIAL *ON YOUR OWN* QUESTIONS |
|---|---|---|
| Graphing Inequalities<br><br>Another Representation<br><br>A New Sign<br><br>Reading Backward and Forward<br><br>Combining Inequalities | **On Your Own**<br>■ Calculators | Questions 1, 2, 4–9 |

*The Think Like a Mathematician Daily Record Sheet should be used daily

---

## MATHEMATICALLY SPEAKING

| ▶ inequality | ▶ solution set | ▶ symbol "≥" | ▶ symbol "≤" |
|---|---|---|---|
| ▶ replacement set | ▶ symbol ">" | ▶ symbol "<" | ▶ symbol "≠" |

# Inequalities

So far, you have worked with equations—statements that show an equal relationship between two quantities. In this section you will learn about inequalities. An inequality compares two quantities. These statements show that one expression is either not equal to ($\neq$), less than ($<$), greater than ($>$), less than or equal to ($\leq$) or greater than or equal to ($\geq$) the other expression. Generally, the solution of an inequality is a set of numbers rather than a single value.

## From Equations to Inequalities

 Start It Off

MATHEMATICALLY SPEAKING

▶ symbol "$\neq$"
▶ symbol "$<$"
▶ symbol "$>$"
▶ symbol "$\leq$"
▶ symbol "$\geq$"

CCCP

1. Find each product or quotient. Use the results to help you answer Questions 2 and 3.

a) $2 \cdot \frac{1}{2} =$     e) $\frac{1}{2} \div \frac{1}{3} =$

b) $2 \div \frac{1}{2} =$     f) $\frac{1}{3} \div \frac{1}{2} =$

c) $2 \div \frac{1}{3} =$     g) $2 \div 3 =$

d) $\frac{1}{3} \div 2 =$     h) $2 \cdot 3 =$

2. When you multiply a positive number by a number greater than 1, is the product greater than or less than the original number? What if you multiply a positive number by a number between 0 and 1?

3. When you divide a positive number by a number greater than 1, is the quotient greater than or less than the original number? What if you divide a positive number by a number between 0 and 1?

4. Does order matter in multiplication? Does order matter in division? Explain.

 Start It Off

1. a) 1

   b) 4

   c) 6

   d) $\frac{1}{6}$

   e) $\frac{3}{2}$

   f) $\frac{2}{3}$

   g) $\frac{2}{3}$

   h) 6

2. The product of any positive number and a number greater than 1 will always be greater than the original number. In Question 1h, 2 multiplied by 3, or 6, is greater than 2. The product of any positive number and a number between 0 and 1 will always be less than the original number. In Question 1a, 2 multiplied by $\frac{1}{2}$, or 1, is less than 2.

   For all $a > 0$ and $b > 1$, $a \cdot b > a$. For all $a > 0$ and $0 < b < 1$, $a \cdot b < a$.

3. The quotient of a positive number and a number greater than 1 will always be less than the original number. Questions 1d and 1g demonstrate this. The quotient of a positive number and a number between 0 and 1 will always be greater than the original number. Questions 1b, 1c, 1e and 1f demonstrate this.

   For all $a > 0$ and $b > 1$, $a \div b < a$. For all $a > 0$ and $0 < b < 1$, $a \div b > a$.

 **NOTE** For negative values, similar properties hold for the absolute values of $a$ and $b$ and their products and quotients.

1 is the multiplicative identity. If $b = 1$, both the product $a \cdot b$ and the quotient $a \div b$ will equal $a$.

4. Order does not matter in multiplication, but it does matter in division. Explanations will vary. Multiplication is commutative. For example, $3 \cdot 6 = 18$ and $6 \cdot 3 = 18$. However, division is not commutative. Questions 1c and 1d illustrate this.

In this lesson, students transition from solving equations to solving inequalities. They compare the similarities and differences between these concepts. Students graph inequalities on a number line and learn how to combine two inequalities as one statement. In addition, students discover that the same inequality can be written in two ways and will still have the same set of numbers as a solution.

## The Space Explorer Ride

Begin the lesson by asking students the following questions:

- *Have you ever encountered a height restriction for an amusement park ride?*

- *If so, what was the restriction?*

- *Why do you think amusement parks have restrictions on some rides?*

Read together about how the Falling Apple Science Museum used algebra to establish a height restriction for the new Space Explorer ride. Discuss how the given inequality is similar to and different from an equation. Introduce the four different inequality symbols to students.

## The Space Explorer Ride

Eleana and Pablo are in line to take a ride on the Space Explorer, a new ride that is part of the Solar System Exhibit at the Falling Apple Science Museum. It is similar to a space shuttle going up into space. This ride has a safety height restriction for passengers. The big question is, "Are they tall enough?" As they get closer to the front of the line, they see the sign below.

Where did this rule come from? The safety engineers at the Science Museum want to make sure a rider is tall enough not to slip through the safety bars on the ride. They based the rule on the fact that 10 hand lengths are approximately equivalent to the height of a person. They made the distance between the dots about $\frac{1}{10}$ the minimum height that is safe for the ride.

You can show the relationship between required height and hand length by writing an inequality.

If $h$ represents approximate height and $l$ represents the distance between the dots in inches, then $h \geq 10l$ describes the heights allowed on the ride.

This is read as "$h$ is greater than or equal to 10 times $l$."

## 💡 Differentiation

**Think Differently:** For students having difficulty distinguishing between the less than and greater than inequality symbols, explain that the less than symbol opens in the same direction as the letter *L*. The less than symbol also points to the left and both the words "less" and "left" begin with the letter *L*. Remind students that the opening of an inequality symbol always faces the greater number.

An **inequality** is a mathematical statement that compares two quantities. There are five different inequality symbols: $\neq$, $<$, $>$, $\leq$ and $\geq$.

| Symbol | Description | Examples |
|--------|-------------|----------|
| $\neq$ | does not equal | $6 + 5 \neq 7 + 3$ |
| $<$ | is less than | $3 < 9$<br>$^-2 < 0$<br>$7 + 1 < 15$ |
| $>$ | is greater than | $9 > 3$<br>$^-8 > ^-10$<br>$\frac{1}{2} > \frac{1}{3}$ |
| $\leq$ | is less than or equal to | $3 \leq 9$<br>$4 \cdot ^-2 \leq ^-1 \cdot 8$ |
| $\geq$ | is greater than or equal to | $1.8 \geq 1 + 0.7589$<br>$6.2 \geq 6.02$ |

In this section, you will solve inequalities that use the last four symbols in the chart.

1. Rewrite the inequality $9 > 3$ using the "is less than" symbol to make a true statement.

2. Is $6.5 \geq 6.5$ a true statement? Explain your answer.

3. Fill in the blanks with the correct symbol: $<$, $=$ or $>$.

    **a)** $60,001$ _____ $60,001$

    **b)** $0.03456$ _____ $0.3456$

    **c)** $\frac{2}{15}$ _____ $\frac{2}{7}$

    **d)** $^-18$ _____ $^-20$

    **e)** $^-2x$ _____ $^-3x$, when $x = ^-1$

    **f)** $^-2x$ _____ $^-3x$, when $x = 1$

    **g)** $^-2x$ _____ $^-3x$, when $x = 0$

---

Have students complete Questions 1–3 independently and compare their responses with a partner. Discuss any discrepancies with the class. When discussing Question 2, guide students to recognize that the word *or* means that only one of the conditions has to be met for the inequality to hold true, not both.

1. $3 < 9$

2. Yes. The *greater than* or *equal to* symbol here means that 6.5 must be *greater than* or *equal to* 6.5. Since 6.5 is *equal to* 6.5, the statement holds true.

3. **a)** $60,001 = 60,001$

    **b)** $0.03456 < 0.3456$

    **c)** $\frac{2}{15} < \frac{2}{7}$

    **d)** $^-18 > ^-20$

    **e)** $^-2x < ^-3x$
       (when $x = ^-1$)

    **f)** $^-2x > ^-3x$ (when $x = 1$)

    **g)** $^-2x = ^-3x$ (when $x = 0$)

Read together the example in the text. Have students discuss Question 4 with a partner and share their responses in a class discussion. Discuss the definition of *replacement set* for a variable in an inequality. Since the replacement set of values in an inequality often includes fractions and decimals, review the definition of *rational numbers* with the class. Guide students to recognize that, because any height equal to or greater than 50 inches will be acceptable, the replacement set includes fractions and decimals. Since students have not studied irrational numbers and do not know the term *real numbers*, we use the phrase "all numbers on the number line" when we want students to graph all real numbers that are part of the solution set.

Have students discuss Question 5 with a partner and share their responses in a class discussion. Read together the definition of *solution set*.

4. a) This means that a person must be at least 50 inches tall to go on the ride.

   b) Yes, a person could be 53 inches, 60 inches or 72 inches.

5. a) positive multiples of $\frac{1}{2}$

   b) positive and negative whole numbers and zero (the set of integers)

   c) positive numbers that have no more than two decimal places

If the distance between the dots on the "Can You Ride?" sign is 5 inches, what is the minimum height necessary to ride the Space Explorer?

To get this answer, substitute 5 inches for $l$ in the formula and solve.

$h \geq 10l$

$h \geq 10(5)$

$h \geq 50$

This is read: "The value of $h$ is greater than or equal to 50."

4. Talk with your partner and discuss:

   a) What does this mean in the situation of the Space Explorer ride?

   b) Could a person ride if his or her height was 53 inches? 60 inches? 72 inches?

As with an equation, a solution to an inequality is any number that will make the statement true. Like some equations, an inequality may have more than one solution.

The set of possible solutions to an equation or an inequality is called the replacement set. The same statement can have different solutions depending on the replacement set. For example, if the replacement set for the equation $3 = 2x$ consists of all numbers, and so includes fractions and decimals, then the solution is $x = 1.5$. If the replacement set is the set of integers, then this equation has no solution.

For real-world problems, you can usually figure out what the replacement set is by considering what the problem is about. For example, when we use the inequality $h \geq 50$ to describe the heights of students allowed to ride the Space Explorer, the replacement set can include only values greater than zero. Can this replacement set include fractions and decimals? Why or why not?

5. Talk to your partner and decide what replacement set would be appropriate from which to choose the following:

   a) U.S. shoe sizes

   b) outdoor temperatures

   c) costs of fruit juices

The solution set of an inequality is the set of all replacement set values that make the inequality true. In our Space Explorer ride situation, any height greater than or equal to 50 inches makes the inequality $h \geq 50$ true. So, the solution set includes 50 and all positive numbers greater than 50.

**MATHEMATICALLY SPEAKING**
▶ replacement set
▶ solution set

## Summarize Day 1

Discuss with students the difference between the replacement set and the solution set. Note that the solution set is a subset of the replacement set. Have the class discuss the inequality $w > 30$. Ask:

- *If the replacement set is the set of integers, what is the solution set?* All positive integers greater than 30. For example: 31, 32, 33 . . .

- *If the replacement set is all positive numbers, what is the solution set?* All positive numbers, including integers and fractions and decimals, greater than 30. For example: 30.5, 35 $\frac{3}{4}$.

## Graphing Inequalities

You graph the inequality $h \geq 50$ on the number line in the following way.

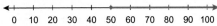

To show that $h$, the height allowed on the Space Explorer, can represent any number greater than 50, a thick line is drawn from 50 to the right on the number line. A filled-in circle on 50 indicates that the value of $h$ can be equal to 50. Any value of the variable that makes the inequality true is a solution to the inequality. In this case, there are an infinite number of solutions.

Suppose that the engineers wanted to change the inequality to limit the ride to people who are taller than 50 inches. The new inequality to represent this situation is $h > 50$.

The graph of the solution to $h > 50$ has an open circle on 50. This open circle indicates that the number 50 is not included in the solution, but any number greater than 50 is included. Again, there are an infinite number of solutions.

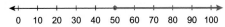

6. List three numbers that are part of the solution set for the inequality $h > 50$.

7. How is the solution set for $h \geq 50$ different from the solution set for $h > 50$?

8. List three numbers that are not part of the solution set for the inequality $h > 50$.

9. Graph the solution set for the following inequalities when the replacement set is i) the set of all numbers on the number line and; ii) the set of integers. Use two different number lines for each example.

   a) $d < 6.5$

   b) $k \geq -2$

   c) $x \leq -15\frac{1}{2}$

---

## DAY 2 TEACHING THE LESSON

## Graphing Inequalities

Discuss how to graph inequalities on a number line. Emphasize that the filled-in circle on the number 50 means that a height of 50 inches is included in the solution. This means $h$ (the height of a rider) can be equal to or greater than 50 inches. Ask students:

- *Can a person who is 50 inches tall go on the ride?* Yes

- *How many solutions to this inequality are there?* There are an infinite number of solutions—a height of 50 inches or any height greater than 50 inches. Realistically, human height has a physical limit.

Have students discuss how the graph of the inequality with an open circle compares to the graph with the filled-in circle. Guide the discussion to emphasize that the graph of the open circle does not include the number 50 as part of the solution. Rather, the solution includes any number greater than 50. Ask:

- *Can a person who is 50 inches tall go on the ride now?* No, only people taller than 50 inches can go on the ride.

- *How many solutions to this inequality are there?* There are an infinite number of solutions—any height greater than 50 inches.

 Have students work independently on Questions 6–9 and then share responses with a partner. Discuss any discrepancies as a class. Use talk moves, such as adding on and agree/disagree and why, to clarify and solidify understanding.

6. Answers will vary. Possible response: 61 inches, $50\frac{1}{2}$ inches and 58 inches.

7. The value of 50 inches is included in $h \geq 50$, but not in $h > 50$.

8. Answers will vary. Possible response: 50 inches, 48 inches and 38 inches.

9. a)

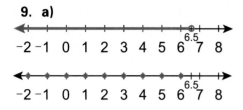

b)

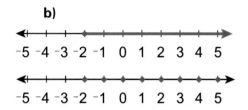

c)

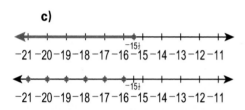

## Another Representation

Next, discuss how to write the same inequality in a different way. Have students complete Question 10 independently and share responses with a partner. Again, discuss any discrepancies.

## A New Sign

10. a) The distance between the dots should be 6.3 inches.

b) $h \geq 63$

c) Answers will vary. Possible heights: 63 inches, $64\frac{1}{2}$ inches, 72 inches, $65\frac{5}{8}$ inches and 78 inches.

d) $0 < h < 63$

e) Answers will vary. Possible heights: $62\frac{3}{4}$ inches, 55 inches, $61\frac{1}{2}$ inches,

---

## Another Representation

The engineers can express the height restriction in a different way. They could say a person is *not* allowed on the ride if his or her height is less than or equal to 50 inches. Since height must be a positive number, we can write this as $0 < h \leq 50$, where $h$ represents an *unacceptable* height.

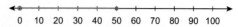

## A New Sign

10. The engineers want to increase the estimated height needed to ride the Space Explorer to 63 inches. Using the estimated height as 10 hand lengths (*l*), they create a new sign.

   a) What is the length between dots on the new sign?

   b) Write and graph an inequality for the new acceptable heights.

   c) List five acceptable heights for the ride.

   d) Write and graph an inequality that shows the heights of people who would not be allowed on the ride.

   e) List three heights of people who would not be allowed on the ride.

## Reading Backward and Forward

Talk with a partner to answer the following question:

11. How is the solution to $h > 50$ similar to or different from the solution $50 < h$?

   **? Hint**
   See page 168

12. Find three different values for $h$ in each situation below.

   a) values that will not be solutions for $h < 58$

   b) values that will be solutions for $-17 < h$

   **? Hint**
   See page 168

13. Rewrite the following inequalities with a different inequality symbol so that they represent the same solution set.

   a) $z > 8$    b) $-\frac{3}{4} \leq a$    c) $-67.2 > x$

---

48 inches and 59 inches.

## Reading Backward and Forward

Have students work with a partner to discuss and answer Question 11. Guide students to recognize that the solutions to the two inequalities are the same set of numbers. The first inequality states that $h$ is greater than 50. The second inequality states that 50 is less than $h$. Any number that is a solution would have to be greater than 50, so these two inequalities represent the same set of numbers. Inequalities, like equations, can be read from right to left or from left to right without affecting the solution. This can help students make sense of inequalities such as $50 < h$. When read from right to left, "$h$ is greater than 50" is

## Combining Inequalities

The inequality $0 < h < 50$ actually combines two inequalities into one. Height is always greater than 0 inches, so $h > 0$. At the same time, those with heights less than 50 inches were not allowed, so $h < 50$.

Similarly, if $3 < x$ and, at the same time, $x < 10$, you can represent this with the combined inequality $3 < x < 10$.

**14. a)** List three values for $x$ that would satisfy this inequality. You might find it easier to rewrite $3 < x$ using a greater than sign.

  **b)** Using all numbers on the number line as the replacement set, graph the solution to this inequality.

  **c)** How would the graph of $3 \leq x \leq 10$ differ from your graph?

  **d)** How do the solution sets of $3 < x < 10$ and $3 \leq x \leq 10$ differ?

**15.** Using all numbers on the number line as the replacement set, list three numbers that would be part of the solution set for each inequality and three numbers that would not be part of the solution set.

  **a)** $5.6 \leq a \leq 5.8$

  **b)** $-2 < b < 0$

  **c)** $-1 > x > -5$

**16. a)** Write the following inequalities using symbols:

  • $n$ is less than or equal to 12

  • $n$ is greater than 5.5

  **b)** Write the two inequalities as one combined inequality. (Write $n$ only once.)

  **c)** Using the set of integers as the replacement set, find all the solutions to this inequality.

  **d)** Graph all integer values for $n$ that satisfy this inequality.

  **e)** Using all numbers on the number line as the replacement set, list five non-integer values that are solutions to this inequality.

 **Hint**
See page 168

  **f)** Using the set of all numbers on the number line, graph all values of $n$ that satisfy this inequality.

---

the same inequality as, "50 is less than $h$."

 **Differentiation**

**Think Differently:** For students who may benefit from graphing the inequalities on number lines, offer Lesson Guide 2.1A: *Number Lines*. This lesson guide has a series of printed number lines for easy graphing.

 **Talk Moves**   Have students complete Questions 12–14 independently. Encourage students to share their responses as a class. Use talk moves, such as agree/disagree and why, to further the discussion and deepen student understanding, especially when examining the

---

inequalities they created for Question 14.

**11.** The set of numbers that represents the solutions to both inequalities is the same.

**12. a)** Answers will vary. Possible values: 60 inches, 59 inches, 70 inches.

  **b)** Answers will vary. Possible values: 36 inches, 48 inches, 45 inches. Note here that all values in the replacement set for possible height (numbers greater than 0) are in the solution set of this inequality.

**13. a)** $8 < z$

  **b)** $a \geq -\frac{3}{4}$

  **c)** $x < -67.2$

## Combining Inequalities

Read the given example together and discuss how two inequalities can be combined. Have students complete Questions 14–16 with a partner. Circulate among pairs to informally assess their understanding of key mathematical ideas from the lesson. Use the *Student Snapshot* observation tool to record observations. Have pairs share responses in a class discussion when finished.

**14. a)** Answers will vary. Possible response: 3.15, 6 and $7\frac{1}{2}$.

  **b)** Possible graph:

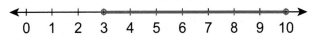

  **c)** The graph of $3 \leq x \leq 10$ would have filled-in circles on 3 and on 10.

  **d)** The solution set for $3 \leq x \leq 10$ includes

the numbers 3 and 10.

**15. a)** Answers will vary. Possible responses that would be part of the solution set: 5.6, 5.65 and 5.8. Possible responses that would not be part of the solution set: 5, 5.5 and 5.9.

**b)** Answers will vary. Possible responses that would be part of the solution set: −0.5, −1 and −1.5. Possible responses that would not be part of the solution set: −2, 0 and 0.5.

**c)** Answers will vary. Possible responses that would be part of the solution set: −2.5, −3 and −4.89. Possible responses that would not be part of the solution set: 0, −1 and −5.

**16. a)** $n \leq 12$, $n > 5.5$

**b)** $5.5 < n \leq 12$ or $12 \geq n > 5.5$

**c)** {6, 7, 8, 9, 10, 11, 12}

**d)**

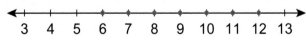

**e)** Answers will vary. Possible responses: 5.6, $8\frac{1}{2}$, $9\frac{3}{4}$ 11.032, $11\frac{2}{3}$

**f)**

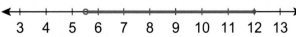

---

How are inequalities and equations alike? How are they different? Give examples of each.

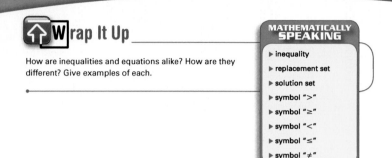
## Wrap It Up

Answers will vary. Responses should include the following key ideas:

Inequalities and equations are alike in the following ways:

- Both are mathematical statements that show a relationship between two expressions.

- The expressions in equations and inequalities may have terms with a variable.

- Equations and inequalities can represent real-life situations.

- The solution(s) to both can be graphed.

Write
About It

1. Natalie, Monique and Joshua are examining the inequality $c \geq 36$.

> The values of $c$ must be at least 36.

> This means that 36 is less than or equal to all values of $c$.

> I think this means that the values for $c$ are greater than or equal to 36.

Who is correct? Explain your reasoning.

2. List three integers and three non-integer values that satisfy each of the following:

a) $b + 4 < 6$

d) $-5 < a$ and $0 > a$

b) $-1 < a \leq 3$

e) $2y \geq 12$

c) $t < 6.2$ and $t \geq -\frac{1}{2}$

## Reflect

Use these questions to help you reflect on the lesson and plan for future instruction.

- Are students able to recognize the similarities and differences between equations and inequalities?

- How accurately are students able to represent a real-life situation as an inequality using appropriate symbols?

- How successful are students in determining and graphing the solution set of an inequality?

Inequalities and equations are different in the following ways:

- The two expressions in an equation are *equal to* each other, and an equal sign (=) is used to show this relationship.

- An inequality compares two expressions that are not necessarily equal; this can be done using the inequality symbols $\neq$, $<$, $>$, $\leq$ and $\geq$.

Example of an equation: $5s + 3 = c$. Example of an inequality: $h > 13$.

## On Your Own

1. Write About It All three students are correct. Reading the inequality from left to right, $c \geq 36$ means the values for $c$ are greater than or equal to 36 as Monique stated. Since the value of $c$ is equal to or greater than 36, Natalie's statement is correct, since the smallest possible value for $c$ is 36. In addition, this inequality can be read from right to left as $36 \leq c$ as Joshua stated. All statements result in the same set of numbers for the solution.

3. Write each statement below with symbols. Using the set of integers as the replacement set, graph the solution set on the number line.

   a) $b$ is greater than $-\frac{7}{3}$.

   b) $h$ is less than or equal to 13 and greater than 7.

   c) 3 is greater than $x$, and $x$ is greater than or equal to 0.

   d) $y$ is not greater than $-5$.

   e) $z$ is at least $-8$.

   f) $y$ is no more than 2.

4. Using the set of all number values as the replacement set, graph the solution set on the number line.

   a) $-6 \leq a \leq -1.4$

   b) $b < 0$ and $b > -1$

   c) $c \geq 3\frac{1}{2}$ and $7 > c$

5. If you consider the integers as the replacement set, which inequality does *not* have the same solution set as the others?

   a) $-5 < x < 10$

   b) $-4 \leq x \leq 9$

   c) $-6 \leq x < 10$

   d) $-5 < x \leq 9$

   e) $x > -5$ and $x < 10$

6. a) How is $-20 > y$ similar to or different from $y < -20$?

   b) Using the set of all numbers as the replacement set, graph the solution set for each inequality on separate number lines and compare.

7. Lucy Vuolo, a buyer for the Newton Discovery Center, shops for tiles for the snack bar at Tiles Surround You. This store sells tiles that range in side length from 4 inches to 48 inches. Write two single inequalities and a combined inequality to represent the range of possible areas ($A$) that an individual tile can cover.

2. a) Accept any integer less than 2 and any rational non-integer numbers less than 2.

   b) Possible integers {0, 1, 2, 3}; accept any rational non-integer numbers greater than $-1$ but less than 3.

   c) Possible integers {0, 1, 2, 3, 4, 5, 6}; accept any rational non-integer numbers equal to or greater than $-\frac{1}{2}$ but less than 6.2.

   d) Possible integers {$-4$, $-3$, $-2$, $-1$}; accept any rational non-integer numbers between $-5$ and 0.

   e) Accept any integer greater than or equal to 6 and any rational non-integer numbers greater than or equal to 6.

3. a) $b > -\frac{7}{3}$. Although a limited number of integers are shown on the number line, all integers greater than 4 are also part of the solution set. This is indicated by the arrow to the right of 4 being made much darker.

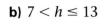
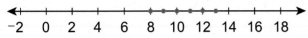

b) $7 < h \le 13$

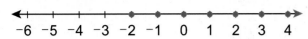

c) $0 \le x < 3$

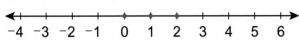

d) $y \le -5$

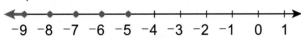

e) $z$ is at least $-8$.

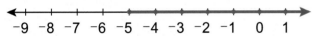

f) $y$ is no more than 2.

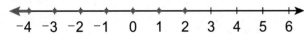

4. a)

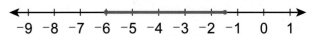

b)

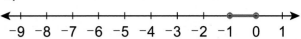

c)

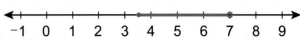

5. c) $-6 \le x < 10$ is not equivalent to the others. The integers $-6$ and $-5$ are only included in the solution set of integers for this inequality, but not in the other solution sets for the other inequalities.

6. a) Both inequalities represent the same relationship between two expressions.

b) The inequality $-20 > y$ means that $-20$ is greater than $y$.

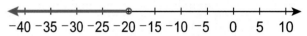

The inequality $y < -20$ means that $y$ is less than $-20$.

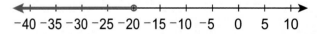

Both inequalities have the same solution set.

7.  The tile sides, $t$, vary from 4 to 48 inches, so $4 \le t \le 48$. Let $A$ = area = $t^2$, so the range for $A$ is $4^2 \le A \le 48^2$ or $16 \text{ in.}^2 \le A \le 2{,}304 \text{ in.}^2$.

8.  $360 \le c < 430$, where $c$ is the number of chocolate chips in a one-pound bag.

---

 Students may benefit from a discussion of the mathematical meaning of the word *between* to help them recognize that the values 86 and 92 should not be included in the values listed.

---

9.  **Think Beyond**

    a)  The replacement set for $d$ (the number of degrees above 85) can be described as $1 < d < 7$. The inequality to determine attendance is: $2{,}550(1 - 0.02 \cdot 7) < n < 2{,}550(1 - 0.02 \cdot 1)$. Solving the inequality: $2{,}193 < n < 2{,}499$, where $n$ represents the number of people in attendance.

    b)  Graphing $2{,}193 < n < 2{,}499$:

    <----+----+----o----+----+----+----+----+----o----+----+---->
    2,100 2,150 2,200 2,250 2,300 2,350 2,400 2,450 2,500 2,550 2,600

    The graph has open circles on the endpoints because the temperature is between, but not equal to, 86 and 92. Therefore, the attendance would be between 2,193 and 2,499, but not equal to either one.

**8.** At Jeff's Cookie Corner, the chocolate chip cookies are a big hit. Jeff estimates that he can get at least 360 but fewer than 430 chocolate chips from each 1-pound bag of chips. Write this as an inequality.

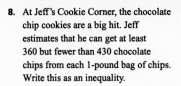

**Think Beyond**

9. Friday is going to be a hot day at the Aquatic Animal Show. The temperature is predicted to be between 86 and 92 degrees Fahrenheit. The formula used to predict the attendance is $n = 2,550 - 2,550 \cdot 2\% \cdot d$ or $n = 2,550(1 - 0.02d)$, where $n$ represents the number of people attending the show and $d$ represents the number of degrees the temperature is above 85°.

**a)** Write an inequality to represent the possible range of attendance at the show for temperatures between 86° and 92°.

**? Hint**
See page 168

**b)** Graph the solution to your inequality. Explain why you used open or filled-in circles.

**Think Beyond**

10. Kayleigh Martin, an architect for the Discovery Center, is designing an elevator for the Falling Apple Science Museum. The maximum area available for the floor of the elevator is 6.25 square yards.

The building code requires that the elevator floor have a minimum area of 4 square yards and that it be in the shape of a square.

**a)** Write an inequality for the possible side lengths ($l$) for the floor of the elevator.

**b)** Graph this inequality on the number line.

**c)** Is 9 feet a possible length for a side of the floor? Explain your answer.

**d)** Is 7 feet a possible length for a side of the floor? Explain your answer.

**Think Beyond**

11. **a)** Give values for $x$ and $y$ so that the graph of the solution set for $n \geq x$ or $n \leq y$ includes only *one* number on the number line.

**b)** Give values for $x$ and $y$ so that the graph of the solution set for $n \geq x$ and $n < y$ includes *no* numbers on the number line.

---

**10.** **Think Beyond**

**a)** 2 yd. $\leq l \leq$ 2.5 yd.

**b)**

```
←+———+———+———+———+———+———+———+———+———+———+→
  -2 -1.5 -1 -0.5  0  0.5  1  1.5  2  2.5  3
```

**c)** No, 9 feet is equivalent to 3 yards. Since 3 yards is greater than 2.5 yards, it is not part of the solution set.

**d)** Yes, 7 feet is a possible length of a side of the floor. Since 7 feet is equivalent to $2.\overline{3}$ yards, it is included in the solution set.

**11.** **Think Beyond**

**a)** Any number will be a solution as long as $x$ is equal to $y$.

**b)** No number will be a solution as long as $x$ is greater than or equal to $y$.

Think
Back

12. If $5w = x - 6$ and $w = 3$, then $x =$

    **A.** $-2$                   **C.** $21$

    **B.** $11$                   **D.** $14$

13. Graph each of these numbers on a number line:

    $8, \quad -3, \quad |-3 - 8|, \quad -|3 + 8|$

14. Molly is shopping for a picnic. She knows she needs enough juice for each of her eight friends to have at least 12 oz. to drink. Is it cheaper for her to buy 32-ounce bottles at $1.25 per bottle or to buy the special on the 6-packs of 10-ounce juice boxes at $1.85 per 6-pack?

15. Write 180 as a product of prime numbers.

16. Solve for $x$. Show your work.

    $-3x - \frac{2}{3} = \frac{7}{12}$

 Think
Back

12. **C.** 21

13.

| | | $|-3-8|$ | |
|---|---|---|---|
| $-|3+8|$ | $-3$ | $8$ | |

$$\xleftarrow{\hspace{0.3cm}} \quad -25 \;\; -20 \;\; -15 \;\; -10 \;\; -5 \quad 0 \quad 5 \quad 10 \quad 15 \quad 20 \quad 25 \xrightarrow{\hspace{0.3cm}}$$

14. You would need three bottles for $3.75 or two 6-packs for $3.70. The 6-packs are cheaper.

15. $180 = 2 \cdot 2 \cdot 3 \cdot 3 \cdot 5$

16. $-3x - \dfrac{2}{3} = \dfrac{7}{12}$

$-3x = \dfrac{7}{12} + \dfrac{2}{3}$

$-3x = \dfrac{7}{12} + \dfrac{8}{12}$

$-3x = \dfrac{15}{12}$

$\left(-\dfrac{1}{3}\right) - 3x = \dfrac{15}{12}\left(-\dfrac{1}{3}\right)$

$x = -\dfrac{15}{36}$

$x = -\dfrac{5}{12}$

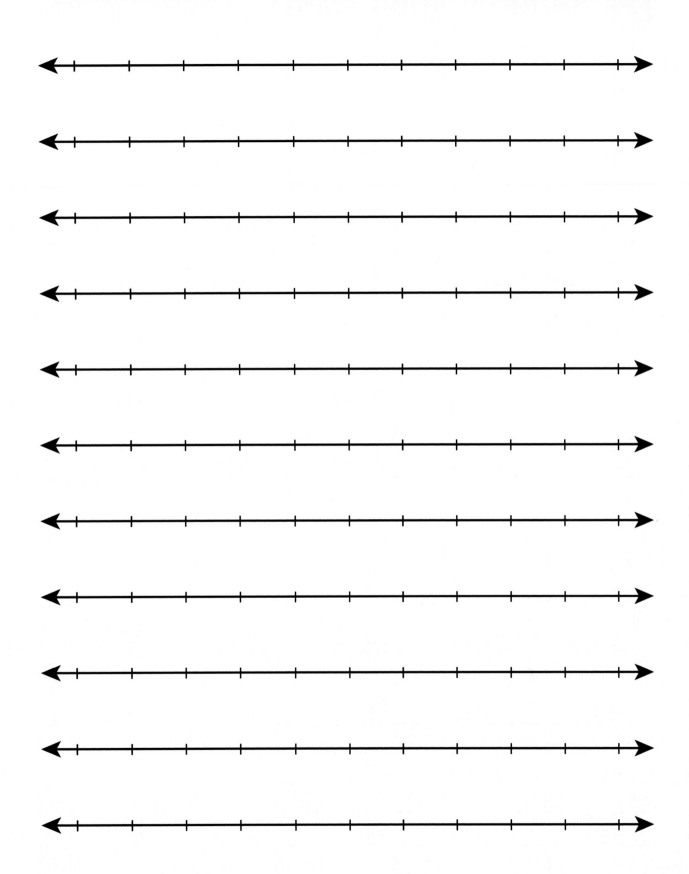

# An Interesting Twist

**Suggested Pacing:** 2 Days

In this lesson, students learn that it is necessary to reverse the direction of the inequality symbol when dividing or multiplying both sides of an inequality by a negative number in order for the resulting inequality to be true.

---

**LESSON OBJECTIVES**

- Students will discover the rules for solving inequalities.
- Students will check their solutions to inequalities by substituting a variety of values for the variables.
- Students will write and solve inequalities that represent real-life situations.

---

| DAY 1 | Materials* | ESSENTIAL *ON YOUR OWN* QUESTIONS |
|---|---|---|
| Strange Happenings<br>Reversing the Inequality<br>Solving Inequalities | **In Class**<br>■ Calculators<br>■ Lesson Guide 2.2: *Strange Happenings*<br>■ Lesson Guide 2.2: *Strange Happenings with Your Own Inequality*<br>■ Lesson Guide 2.2A: *Do You See a Pattern?*<br>■ Lesson Guide 2.2A: *Checking the Solution to an Inequality*<br><br>**On Your Own**<br>■ Calculators | Questions 1, 2, 10–14 |

| DAY 2 | Materials* | ESSENTIAL *ON YOUR OWN* QUESTIONS |
|---|---|---|
| Another Way to Find a Solution<br>Using Inequalities to Understand Situations | **In Class**<br>■ Lesson Guide 2.2: *Make a Match Cards*<br>■ Calculators<br><br>**On Your Own**<br>■ Calculators | Questions 3–8 |

\* The Think Like a Mathematician Daily Record Sheet should be used daily

---

## MATHEMATICALLY SPEAKING

▶ addition property of inequality

▶ multiplication property of inequality for multiplication by a positive number

▶ multiplication property of inequality for multiplication by a negative number

---

# LESSON 2.2 An Interesting Twist

 **Start It Off**

Look at the multiplication and division examples in the Start It Off from the previous lesson on page 51. There are some pairs that should look very similar, either in the example or in your answer.

Talk to your partner about what is the same and what is different about each of the following pairs. Why?

1.  a and b

2.  c and d

3.  e and f

4.  f and g

5.  c and h

## Strange Happenings

You know that when you add, subtract, multiply or divide both sides of an equation by the same number, you get another true equation. Now, you will explore what happens when you perform the same operations on both sides of an inequality.

**1.** Fill in the table below. Start with the inequality $6 > 3$ in each row.

| Directions: | Write the new inequality showing operations. | Write the result. | Is this true? |
|---|---|---|---|
| **Using Positive Numbers** | | | |
| Add 3 to both sides. | $6 + 3 > 3 + 3$ | $9 > 6$ | Yes |
| Multiply both sides by 3. | $6 \cdot 3 > 3 \cdot 3$ | | |
| Subtract 3 from both sides. | | | |
| Divide both sides by 3. | | | |
| **Using Negative Numbers** | | | |
| Add −3 to both sides. | | | |
| Multiply both sides by −3. | | | |
| Subtract −3 from both sides. | | | |
| Divide both sides by −3. | | | |

**2.** Create another inequality. Fill in the table on the Lesson Guide.

 **Start It Off**

1.  Parts a and b have the same numbers, but different operations. When you multiply by a proper fraction, the solution is less than the other factor. When you divide by a proper fraction, the solution is greater than the dividend. The solution to Part a is 1, which is less than 2. The solution to Part b is 4, which is greater than 2—there are four $\frac{1}{2}$s in 2 wholes.

2.  Parts c and d show that order matters in division. If you switch the order of the terms, the solutions are reciprocals of each other.

3.  Parts e and f show that order matters in division. If you switch the order of the terms, the solutions are reciprocals of each other.

4.  Parts f and g are different problems but have the same answer. Part f asks how many halves are in $\frac{1}{3}$ and Part g asks how many threes are in 2. In both cases, you cannot "measure out" or subtract one whole set that represents the value of the divisor from the dividend (only $\frac{2}{3}$ of it).

5.  Parts c and h both have the same answer (6) but different operations. The first terms are the same in both problems, but the second terms are reciprocals of each other. Part h is a multiplication problem and can be interpreted as repeatedly adding 3 two times for a total of 6. Part c is a division problem and can be interpreted as repeatedly subtracting one-third from 2 wholes. There are 6 thirds in 2 wholes, thus both problems have the same answer.

# DAY 1 TEACHING THE LESSON

In this lesson, students learn important rules for solving inequalities. As they encounter a variety of operations and signed numbers when solving inequalities, they come to an important realization—they must reverse the direction of the inequality symbol when dividing or multiplying both sides of an inequality by a negative number in order for the resulting inequality to hold true.

## Strange Happenings

Distribute copies of Lesson Guide 2.2: *Strange Happenings* to students and have them complete the table in Question 1 with a partner. Encourage students to share their answers and discoveries as a class when finished. Help students formulate the hypothesis that multiplying and dividing expressions on both sides of an inequality by a negative number does not result in a true statement using the original inequality sign. The direction of the inequality sign must be reversed for the statement to hold true.

 **Talk Moves** Distribute Lesson Guide 2.2: *Strange Happenings with Your Own Inequality*. Encourage students to test this hypothesis by completing Question 2 independently and comparing their results with a partner. Next, have partners discuss Question 3 and then share the generalizations they derived with the class. Use talk moves, such as agree/ disagree and why and adding on, to further the discussion and clarify students' understanding. Guide the discussion to help students conclude that when multiplying and dividing by the same negative number on both sides of an inequality, the direction of the inequality sign must be reversed in order for the statement to hold true.

**1.**

| Directions: | Write the new inequality showing operations. | Write the result. | Is this true? |
|---|---|---|---|
| **Using Positive Numbers** | | | |
| Add 3 to both sides. | $6 + 3 > 3 + 3$ | $9 > 6$ | Yes |
| Multiply both sides by 3. | $6 \cdot 3 > 3 \cdot 3$ | $18 > 9$ | Yes |
| Subtract 3 from both sides. | $6 - 3 > 3 - 3$ | $3 > 0$ | Yes |
| Divide both sides by 3. | $6 \div 3 > 3 \div 3$ | $2 > 1$ | Yes |
| **Using Negative Numbers** | | | |
| Add $-3$ to both sides. | $6 + (-3) > 3 + (-3)$ | $3 > 0$ | Yes |
| Multiply both sides by $-3$. | $6 \cdot {}^-3 > 3 \cdot {}^-3$ | $^-18 > {}^-9;$ $^-18 < {}^-9$ | No Yes |
| Subtract $-3$ from both sides. | $6 - (-3) > 3 - (-3)$ | $9 > 6$ | Yes |
| Divide both sides by $-3$. | $6 \div {}^-3 > 3 \div {}^-3$ | $^-2 > {}^-1;$ $^-2 < {}^-1$ | No Yes |

**2.** Answers will vary.

**3. a)** When you add or subtract the same number from both sides of an inequality, the resulting inequality is a true statement.

**b)** When you multiply or divide both sides of an inequality by the same positive number, the resulting inequality is a true statement.

When you multiply or divide the same negative number on both sides of an inequality, the resulting inequality is a true statement only if the direction of the original inequality symbol is reversed.

3. Talk to your partner and look for patterns.

   a) How does adding the same number to or subtracting the same number from both sides of an inequality affect the inequality?

   b) How does multiplying or dividing both sides of an inequality by the same number affect the inequality?

You should have found the following:

**MATHEMATICALLY SPEAKING**

▶ addition property of inequality

▶ multiplication property of inequality for multiplication by a positive number

▶ multiplication property of inequality for multiplication by a negative number

- When you add the same number to or subtract the same number from both sides of an inequality, the direction of the inequality symbol remains the same and the resulting inequality is true. It does not matter whether you add or subtract a positive or a negative number. This is the addition property of inequality.

- When you multiply or divide both sides of an inequality by the same positive number, the direction of the inequality symbol remains the same and the resulting inequality is true. This is the multiplication property of inequality for multiplication by a positive number.

- When you multiply or divide both sides of an inequality by a negative number, you must reverse the direction of the inequality to create a true statement. This is the multiplication property of inequality for multiplication by a negative number.

## Reversing the Inequality

Look at the last statement: When you multiply or divide both sides of an inequality by a negative number, you must *reverse* the direction of the inequality to create a true statement. Why do you think this happens?

4. Consider the following: Start with $6 > 3$. Is the opposite of 6 greater than the opposite of 3? Talk to your partner and explain how this is related to multiplying and dividing by negative numbers and the resulting inequalities.

## Reversing the Inequality

Have students discuss Question 4 with a partner and then share their ideas in a class discussion.

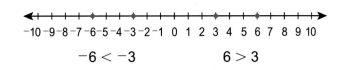

$$-6 < -3 \qquad\qquad 6 > 3$$

4. Comparing the opposite of 6 and the opposite of 3 is the same as multiplying or dividing 6 and 3 by $-1$ and then comparing. Given the original inequality $6 > 3$, when you multiply or divide both sides of the inequality by $-1$, the resulting inequality is $-6 > -3$. This statement does not hold true unless the inequality sign is reversed, $-6 < -3$.

## Solving Inequalities

Use the rules you have learned to solve each inequality below.

**5. a)** Solve $x + 15 < 22$. (If not mentioned, use the replacement set as the set of all numbers on the number line.)

Start by adding −15 to both sides.

| Inequality | Justification |
|---|---|
| **b)** $x + 15 + (^-15) < 22 + (^-15)$ | |
| **c)** $x + 0 < 22 + (^-15)$ | |
| **d)** $x < 22 + (^-15)$ | |
| **e)** $x < 7$ | |

So, any number less than 7 is a solution to the inequality.

**b)** Using the set of all numbers on the number line as the replacement set, graph the solution set for the inequality.

$$-2 \quad -1 \quad 0 \quad 1 \quad 2 \quad 3 \quad 4 \quad 5 \quad 6 \quad 7 \quad 8 \quad 9 \quad 10 \quad 11 \quad 12 \quad 13 \quad 14$$

Here is a way to check your work.

• First, check to see when the related equation holds true.
Solve the related equation, $x + 15 = 22$.
The solution is $x = 7$.

• Replace $x$ in $x + 15 < 22$ with a number *greater than* 7.
Is the resulting inequality true?
For example, $8 + 15 < 22$ is false since 23 is not less than 22.

Try a few more numbers greater than 7. Do they work?

• Replace $x$ in $x + 15 < 22$ with a number *less than* 7.
Is the resulting inequality true?
For example, $6 + 15 < 22$ is true since 21 is *less than* 22.

**6. a)** Try at least four more numbers less than 7 to see if the inequality holds true.

| Value for $x$ | $x + 15$ | $x + 15 < 22$? |
|---|---|---|
| 6 | 21 | Yes |
| 5 | 20 | Yes |
| 4 | 19 | Yes |
| 3 | | |
| | | |
| | | |
| | | |

**b)** Do you see a pattern in your answers?

**c)** Why will letting $x$ equal any number less than 7 always work?

## Solving Inequalities

Explore as a class how the inequality in Question 5 was solved. Discuss student justifications for each step in the solution process. Emphasize the importance of checking solutions when solving inequalities. Have students work independently on Question 6 and share their answers with a partner. Then discuss Questions 6b and 6c as a class. Guide the discussion to help students recognize that as the values for $x$ that are less than 7 decrease, the sum of $x + 15$ also decreases and will always be less than 22. Ask students:

• *Did anyone try any non-integer numbers less than 7?*

If no one tried any non-integer rational numbers, encourage students to select a few to make sure these numbers are part of the solution set, as long as their values are less than 7.

### Differentiation

**Think Differently:** Offer Lesson Guide 2.2A: *Do You See a Pattern?* for students who need help organizing and analyzing their answers to Question 6a. This lesson guide will enable students to more readily identify a pattern.

**Talk Moves** Have students complete Questions 7 and 8 independently. Circulate as students solve these problems to informally assess their understanding of key ideas. Use the *Student Snapshot* observation tool to record observations. Discuss student responses as a class when finished. Encourage a student volunteer to share his or her graph of the inequality for Question 7b on the overhead or interactive white board. Use the talk move agree/disagree and why to stimulate discussion and clarify student understanding.

### Differentiation

**Think Differently:** Offer Lesson Guide 2.2A: *Checking the Solution to an Inequality* for students who may need help organizing and analyzing the values they test to check the solution of the inequality.

**7. a)** Solve for $b$: $16 - 3b \geq 61$

| Inequality | Justification |
|---|---|
| $16 + (-16) + (-3b) \geq 61 + (-16)$ | |
| | additive inverse property |
| $-3b \geq 61 + (-16)$ | |
| | combining like terms |
| $-\frac{1}{3}(-3b) \leq 45\left(-\frac{1}{3}\right)$ | |
| $1 \cdot b \leq -15$ | |
| $b \leq -15$ | |

Why is the inequality sign *reversed* here?

**b)** Using the set of all numbers as the replacement set, graph the solution set for this inequality on the number line.

**c)** Next, you need to check your work.

• First, solve the related equation $16 - 3b = 61$ to get $b = -15$.

• Try a number *greater than* $-15$ to see if it works. For example, try 0. Is $16 - 3(0) \geq 61$? No.

• Try a number *less than* $-15$. For example, try $-20$. Is $16 - 3(-20) \geq 61$? $16 - (-60) \geq 61$. So, $76 \geq 61$. Yes, this works.

**8. a)** To ensure that all numbers less than $-15$ work, try at least four more numbers less than $-15$.

**b)** Will any number less than $-15$ work? Why?

---

> **NOTE** Remember to reverse the inequality sign to make this a true statement.
> So our solution is $b \leq -15$.

---

**5. a)**

| Inequality | Justification |
|---|---|
| **b)** $x + 15 + (-15)$ $< 22 + (-15)$ | addition property of inequality |
| **c)** $x + 0 < 22 + (-15)$ | additive inverse property |
| **d)** $x < 22 + (-15)$ | additive identity property |
| **e)** $x < 7$ | combining like terms |

**f)**

**6. a)** Numbers selected will vary. All numbers less than 7 will make the inequality a true statement.

**b)** Yes, there is a pattern.

**c)** As the values for $x$ decrease, the sum of $x + 15$ decreases. Using values that are less than 7, $x + 15$ is always less that 22, which makes the inequality a true statement.

**7. a)**

| Inequality | Justification |
|---|---|
| $16 + (-16) + (-3b) \geq 61 + (-16)$ | addition property of inequality |
| $0 + (-3b) \geq 61 + (-16)$ | additive inverse property |
| $-3b \geq 61 + (-16)$ | additive identity property |
| $-3b \geq 45$ | combining like terms |
| $-\frac{1}{3}(-3b) \leq 45\left(-\frac{1}{3}\right)$ | multiplication property of inequality |
| $1 \cdot b \leq -15$ | multiplicative inverse property |
| $b \leq -15$ | multiplicative identity property |

## Another Way to Find a Solution

You can also solve inequalities a different way.

**9.** Fill in the blanks. You may need to use more than one property for some of the steps.

| Inequality | Justification |
|---|---|
| $16 - 3b \geq 61$ | |
| $(^-61) + 16 - 3b \geq 61 + (^-61)$ | |
| $^-45 - 3b \geq 0$ | |
| $^-45 - 3b + (+3b) \geq 0 + 3b$ | |
| $^-45 + 0 \geq 3b$ | |
| $^-45 \geq 3b$ | |
| $\left(\frac{1}{3}\right)(^-45) \geq \left(\frac{1}{3}\right)3b$ | |
| $^-15 \geq b$ | |

**10.** Talk to a partner and discuss:

  **a)** Why isn't the inequality sign reversed in Question 9?

  **b)** Is the solution in Question 9 the same as the solution in Question 7? Explain.

  **c)** Which solution method do you prefer? Why?

**11.** Solve the following inequalities. Check your work.

  **a)** $^-25 \geq c - 7$    **d)** $^-3a + 6 < 26 - a$

  **b)** $^-0.4b \geq ^-2.4$    **e)** $\frac{1}{3}b + 7 \geq ^-2 - \frac{2}{3b}$

  **c)** $^-13 - 2x < 29 + 5x$    **f)** $^-6 \leq 3(y - 2) + 6$

**12.** Play Make a Match with a partner.

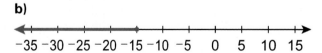

### Make a Match

**Players: 2–4**

**Materials:** Make a Match **game cards**

**Directions:**

  1. Shuffle and place all cards face down in 5 rows with 5 cards in each row.

  2. Players take turns. On each turn, the player turns over two cards.

  3. If the inequalities on the cards have the same solution set, she or he keeps the cards. If not, the player turns the cards back over.

  4. There is one wild card that will match with any other card.

  5. Play continues until no more matches can be made. The player with the most matches wins.

When both sides of the inequality were multiplied by a negative number $\left(^-\frac{1}{3}\right)$, the inequality symbol had to be reversed for the resulting statement to be true.

**b)**

**8. a)** Numbers selected will vary.

  **b)** Yes, any number less than $^-15$ will work, including $^-15$. As $x$ gets smaller, $16 - 3b$ gets larger. For any number less than or equal to $^-15$, $16 - 3b$ is greater than or equal to 61.

## Summarize Day 1

Have students discuss the following question with a partner and share their answers in a class discussion.

  • *Compare the inequalities $6a > 72$ and $^-6a > 72$. How would you solve each? Graph the solutions on a number line and discuss how the graphs are the same and different.*

Students should recognize that when dividing by a negative number, the inequality sign must be reversed. If $^-a > 12$, then $a < ^-12$.

### DAY 2 TEACHING THE LESSON

## Another Way to Find a Solution

Explain to students that they will explore another way to solve the same inequality. Have students complete Questions 9 and 10 with a partner. Discuss their responses as a class when finished. To stimulate discussion about Question 10, ask:

  • *How is this method similar to the first method used to solve the inequality?*

  • *How is it different?*

Have students practice solving inequalities by working independently on Question 11. When finished, have them compare solutions with a partner. Discuss any discrepancies with the class. Have students justify their solutions if they reversed the inequality sign when solving the problems.

Have students play the Make a Match card game in Question 12 with a partner. Circulate as students play the game to informally assess their understanding of key ideas. Use the *Student Snapshot* observation tool to record observations. After playing the game, have students complete Question 13 independently. Check to make sure students create matching pairs. Students can then add the new pairs to their game, or the new pairs can be collected and become a new class game.

9.

| Inequality | Justification |
|---|---|
| $16 - 3b \geq 61$ | given |
| $(-61) + 16 - 3b \geq 61 + (-61)$ | addition property of inequality |
| $-45 - 3b \geq 0$ | additive inverse property |
| $-45 - 3b + (+3b) \geq 0 + 3b$ | addition property of inequality |
| $-45 + 0 \geq 3b$ | additive inverse property |
| $-45 \geq 3b$ | additive identity property |
| $\left(\frac{1}{3}\right)(-45) \geq \left(\frac{1}{3}\right)3b$ | multiplication property of inequality |
| $-15 \geq b$ | multiplicative inverse property and multiplicative identity property |

10. a) Both sides of the inequality were multiplied by a positive number ($\frac{1}{3}$).

b) Yes. $-15 \geq b$ and $b \leq -15$ have the same solution set since they are equivalent statements.

c) Answers will vary. Students may find it easier working with a positive value for the coefficient of a variable when solving inequalities, since they don't have to reverse the inequality sign when multiplying or dividing by a positive number.

11. a) $-18 \geq c$ or $c \leq -18$

b) $b \leq 6$ or $6 \geq b$

c) $-6 < x$ or $x > -6$

d) $-10 < a$ or $a > -10$

e) $b \geq -9$ or $-9 \leq b$

f) $-2 \leq y$ or $y \geq -2$

12. Students play Make a Match card game.

## Using Inequalities to Understand Situations

**Talk Moves** Introduce the baby stroller rental scenario to the class. Have students complete Question 13 independently and compare their responses with a partner. Discuss Question 13c as a class. Use the talk move agree/disagree and why to build a consensus among students as they relate their mathematical inequality to a real-life situation.

**13. a)** The variable is the number of hours Dan's mom will rent the stroller.

**b)** $45 \geq 5.25h + 10$ or $5.25h + 10 \leq 45$, where $h$ represents the number of hours the baby stroller is rented.

$5.25h + 10 \leq 45$

$5.25h + 10 + (-10) \leq 45 + (-10)$

$5.25h + 0 \leq 35$

**c)** $5.25h \leq 35$

$(\frac{1}{5.25})(5.25h) \leq 35 \cdot (\frac{1}{5.25})$

$h \leq 6.\overline{6}$

**d)** Since the baby strollers can only be rented by whole hours, the maximum number of hours Dan's mom can rent the stroller is 6 hours.

## Wrap It Up

Responses will vary. The discussion should include the following key ideas:

Solving equations and inequalities are alike in the following ways:

- Both equations and inequalities indicate a relationship between expressions. The expressions consist of terms with variables and/or numerical values.

- Like terms are combined to simplify expressions.

- Algebraic properties are used to write equivalent expressions to simplify them when solving equations and inequalities.

- To solve inequalities and equations, the variable is isolated on one side of the equation.

- The solutions can be graphed.

Solving equations and inequalities are different in the following ways:

- An equation indicates that two expressions have the same value using an equal sign. An inequality compares two expressions using $<$, $>$, $\leq$ or $\geq$.

- When you add, subtract, multiply or divide the same number from or by expressions on both sides of an equation, the equal sign does not change. When you multiply or divide expressions on both sides of an inequality by the same negative number, the direction of the inequality symbol must be reversed.

- When you solve linear equations, there is usually one value for the variable that makes the statement true. When you solve inequalities, there may be more than one value for the variable that makes the inequality true.

## Reflect

Use these questions to help you reflect on the lesson and plan for future instruction.

- How skilled are students at solving inequalities?

- Are students able to recognize when the direction of an inequality symbol must be reversed when solving inequalities?

- What are some lingering student misconceptions about inequalities that need to be addressed in future instruction?

See corresponding assessments in Assessment Resources.

## Using Inequalities to Understand Situations

Visitors to the Newton Discovery Center can rent baby strollers for $5.25 an hour. When determining the total price, any part of an hour is rounded up to the next hour. Skyler's mom needs to rent a stroller for his younger sister. His mother wants to spend at most $45, including the stroller rental and $10 for snacks. (Notice the sign says: $5.25 an hour includes any part of the hour.)

13. **a)** What is the variable in this situation?

    **b)** Write an inequality that describes this situation.

    **c)** Solve the inequality. What is the replacement set?

    **d)** What is the maximum number of hours she can rent a stroller?

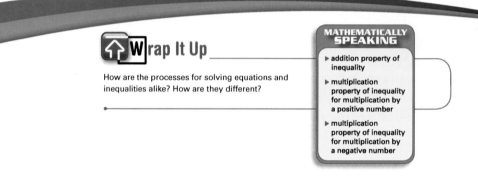

### Wrap It Up

How are the processes for solving equations and inequalities alike? How are they different?

**MATHEMATICALLY SPEAKING**

▶ addition property of inequality

▶ multiplication property of inequality for multiplication by a positive number

▶ multiplication property of inequality for multiplication by a negative number

**Write About It**

1. Explain to a friend who was absent today why you need to switch the direction of an inequality symbol when multiplying or dividing both sides by a negative number. Use an example.

2. Solve each inequality below. Use all the numbers on the number line as the replacement set. Graph each solution on a number line.

   a) $4c - 3 < 45$

   b) $2.2z > {}^-0.6z + 7$

   c) $44 - d \leq 12d - 8$

   d) $^-20 + 12g < {}^-5 - 3g$

3. The Silky Smooth snack bar at the Discovery Center buys fruit in bulk to make drinks. One case of oranges costs $22.50 and will make no more than 48 drinks.

   a) Find the maximum number of cases you can buy for less than $300.

   b) If Katherine, who runs the snack bar, wants to make at least 500 drinks each day, what is the minimum number of cases she needs to buy?

4. James and Anthony were discussing solving inequalities. James said he only wants to multiply or divide by positive numbers and will use properties to make the term with the variable have a positive value.

   a) Why do you think he wants this term to be positive?

   b) Anthony thinks this is not always possible. Do you agree or disagree? Justify your answer.

5. Solve the following inequalities. Check your answers by testing several values.

   a) $-\frac{1}{2x} \leq 2(x + 5)$

   b) $6 - (3x + 7\frac{2}{3}) > 15 + 22\frac{1}{3}$

   c) $34 - 2(a - 25) \geq 15 - a$

   d) $5(n - 7) < \frac{2}{3}(3 + 9n)$

**On Your Own**

**Write About It**

1. Answers will vary. Possible response: When you multiply or divide the expressions on both sides of an inequality by a negative number, the direction of the inequality symbol must be reversed for the resulting inequality to hold true.

| Example: | $3 > 2$ | true |
|---|---|---|
| Now multiply the expressions on both sides of the inequality by $^-4$. | $^-4 \cdot 3 > {}^-4 \cdot 2$ <br> $^-12 > {}^-8$ | not true |
| Reverse the direction of the inequality sign. | $^-12 < {}^-8$ | true |

**2.** **a)** $c < 12$ or $12 > c$

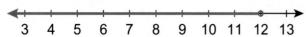

**b)** $z > 2.5$ or $2.5 < z$

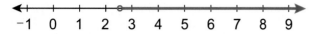

**c)** $4 \leq d$ or $d \geq 4$

**d)** $g < 1$ or $1 > g$

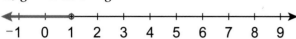

**3.** **a)** 13 cases

**b)** 11 cases

**4.** **a)** When the term with the variable has a positive coefficient, James does not have to multiply or divide both sides of the inequality by a negative number to isolate the variable. So the resulting statement will be true without reversing the direction of the inequality sign.

**b)** It is always possible to write an inequality so the term with the variable has a positive coefficient. If the term with the variable has a negative coefficient, add the opposite of the term to both sides of the inequality. This may involve a few more steps when solving the inequality.

Example: $6 > {}^-2a$

$$6 + 2a > {}^-2a + 2a$$    Add the
$$6 + 2a > 0$$    opposite of
$$6 + ({}^-6) + 2a > 0 + ({}^-6)$$    the variable
$$0 + 2a > {}^-6$$    term to both
$$2a > {}^-6$$    sides of the
$$\tfrac{1}{2} \cdot 2a > \tfrac{1}{2} \cdot {}^-6$$    inequality.
$$1 \cdot a > {}^-3$$
$$a > {}^-3$$

**5. a)** $-4 \leq x$ or $x \geq -4$

Possible values to test:

| Value for $x$ | $-\frac{1}{2}x$ | $2(x + 5)$ | $-\frac{1}{2}x \leq 2(x + 5)$? |
|---|---|---|---|
| −4 | 2 | 2 | Yes |
| 1 | $\frac{-1}{2}$ | 12 | Yes |
| −6 | 3 | −2 | No |

So, "$x$ is greater than or equal to $-4$" holds true.

**b)** $x < -13$ or $-13 > x$

| Value for $x$ | $6 - (3x + 7\frac{2}{3})$ | $15 + 22\frac{1}{3}$ | $6 - (3x + 7\frac{2}{3}) > 15 + 22\frac{1}{3}$? |
|---|---|---|---|
| −20 | $58\frac{1}{3}$ | $37\frac{1}{3}$ | Yes |
| −14 | $40\frac{1}{3}$ | $37\frac{1}{3}$ | Yes |
| 1 | $-4\frac{2}{3}$ | $37\frac{1}{3}$ | No |

So, "$x$ is less than $-13$" holds true.

**c)** $69 \geq a$ or $a \leq 69$

| Value for $a$ | $34 - 2(a - 25)$ | $15 - a$ | $34 - 2(a - 25) \geq 15 - a$ |
|---|---|---|---|
| 25 | 34 | −10 | Yes |
| 69 | −54 | −54 | Yes |
| 75 | −66 | −60 | No |

So, "$a$ is less than or equal to $69$" holds true.

**d)** $n > -37$ or $-37 < n$

| Value for $n$ | $5(n - 7)$ | $\frac{2}{3}(3 + 9n)$ | $5(n - 7) < \frac{2}{3}(3 + 9n)$ |
|---|---|---|---|
| −30 | −185 | −178 | Yes |
| 1 | −30 | 8 | Yes |
| −40 | −235 | −238 | No |

So, "$n$ is greater than $-37$" holds true.

**6. a)** $11r - 7 + 20 \leq 300$ or $11r + 13 \leq 300$, where $r$ is the number of rides.

---

Each full turn will take a total of 11 minutes (4 minutes to go on the ride and 7 minutes to wait in line). However, Skyler does not have to wait in line after his last ride, so students should subtract 7 minutes.

---

**b)** $r \leq 26.0\overline{9}$. Therefore, the maximum number of rides Skyler can take is 26.

**7.** $0.15t + 3.50 \leq 9.50$ or $9.50 \geq 0.15t + 3.50$, where $t$ represents the number of minutes Sierra can be on the computer. The solution is $t \leq 40$, so Sierra can spend a maximum of 40 minutes on the computer.

**8.** Answers will vary.

6. Sierra can stay at the Newton Discovery Center from 10 am until 3 pm. She wants to ride the Space Explorer as many times as possible. Each ride lasts 4 minutes and it takes about 7 minutes to get off the ride, get back in line, and get back on the ride. He needs 20 minutes for a lunch break.

    a) Write an inequality to find the maximum number of rides Sierra can take.

    b) Solve your inequality.

    **? Hint**
    See page 168

7. Thursday mornings are special at the Falling Apple Science Museum. The price of admission is just $3.50! At the Create Your Own Computer Game exhibit, computer time costs just $0.15 per minute. One Thursday morning, Skyler brought $9.50 with him and planned to spend the entire time at this exhibit.

    Write an inequality for this situation, using $t$ to represent the amount of time Skyler can spend at this exhibit. Then solve your inequality.

8. Look for a newspaper or magazine article where a range of numbers is listed. Write this range as an inequality.

**Think Beyond**

9. a) For the inequality $y > 2x - 3$, name five coordinate pairs $(x, y)$ that are solutions, assuming the replacement set is the set of all numbers.

    b) Graph the equation $y = 2x - 3$. Where are the pairs from Part a in relation to the graph of $y = 2x - 3$?

    c) Predict where all the solutions of the inequality will be found on a graph. Explain your reasoning.

**Think Beyond**

9.

a) Answers will vary. Possible solutions:

$y > 2x - 3$

| x | y | (x, y) |
|---|---|--------|
| −1 | −4 | (−1, −4) |
| 0 | −2 | (0, −2) |
| 1 | 0 | (1, 0) |
| 2 | 2 | (2, 2) |
| 3 | 4 | (3, 4) |

b) The pairs are above and to the left of the line.

$y = 2x - 3$

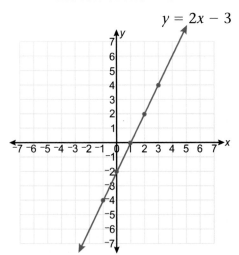

c) The solutions of the inequality will be found in the region above the graph of the line $y = 2x - 3$. For each point $(x, y)$ on the line $y = 2x - 3$, the associated $y$-values in the replacement set for $y > 2x - 3$ would all be greater than (or above) the $y$-value of that point.

$y = 2x - 3$

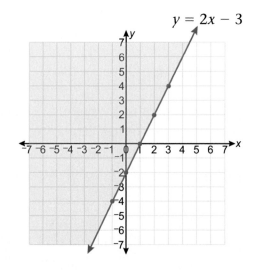

10. Shannon told Hayden that she had a coupon for 20% off one admission to Five Flags Theme Park. Using her coupon, she paid $20 for a ticket. Her friend Hayden did not have the coupon, so she added 20% of $20 and handed the ticket seller $24 for her admission. The ticket seller said he needed another dollar. Why?

11. Hector rides his bike to school at an average of 18 miles per hour. If his school is 3 miles away, how many minutes does it take him to get there? If he has to be in class at 8:05 and it takes him 3 minutes to lock up his bike, what time must he leave home to keep from being late? Explain your answer.

12. Alana had a box of fruit chews. There were 6 cherry, 5 lemon, 3 orange and 8 grape. Mariko only likes the orange and lemon ones. If Alana lets Mariko pull one fruit chew from the box, what is the probability that she will get one she likes?

13. Which set of numbers is ordered from least to greatest?

   **A.** $0.65, 0.68, \frac{2}{3}, \frac{5}{8}$      **C.** $\frac{5}{8}, 0.65, \frac{2}{3}, 0.68$

   **B.** $0.65, \frac{5}{8}, \frac{2}{3}, 0.68$      **D.** $\frac{5}{8}, \frac{2}{3}, 0.65, 0.68$

14. In an isosceles triangle, one side is 2.4 cm and another side is 1.8 cm. What are the two possible perimeters for this triangle?

Optional Technology Lesson for this section available at **www.mymathinnovations.com**

Think
Back

10. The 20% discount was off the original price, but Hayden calculated 20% of the discounted price—20% of $20 is $4. Hayden then added $20 + $4 to get a total cost of $24. To find the original cost of the ticket, Hayden could have set up the equation $20 = 0.80x$, since $20 represents 80% of the original cost. Solving the equation, she would find that the correct cost is $25.

11. It would take Hector 10 minutes to get to school.

   $$\frac{18 \text{ miles}}{60 \text{ minutes}} = \frac{3 \text{ miles}}{x \text{ minutes}}$$

   8:05 − 10 minutes − 3 minutes = 7:52 am. He would have to leave home by 7:52 am.

12. $\frac{8}{22}$ or $\frac{4}{11}$

13. **C** $\frac{5}{8}, 0.65, \frac{2}{3}, 0.68$

14. Since two sides of an isosceles triangle have the same length, the perimeter is either 6.6 cm (2.4 cm + 2.4 cm + 1.8 cm) or 6 cm (1.8 cm + 1.8 cm + 2.4 cm).

Optional Technology Lesson for this section available at **www.mymathinnovations.com**

**1.** **Start with the inequality 6 > 3 and complete the table below.**

| Directions: | Write the new inequality showing operations. | Write the result. | Is this true? |
|---|---|---|---|
| **Using Positive Numbers** | | | |
| Add 3 to both sides. | $6 + 3 > 3 + 3$ | $9 > 6$ | Yes |
| Multiply both sides by 3. | $6 \cdot 3 > 3 \cdot 3$ | | |
| Subtract 3 from both sides. | | | |
| Divide both sides by 3. | | | |
| **Using Negative Numbers** | | | |
| Add $-3$ to both sides. | | | |
| Multiply both sides by $-3$. | | | |
| Subtract $-3$ from both sides. | | | |
| Divide both sides by $-3$. | | | |

2. Now make up another inequality. _____
   Use your inequality to fill in the table below.

| Directions: | Write the new inequality showing operations. | Write the result. | Is this true? |
|---|---|---|---|
| **Using Positive Numbers** | | | |
| Add 3 to both sides. | | | |
| Multiply both sides by 3. | | | |
| Subtract 3 from both sides. | | | |
| Divide both sides by 3. | | | |
| **Using Negative Numbers** | | | |
| Add −3 to both sides. | | | |
| Multiply both sides by −3. | | | |
| Subtract −3 from both sides. | | | |
| Divide both sides by −3. | | | |

Accommodation Guide

**5.**

| Value for $x$ | $x + 15$ | $x + 15 < 22$? |
|:---:|:---:|:---:|
| 6 | 21 | Yes |
| 5 | 20 | Yes |
| 4 | 19 | Yes |
| 3 | | |
| | | |
| | | |
| | | |
| | | |
| | | |
| | | |
| | | |
| | | |
| | | |
| | | |
| | | |

© Kendall Hunt Publishing Company

**6.**

| Value for $b$ | $16 - 3b$ | $16 - 3b \geq 61$? |
|---|---|---|
| −15 | 61 | Yes |
| −20 | 78 | Yes |
| | | |
| | | |
| | | |
| | | |
| | | |
| | | |
| | | |
| | | |
| | | |
| | | |
| | | |
| | | |

| | | | | |
|---|---|---|---|---|
| Wild Card | $-18 \le x - 6$ | $x \ge -12$ | $-2(x + 3) > 18$ | |
| $2 < x \le 5$ | $x > 2$ and $x \le 5$ | $x < -4$ | $\frac{1}{2}x > \frac{3}{2}x + 4$ | $2x - 2 > -10$ |
| | $x$ is less than $-2$ and $x$ is greater than $-10$. | $-2 > x > -10$ | | The replacement set is the set of integers. $0 < x \le 1$ |
| **1** | | The replacement set is the set of positive integers. $-1 < x < 2$ | $3x - 4 \ge 2x + 1$ | $x \ge 5$ |
| The replacement set is the set of all positive numbers. $-3 \le 2(x - 1) + 3$ | | $-50x \le 100$ | | $-2x + 6 > 14$ |

| | | | | |
|---|---|---|---|---|
| **MAKE A MATCH!** | **MAKE A MATCH!** | **MAKE A MATCH!** | **MAKE A MATCH!** | **MAKE A MATCH!** |
| **MAKE A MATCH!** | **MAKE A MATCH!** | **MAKE A MATCH!** | **MAKE A MATCH!** | **MAKE A MATCH!** |
| **MAKE A MATCH!** | **MAKE A MATCH!** | **MAKE A MATCH!** | **MAKE A MATCH!** | **MAKE A MATCH!** |
| **MAKE A MATCH!** | **MAKE A MATCH!** | **MAKE A MATCH!** | **MAKE A MATCH!** | **MAKE A MATCH!** |
| **MAKE A MATCH!** | **MAKE A MATCH!** | **MAKE A MATCH!** | **MAKE A MATCH!** | **MAKE A MATCH!** |

**Note:** Wild Card can be used to match any card.

| | |
|---|---|
| $-18 \leq x - 6$ | $x \geq {-12}$ |
| $-2(x + 3) > 18$ | $-18 \ -12 \ -6 \quad 0 \quad 6 \quad 12 \ 18$ |
| $2 < x \leq 5$ | $x > 2$ and $x \leq 5$ |

| | | |
|---|---|---|
| $x < {-4}$ | $\frac{1}{2}x > \frac{3}{2}x + 4$ | $-2x + 6 > 14$ |

| | |
|---|---|
| $2x - 2 > -10$ | $-4 \ -3 \ -2 \ -1 \ \ 0 \ \ 1 \ \ 2 \ \ 3 \ \ 4$ |
| $x$ is less than $-2$ and $x$ is greater than $-10$. | $-2 > x > -10$ |
| $-2 \ -1 \ 0 \ 1 \ 2 \ 3 \ 4 \ 5 \ 6 \ 7 \ 8 \ 9 \ 10$ | Wild Card |

| | | |
|---|---|---|
| The replacement set is the set of integers. $0 < x \leq 1$ | **1** | The replacement set is the set of positive integers. $--1 < x < 2$ |

| | |
|---|---|
| $0 \ \ 1 \ \ 2 \ \ 3 \ \ 4 \ \ 5 \ \ 6 \ \ 7$ | Wild Card |
| $3x - 4 \geq 2x + 1$ | $x \geq 5$ |
| The replacement set is the set of all positive numbers. $-3 \leq 2(x - 1) + 3$ | $-2 \ -1 \ \ 0 \ \ 1 \ \ 2 \ \ 3 \ \ 4 \ \ 5$ |
| $-50x \leq 100$ | $-3 \ -2 \ -1 \ \ 0 \ \ 1 \ \ 2 \ \ 3 \ \ 4 \ \ 5$ |

The Sum It Up summarizes the important mathematics students should have learned in this section. Encourage students to use this Sum It Up as they complete the Study Guide and prepare for quizzes and tests.

# Sum It Up

In this section you learned about inequalities—mathematical statements that compare two expressions. The solution to an inequality is a set of values of the variable that make the inequality true. You can graph solutions to inequalities on a number line. You solved equations using properties of equality. Similarly, you can solve inequalities using properties of inequality and inverse properties. With inequalities, however, you must be careful with the directions of symbols. The following are important ideas you learned in this section.

## Reading and Writing Inequalities

■ Inequalities use different symbols to represent the relationship between expressions.

| Symbol | Description |
|--------|-------------|
| $\neq$ | does not equal |
| $<$ | is less than |
| $>$ | is greater than |
| $\leq$ | is less than or equal to |
| $\geq$ | is greater than or equal to |

■ Inequalities can be read from left to right or from right to left. For example, $5 < x$ can be read as "5 is less than $x$" or "$x$ is greater than 5."

■ Inequalities can be combined into a single statement. For example, "$x$ is less than 2" and "$x$ is greater than $-1$" can be written as $-1 < x < 2$.

## Solving Inequalities

■ To solve inequalities:

- When you add the same number to or subtract the same number from both sides of an inequality, the resulting inequality is true. This is the addition property of inequality.

If $4 > x$, then $4 + 3 > x + 3$.
If $4 > x$, then $4 - 3 > x - 3$.

■ When you multiply or divide both sides of an inequality by the same *positive* number, the resulting inequality is true. This is the multiplication property of inequality for multiplication by a positive number.

If $x > 4$, then $3 \cdot 4 > 3 \cdot x$.
If $4 > x$, then $\frac{4}{3} > \frac{x}{3}$.

- When you multiply or divide both sides of an inequality by the same negative number, you must reverse the inequality symbol for the resulting inequality to be a true statement. This is the multiplication property of inequality for multiplication by a negative number.

$4 > x$, so $4(-3) < (-3x)$

$4 > x$, so $\frac{4}{-3} < \frac{x}{-3}$

■ To find the solution set for an inequality, you must first consider the replacement set. For example, if the replacement set for $4 > x$ is the set of positive integers, the solution set is $\{1, 2, 3\}$. If the replacement set is all real numbers, the solution set includes all real numbers less than 4.

## Graphing Inequalities

■ An open circle on a number indicates that the number is not part of the solution set. For example: The solution set of $x < 7$ does not include $x = 7$.

**a)** The graph below is the solution when the replacement set is the set of all numbers on the number line.

**b)** The graph below is the solution set when the replacement set is the set of integers. Note that an open circle on 7 is not needed in this case and is usually not used.

• A filled-in circle on a number identifies that number as part of the solution set. For example: When the replacement set is the set of all numbers on the number line, the solution set of $x \geq 7$ includes $x = 7$.

---

### MATHEMATICALLY SPEAKING

Do you know what these mathematical terms mean?

▶ addition property of inequality

▶ inequality

▶ multiplication property of inequality for multiplication by a positive number

▶ multiplication property of inequality for multiplication by a negative number

▶ replacement set

▶ solution set

▶ symbol ">"

▶ symbol "≥"

▶ symbol "<"

▶ symbol "≤"

▶ symbol "≠"

# Study Guide

Solve It: Focusing on Equations,
Inequalities and Exponents

## Part 1. What did you learn?

1. List three integers and three non-integers that satisfy each of \the following inequalities.

   **a.** $a + 5 < 8$

   **b.** $-4 \leq b < -0.5$

   **c.** $c < 1$ and $c \geq -2$

   **d.** $4d \geq -12$

2. The following table shows the steps and justification for the solution of the inequality $2x + 4 \leq 24$. Complete the missing entries.

| Step | Justification |
|---|---|
| **a.** $2x + 4 \leq 24$ | **b.** Original inequality |
| **c.** $2x + 4 + {}^{-}4 \leq 24 + {}^{-}4$ | **d.** |
| **e.** $2x \leq 20$ | **f.** Combine like terms |
| **g.** | **h.** Multiplication Property of Equality |
| **i.** | **j.** Solution |

3. Graph the solution from Question 2 on a number line.

4. Solve for $b$: $20 - 2b \geq -32$. Show your steps. Graph your solution on the number line.

5. Solve for $c$: $c + 4 < 20 - c$. Show your steps. Graph your solution on the number line.

6. When graphing an inequality, how do you know whether the arrow away from the endpoint should point left or right?

7. When graphing an inequality, how do you know whether the circle at the endpoint should be open or closed?

8. How is solving $3x = 12$ similar to solving $3x > 12$? How is it different?

Section 2: Inequalities • Study Guide   **75**

**3.**

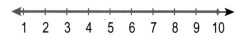

**4.**
$$20 - 2b \geq -32$$
$$20 - 2b + {}^{-}20 \geq -32 + {}^{-}20$$
$$2b \geq -52$$
$$-\frac{1}{2} \cdot {}^{-}2b < -52 \cdot -\frac{1}{2}$$
$$b \leq 26$$

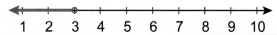

**5.**
$$c + 4 < 20 - c$$
$$c + 4 + c < 20 - c + c$$
$$2c + 4 < 20$$
$$2c + 4 + {}^{-}4 < 20 + {}^{-}4$$
$$2c < 16$$
$$\frac{1}{2} \cdot 2c < 16 \cdot \frac{1}{2}$$
$$c < 8$$

# Study Guide

1. Answers will vary. Possible answers are given below.

   **a.** 0, 1, 2; -0.5, 0.75, 1.5

   **b.** -3, -2, -1; -1.5, -1.6, -1.7

   **c.** -2, -1, 0; 0.5, 0.6, 0.7

   **d.** -2, -1, 0; 1.5, 2.5, 3.5

2. **d.** Addition Property of Equality

   **g.** $\frac{1}{2} \cdot 2x \leq 20 \cdot \frac{1}{2}$

   **i.** $x \leq 10$

6. Answers will vary. Possible answer: If the solution to the inequality is of the form "$x <$", then the arrow should point to the left. If the solution to the inequality is of the form "$x >$", then the arrow should point to the right.

7. Answers will vary. Possible answer: If the solution to the inequality uses $<$ or $>$, then the circle should be open. If the solution to the inequality uses $\leq$ or $\geq$, then the circle should be closed.

8. Answers will vary. Possible answer: To solve both the equation and inequality, we use the multiplication property of equality to multiply both sides by $\frac{1}{3}$. This isolates the variable $x$. In the equation, $x = 4$ means that the only value that can replace the variable to make the equation true is 4. But in the inequality, $x > 4$ means that any number greater than 4 can replace the variable to make the inequality true. So, the equation has one solution and the inequality has infinitely many solutions.

9. Kellie was asked the following multiple-choice question on a recent quiz.

> If $x$ represents the speed at which a car is permitted to travel, which inequality below could be used to represent a speed limit of 55 miles per hour?
>
> **A.** $x \leq 55$      **C.** $x < 55$
>
> **B.** $x \geq 55$      **D.** $x > 55$

Kellie chose letter C but her answer was marked wrong. Why? What could you say or do to help Kellie find the correct answer?

10. Jerry thinks $5 < x$ is the same as $x < 5$. Veronica disagrees. She thinks $5 < x$ is the same as $x > 5$. Who do you agree with? Why?

9. Answers will vary. Possible answer: Letter C is not the correct choice because it only includes values less than 55 mph. But, the speed limit is 55 mph or less. So, the correct choice is letter A. I would remind Kellie to think about the difference between "less than" and "less than or equal to." In this situation, a car's speed can be either less than 55 mph or equal to 55 mph.

10. Answers will vary. Possible answer: I agree with Veronica. $5 < x$ is not the same as $x < 5$. You can check this by plugging in values for $x$. If $x = 7$, $5 < 7$ but it is not true that $7 < 5$. But, $5 < x$ is the same as $x > 5$. $5 < x$ means that 5 is less than some number, $x$, and that is the same as saying some number, $x$, is greater than 5 which can be written as $x > 5$, if $x = 7$, $5 < 7$ and $7 > 5$.

# Exponents and Scientific Notation

**LESSON 3.1**

## Thinking Really Big

**Suggested Pacing: 2 Days**

In this lesson, students will read, write and compare very large numbers. They will explore the rules for scientific notation and use exponents to express powers of ten. They will solve problems and play card games that involve large numbers written in scientific notation and standard notation. They will learn how a calculator records and displays numbers in scientific notation.

---

**LESSON OBJECTIVES**

- Students will read, write and interpret large numbers written in scientific notation.
- Students will translate, order and compare large numbers written in standard and scientific notation.
- Students will solve real-life problems with large numbers using scientific notation.
- Students will interpret how a calculator records and displays numbers in scientific notation.

---

| DAY 1 | Materials* | ESSENTIAL *ON YOUR OWN* QUESTIONS |
|---|---|---|
| The Solar System Exhibit <br><br> Mathematicians' Shortcut <br><br> Finding Distances in Our Solar System | **In Class** <br> ■ Calculators <br> ■ Lesson Guide 3.1A: *Do You Know the Powers of 10?* | Questions 1–4, 6, 14–16 |

| DAY 2 | Materials* | ESSENTIAL *ON YOUR OWN* QUESTIONS |
|---|---|---|
| Big Numbers Rule! <br><br> Using the Calculator | **In Class** <br> ■ Calculators <br> ■ Lesson Guide 3.1: *Big Numbers Rule!* <br> ■ Scissors <br><br> **On Your Own** <br> ■ Calculators <br> ■ Internet or newspapers and magazines | Questions 5, 7, 8–12, 17, 18 |

\* The Think Like a Mathematician Daily Record Sheet should be used daily

---

## MATHEMATICALLY SPEAKING

▶ astronomical unit (AU)          ▶ exponent          ▶ scientific notation

▶ base          ▶ mantissa          ▶ standard notation

SECTION **3**

THINKING LIKE A MATHEMATICIAN

# Exponents and Scientific Notation

In this section, you will learn how to use exponents with scientific notation and how this helps us read, write and work with numbers efficiently. You will learn rules that mathematicians use when multiplying and dividing by powers of 10. These rules will help you compare very large numbers, as well as very small numbers. You will learn that exponents in expressions can be either positive or negative, and you will learn how to multiply and divide exponential expressions.

 **LESSON 3.1** Thinking Really Big

 Start It Off

1. Multiply the following without using a calculator.

   **a)** $10 \cdot 5{,}000 =$     **d)** $600 \cdot 200{,}000 =$

   **b)** $100 \cdot 40{,}000 =$     **e)** $10{,}000 \cdot 10{,}000 =$

   **c)** $4{,}000 \cdot 70{,}000 =$

2. Describe a shortcut rule to solve these multiplication problems mentally.

The number 34,000,000,000 is quite large! Did you know that there is a way to write large numbers so they are easier to understand and work with?

 Start It Off

1. **a)** 50,000

   **b)** 4,000,000

   **c)** 280,000,000

   **d)** 120,000,000

   **e)** 100,000,000

2. You can solve them mentally by multiplying the front-end (nonzero) digits of the factors and counting the number of zeros in each factor to determine the total number of zeros. Move the decimal point of the front-end digit product to the right the number of places represented by the total number of zeros in the original factors.

## The Solar System Exhibit

As Director of the Newton Discovery Center, you have hired a group to redo the solar system exhibit in the Falling Apple Science Museum. This is necessary after the surprising announcement that Pluto is no longer considered a planet! Your current exhibit shows nine planets orbiting the sun.

Why isn't Pluto considered a planet? The group found a newspaper clipping online. Notice the important role that numbers play in determining Pluto's new status.

## DAY 1 TEACHING THE LESSON

In this lesson, students discover how to read, write and compare very large numbers efficiently. They explore the rules for scientific notation and review how to use exponents to express powers of ten. Using real-life contexts related to the Newton Discovery Center, students solve problems that involve large numbers written in scientific notation as well as standard notation. Students will play a card game to hone their skills in comparing large numbers in different forms. They will also discover how a calculator records and displays numbers in scientific notation.

## The Solar System Exhibit

Explain to students that they must hire a group to redo the Newton Discovery Center's solar system exhibit due to the fact that Pluto is no longer considered a planet. Have students complete Question 1 with a partner.

Encourage students to estimate the size of the numbers needed to complete each statement in order for the story to make sense before selecting a number from the box. Have student pairs compare their responses in a class discussion. Encourage them to share their strategies they used for selecting appropriate numbers to complete the given statements.

**1.** Fill in the blanks in the report with the correct numbers from this list.

| | | | |
|---|---|---|---|
| 3,000 kilometers | 3 | 2,500 | 149,000,000 km |
| 2006 | 1,467 miles | 248 | |
| 8 | 2015 | 3,647,000,000 miles | |

**News Bulletin: August _____**
                                   1

### And Then There Were _____
                                                  2

About _____ scientists
                    3
met in Prague to adopt important
new guidelines that demote the small
distant world of Pluto from planet to
"dwarf planet."

The International Astronomical
Union's decision means science text-
books and museum exhibits will now
have to describe a solar system with just
eight major planets. Pluto's status has
been argued for many years. At just
_____ in diameter, it is
              4
considerably smaller than the other
"traditional" planets in our solar system.

The final argument for Pluto came
with the discovery _____ years
                                5
ago of an object currently named
2003UB313 that was shown to be some

_____ in diameter, much larger
            6
than Pluto. It is also farther away than
all the other planets with a distance of
_____ from the sun. In contrast,
            7
our planet Earth is _____ from
                                  8
the sun. It takes _____ Earth
                              9
years for Pluto to complete a single
circuit around the sun. An unmanned
U.S. spacecraft, *New Horizons,* is sched-
uled to fly by Pluto in _____.
                                      10

Some scientists at the meeting were
just as distraught as the general public at
having to demote Pluto. In fact, Professor
Iwan Williams, chair of the panel working on the topic, stated, "I have a tear in
my eye today, yes; but at the end of the
day we have to describe the solar system
as it really is, not as we would like it to be."

 **Hint**
See page 169

**1.**

**1** 2006

**2** 8

**3** 2,500

**4** 1,467 miles

**5** 3

**6** 3,000 kilometers

**7** 3,647,000,000 miles

**8** 149,000,000 km

**9** 248

**10** 2015

# Mathematicians' Shortcut

Explain to students that mathematicians created a system to help write very large numbers. Discuss the format of scientific notation and how to determine the mantissa and the appropriate exponent of 10. Remind students that multiplying by 10 results in moving the decimal point one place to the right.

 **Differentiation**

**Think Differently:** For students experiencing difficulty identifying the appropriate power of 10 when writing a number in scientific notation, offer Lesson Guide 3.1A: *Do You Know the Powers of Ten?* for additional practice. Guide students to recognize that the number of decimal places moved represents the exponent of the power of 10.

## Mathematicians' Shortcut

Some of the numbers in this news release are very large. Mathematicians have created a system to write very large numbers to make calculations and comparisons with these numbers much easier. It is called scientific notation. A number written in scientific notation has the following form:

| a number greater than or equal to 1 and less than 10 | $\times$ | 10 raised to a power (using an exponent) |

For example, 31,000 would be written as $3.1 \times 10^4$.

Note: $3.1 \cdot 10,000 = 3.1 \cdot 10 \cdot 10 \cdot 10 \cdot 10 = 3 \times 10^4$.

In scientific notation, the first number—in this case, 3.1—is called the mantissa. In the exponential part, $10^4$, 10 is the base and 4 is the exponent.

**Let's Review** Remember that multiplying a number by 10 moves the decimal point one place to the right.
$2.4 \cdot 10 = 24$

**Example**

To write 3,260 in scientific notation, first create the mantissa, 3.26, and then figure out how many times you need to multiply by 10 to make the orginal number 3,260. The decimal point needs to be moved three places to the right. This is the same as multiplying by 1,000 or $10^3$.
$3,260 = 3.26 \times 10^3$

6,240,000 written in scientific notation is $6.24 \times 10^6$. Can you explain why?

2. Write the following numbers in scientific notation.

   a) 1,000,000

   b) 2,030,000,000

   c) 64 million

   d) 522 trillion

   e) 1.7 billion

   f) the distance from Earth to the sun in kilometers

   g) the distance from Pluto to the sun in miles

 **Talk Moves** Have students complete Questions 2–5 independently and compare their responses with a partner before discussing the solutions as a class. Use talk moves, such as agree/disagree and why, to clarify misconceptions and deepen student understanding. Learn more about the talk moves in the Teaching and Learning Strategies on p. T5. Note that the distances needed for Question 2f and 2g can be obtained from Question 1.

2. **a)** $1 \times 10^6$

   **b)** $2.03 \times 10^9$

   **c)** $6.4 \times 10^7$

   **d)** $5.22 \times 10^{14}$

   **e)** $1.7 \times 10^9$

   **f)** $1.49 \times 10^8$ kilometers (This distance is given in Question 1.)

   **g)** $3.647 \times 10^9$ miles (This distance is given in Question 1.)

**Think Beyond**

3. In Parts a–c, write your answers in both standard and scientific notation.

   a) Write the distance from Earth to the sun in miles.

   b) Write the distance from Pluto to the sun in kilometers.

   c) How much greater is the distance from Pluto to the sun than the distance from Earth to the sun in miles? In kilometers?

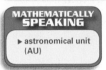 **MATHEMATICALLY SPEAKING**

▶ standard notation

4. Write the following numbers in standard notation.

   a) $9.0 \times 10^5$   b) $7.462 \times 10^7$   c) $1.25 \times 10^{10}$

5. Use your answers to Question 4 and write these numbers in words.

## Finding Distances in Our Solar System

**MATHEMATICALLY SPEAKING**

▶ astronomical unit (AU)

To create the new exhibit, the engineering team needs to find the distance of each of the eight planets from the sun. The team will use distances in astronomical units (AU), used by astronomers to measure each planet's distance from the sun.

1 AU is the average distance from the sun's center to Earth's center. 1 AU is approximately 93,000,000 miles.

 only ← ho ✗

6. Write the distance of 1 AU in miles using scientific notation.

7. Write the distance of 1 AU in kilometers using scientific notation.

**? Hint**
See page 169

---Example---

Calculate the distance from Jupiter to the sun in miles.

Jupiter has a distance of 5.203 AU. This means the distance is 5.203 times the distance from Earth to the sun or $5.203 \cdot (9.3 \times 10^7)$ miles.

$5.203 \cdot 9.3 \cdot 10^7 = 48.3879 \cdot 10^7 = 483,879,000$

---

3.  **Think Beyond**

a) Standard notation: $149,000,000 \cdot 0.6 = 89,400,000$ miles
Scientific notation: $8.94 \times 10^7$ miles

b) Standard notation: $3,647,000,000 \div 0.6 = 6,078,333,333$ kilometers
Scientific notation: $6.078333333 \times 10^9$ kilometers

c) Standard notation: $3,647,000,000 - 89,400,000 = 3,557,600,000$ miles
Scientific notation: $3.5576 \times 10^9$ miles

Standard notation: $6,078,333,333 - 149,000,000 = 5,929,333,333$ kilometers

Scientific notation: $5.929333333 \times 10^9$ kilometers

4. a) 900,000

   b) 74,620,000

   c) 12,500,000,000

5. a) nine hundred thousand

   b) seventy-four million, six hundred twenty thousand

   c) twelve billion, five hundred million

## Finding Distances in Our Solar System

Introduce students to the astronomical unit, or AU, by asking:

- ***Does anyone know the name of a unit used by astronomers to measure the distance from planets to the sun?***

If no one is familiar with this unit of measure, have students read about it as a class. Emphasize that one AU is the average distance from the sun's center to Earth's center. Have students work with a partner to complete Questions 6 and 7 and then share their responses with the class. Encourage pairs to share their solution strategies as well as their answers.

Next, explain to students that they have been assigned to help engineers calculate the distances of various planets to the sun. Have them discuss and complete Questions 8a and 8b as a class.

To make sure students understand how to convert AUs to miles, ask:

- ***Why did we have to multiply 5.203 by $9.3 \times 10^7$ to determine the distance from Jupiter to the sun in miles?***

Work together as a class to determine the distance from Earth to the sun in kilometers for Question 9. Guide students to recognize that they need to divide the number of miles by approximately 0.6 to determine the number of kilometers. Then have them work with a partner to complete the rest of the table. Circulate among pairs to informally assess student understanding. Use the *Student Snapshot* observational tool to record observations and notes. Have student partners compare their answers with another pair and discuss any unresolved discrepancies as a class.

6.  $9.3 \times 10^7$ miles

7.  $1.49 \times 10^8$ kilometers

**8. a)** The number is not in scientific notation because the mantissa is not greater than or equal to 1 and less than 10.

**b)** $48.3879 \times 10^7 = 48.3879 \cdot 10{,}000{,}000 = 4.83879 \cdot 100{,}000{,}000 = 4.83879 \times 10^8$

**9.**

| Planet | Distance from the Sun (AU) | Distance from the Sun (mi.), in Scientific Notation | Distance from the Sun (km), in Scientific Notation |
|---|---|---|---|
| Earth | 1 | $9.3 \times 10^7$ | $\mathbf{1.55 \times 10^8}$ |
| Jupiter | 5.203 | $4.83879 \times 10^8$ | $\mathbf{8.06465 \times 10^8}$ |
| Mars | 1.524 | $1.41732 \times 10^8$ | $\mathbf{2.3622 \times 10^8}$ |
| Mercury | 0.39 | $3.627 \times 10^7$ | $\mathbf{6.045 \times 10^7}$ |
| Neptune | 30.06 | $2.79558 \times 10^9$ | $\mathbf{4.6593 \times 10^9}$ |
| Saturn | 9.539 | $8.87127 \times 10^8$ | $\mathbf{1.478545 \times 10^9}$ |
| Uranus | 19.18 | $1.78374 \times 10^9$ | $\mathbf{2.9729 \times 10^9}$ |
| Venus | 0.723 | $6.7239 \times 10^7$ | $\mathbf{1.12065 \times 10^8}$ |

## Summarize Day 1

As a Wrap It Up discussion for Day 1, ask students:

- *What is scientific notation and why do we use it?*

Students should indicate that scientific notation is a way to write very large numbers that makes calculations and comparisons much easier.

Have students discuss the following example, comparing both notations and identifying the mantissa, the base and the exponent.

$$64{,}000{,}000 = 6.4 \times 10^7$$

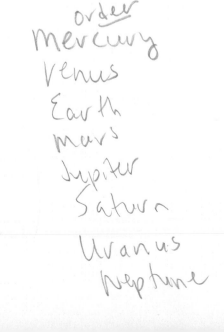

### Big Numbers Rule!

Explain to students that they will play a game to hone their skills comparing large numbers written in a variety of notations. Distribute a copy of Lesson Guide 3.1: *Big Numbers Rule!* to each pair of students. Have students cut out the cards and shuffle them. Next, read the rules of the game with the class. Model one turn of the game to make sure students understand the directions. Have students play the game until a winner is declared or as time allows.

Circulate as students play the game to informally assess their understanding of large numbers written in a variety of notations. Note strategies students use to determine which number has the greater value. You may wish to record observations and notes using the *Student Snapshot* observation tool. It is important to set aside time to discuss these strategies when students have finished playing the game. Ask:

- *Were there any numbers that were particularly challenging to compare?*

- *What strategies did you find helpful to use when comparing these numbers?*

 **Talk Moves** Use talk moves, such as repeat/rephrase and adding on, to clarify student ideas and extend understanding.

**10.** Answers will vary.

## Using the Calculator

Point out that different calculators have different ways of displaying large numbers. Work together as a class to answer Questions 11a and 11b. Have students work individually on Question 11c and share their solutions with a partner. Discuss student responses as a class, encouraging students to justify why they think their answers are correct. Focus the discussion on the strategies students used to determine appropriate factors.

One strategy students might use is to find a factor or divisor that divides evenly into the mantissa. The resulting quotient will be the second factor. Students then must identify two addends that will create a sum equal to the exponent of the power of 10. The value of each addend will then be the exponent of the power of 10 for each factor.

Example: 2.5 E 10

$2.5 \div 5 = 0.5$; The two partial factors are 0.5 and 5. Two addends that have a sum of 10 are 3 and 7. Therefore, two factors that can be multiplied to get a product of 2.5 E 10 are $5 \times 10^3$ and $0.5 \times 10^7$ or $5,000 \cdot 5,000,000$.

**8 a)** Notice that $48.3879 \times 10^7$ is not in scientific notation. Why not?

- To change $48.3878 \times 10^7$ to scientific notation, first change the mantissa to a number between 1 and 10.

    4.83879

- Since you divide by 10 to make this change, you must multiply $10^7$ by 10 so it becomes $10^8$.

- So $48.3879 \times 10^7 = 4.83879 \times 10^8$

**b)** By writing both numbers in standard notation, show that $48.3879 \times 10^7 = 4.83879 \times 10^8$.

**9.** Help the engineers complete the table below to find the distances from each planet to the sun.

| Planet | Distance from the Sun (AU) | Distance from the Sun (mi.) in Scientific Notation | Distance from the Sun (km) in Scientific Notation |
|---|---|---|---|
| Earth | 1 | $9.3 \times 10^7$ | |
| Jupiter | 5.203 | $4.83879 \times 10^8$ | |
| Mars | 1.524 | | |
| Mercury | 0.39 | | |
| Neptune | 30.06 | | |
| Saturn | 9.539 | | |
| Uranus | 19.18 | | |
| Venus | 0.723 | | |

## Big Numbers Rule!

### GAME · · · · · Big Numbers Rule! · · · · ·

Players: 2

Directions:

1. Shuffle, and deal one card at a time, face down, to each player. Use the entire deck.

2. Each player turns his top card over and the pair decides which card is greater in value. The person who turned that card over keeps the pair.

3. If the cards are equal in value, then the players each put two cards on top of their card face down and turn a third card face up. Whoever turned over the third card with the greater value takes this pile of eight cards from both players.

The game ends when a player has no more cards to turn over. The other player is the winner! (This is similar to the popular card game of War.)

**10.** Play one round of Big Numbers Rule! with a partner.

How does your calculator display large numbers? Different calculators show scientific notation in different ways.

11. Multiply 300,000 by 300,000 on your calculator.

a) What appears on your display?

b) Explain what the number in the display means. Use what you know about scientific notation.

c) Experiment with your calculator to figure out how to get the following products on the screen.

| | | | |
|---|---|---|---|
| 2.5 E 12 | or | 2.5 | 12 |
| 5.0204 E 10 | or | 5.0204 | 10 |
| 6.4598 E 15 | or | 6.4598 | 15 |

### ⬆W rap It Up

Describe how you would translate the number 17,352,246 into scientific notation and how you would translate $5 \times 10^{13}$ into standard notation.

**MATHEMATICALLY SPEAKING**

▸ astronomical unit (AU)
▸ base
▸ exponent
▸ mantissa
▸ scientific notation
▸ standard notation

11. a) 9 E 10 or $9^{10}$

b) 9 is the mantissa and 10 is the exponent of the power of 10.

c) Answers will vary. Possible responses:

| | |
|---|---|
| 2.5 E 12 | 50,000,000,000 • 50 |
| 5.0204 E 10 | 25,102,000 • 2,000 |
| 6.4598 E 15 | 16,149,500 • 400,000,000 |

### ⬆W rap It Up

Responses will vary. The discussion should include the following key ideas:

Steps to translate 17,352,246 into scientific notation:

- Create two factors: *a mantissa × a power of 10.*

- Identify a mantissa for the given number. (1.7352246)

- Count the number of places the decimal point has to be moved (7). This number represents the number of times the mantissa needs to be multiplied by 10 to convert it back to the original number. It is the exponent of 10.

  Therefore,
  $17,352,246 = 1.7352246 \times 10^7$

Steps to translate $5 \times 10^{13}$ into standard notation:

- Each time a number is multiplied by ten, the decimal point moves one place value to the right. Since 5 is being multiplied by 10 thirteen times (as indicated by the exponent), move the decimal point 13 places to the right.

  Therefore,
  $5 \cdot 10^{13} = 50,000,000,000,000$

### Reflect

Use these questions to help you reflect on the lesson and plan for future instruction.

- Are students able to interpret large numbers in scientific notation?

- What strategy did students use to compare and order large numbers written in different notations?

## On Your Own

1. **Write About It** Answers will vary. Possible response: Scientific notation helps us read, write and work with very large numbers more efficiently. To convert a number into scientific notation, you need to create two factors: a mantissa and a power of 10. The first factor is the mantissa. It is a number that is greater than or equal to 1 and less than 10. The second factor is a power of 10. When the two factors are multiplied, the result should be the original number.

Example: 2,430,700

The mantissa is 2.4307. Therefore $2,430,700 = 2.4307 \times 10^6$.

2. **a)** 330,000,000,000,000,000,000,000 kg

**b)** Answers will vary. Possible response: These numbers are very large in value. Using standard notation, they are difficult to read and cumbersome to write. Scientific notation enables us to work more efficiently with these numbers.

---

### Write About It

1. Explain to a friend who was absent why scientific notation is useful and how to convert a number from standard notation into scientific notation. Use examples.

2. The mass, or amount of matter, in a planet is generally written in scientific notation.

   For example, the mass of Mercury is $3.3 \times 10^{23}$ kg.

   **a)** Write the mass of Mercury in standard notation.

   **b)** Mercury has the smallest mass of all the planets. Explain why the masses of planets are usually written in scientific notation.

   *Mercury*

3. Write the following numbers in scientific notation.

   **a)** 250,135
   **d)** 54,675,009

   **b)** 3 trillion
   **e)** 580,744,267,100

   **c)** 2.48 million

4. Which number is greater?

   **a)** $4.32 \times 10^5$ or $3.42 \times 10^6$

   **b)** $5.68885 \times 10^{23}$ or $5.5 \times 10^{25}$

   **c)** $2.234 \times 10^7$ or $22.34 \times 10^6$

5. The walking stride of a typical person is about 1 yard in length.

   **a)** How many strides would it take for a person to cover the same distance as the length of the diameter of Pluto? Write your answers in standard notation and in scientific notation.

   **b)** How many strides would it take for a person to cover the same distance as the length of the diameter of Earth? Write your answers in standard and in scientific notation.

   **c)** How many strides would it take to cover the distance from Earth to the sun? Write your answer in scientific notation.

### Think Beyond

   **d)** How many strides would it take to walk the same distance as the distance from the sun to the farthest planet from the sun? Perform your calculations using scientific notation.

84    Course 3: Solve It: Focusing on Equations, Inequalities and Exponents

---

3. **a)** $2.50135 \times 10^5$

   **b)** $3 \times 10^{12}$

   **c)** $2.48 \times 10^6$

   **d)** $5.4675009 \times 10^7$

   **e)** $5.807442671 \times 10^{11}$

4. **a)** $3.42 \times 10^6$

   **b)** $5.5 \times 10^{25}$

   **c)** Both numbers are the same.

6. As Director of the Newton Discovery Center, you are concerned about recycling the many food and drink containers used at the center.

**Did you know?** Every year, Americans throw away 50 billion food and drink cans, 27 billion glass bottles and jars, and 65 million plastic and metal jar and can covers.

a) Write these numbers both in standard and scientific notation.

b) At the Newton Discovery Center, each person visiting consumes about 2 canned drinks. Last year attendance at the center was 1,005,329. Approximately how many cans were consumed last year, written in scientific notation?

c) If attendance remains the same, how many cans will be consumed over the next 12 years? Write your answer in both standard and scientific notation.

**Did you know?** Aluminum can take anywhere from 100 to 400 years to decompose. Glass has been found in perfect condition after 4,000 years in the earth!

Roman glass from the 2nd century

7. A bottlenose dolphin at the water's surface has a heartbeat of about 110 beats per minute. The average dolphin lives from 30 to 50 years. Find the minimum and maximum number of heartbeats a bottlenose dolphin experiences in a lifetime. Write the numbers in standard and scientific notation.

5. a) Pluto's diameter is approximately 1,467 miles, since there are 1,760 yards per mile, 1,467 • 1,760 = 2,581,920 yards. The number of strides needed to walk the diameter of Pluto is 2,581,920 in standard notation and $2.58129 \times 10^6$ in scientific notation.

b) Earth's diameter is approximately 7,926 miles, since there are 1,760 yards per mile, 7,926 • 1,760 = 13,949,760 yards. The number of strides needed to walk the diameter of Earth is 13,949,760 in standard notation and $1.394976 \times 10^7$ in scientific notation.

c) The distance from Earth to the sun is about 93,000,000 miles. This is equivalent to 163,680,000,000 yards. The number of strides is 163,680,000,000 in standard notation and $1.6368 \times 10^{11}$ in scientific notation.

d) **Think Beyond** Uranus is the planet farthest from the sun, since Pluto is no longer considered a planet. It is $1.78374 \times 10^9$ miles away from the sun.

$1.78374 \times 10^9 • 1,760 = 1.78374 \times 10^9 • 1.76 \times 10^3 = 3.1393824 \times 10^{12}$ yards

Therefore, the number of strides from Uranus to the sun is $3.1393824 \times 10^{12}$.

6. a) $50,000,000,000 = 5.0 \times 10^{10}$ cans; $27,000,000,000 = 2.7 \times 10^{10}$ glass bottles and jars; $65,000,000 = 6.5 \times 10^7$ covers

b) 2 • 1,005,329 = 2,010,658 cans. Scientific notation: $2.010658 \times 10^6$

c) 12 • 2,010,658 = 24,127,896 cans. Scientific notation: $2.4127896 \times 10^7$

8. A blue whale eats up to 8,000 lb. of krill each day for about 120 days per year.

   **a)** How many pounds of krill will a blue whale eat over the next year?

   **b)** How much krill will a blue whale eat during an average lifespan of 34 years? Write your answer in scientific notation and in standard notation.

9. People from different countries visit the Discovery Center. Each visitor puts a pushpin on a large map at the entry to indicate where he or she is from. From January through June of 2008, the following countries were marked. We have listed the population of each country in 2008.

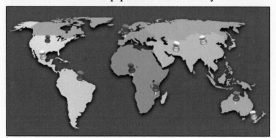

   **a)** Put the countries in order according to the population from the least to the greatest.

| Country | 2008 Population |
|---|---|
| Jamaica | $2.804 \times 10^6$ |
| United States | 303,825,100 |
| Australia | twenty million, 601 thousand |
| India | one billion, one hundred forty-seven million, nine hundred ninety-six thousand |
| China | 1,330,045,000 |
| Ecuador | $1.3928 \times 10^7$ |
| Mexico | $1.09955 \times 10^8$ |
| Spain | forty million, four hundred ninety-one thousand |
| Tanzania | 40,213,000 |
| Central African Republic | $4.4357 \times 10^6$ |
| New Zealand | 4,173,000 |

Data Sources: *CIA World Factbook*, and other public domain resources (July, 2008)

   **b)** Write each population in standard notation.

---

**7.**

  **NOTE**

Assume there are 365 days in one year.

$110 \cdot 60 = 6,600$ heartbeats per hour

$6,600 \cdot 24 = 158,400$ heartbeats per day

$158,400 \cdot 365 = 57,816,000$ heartbeats per year

$57,816,000 \cdot 30 = 1,734,480,000$ or $1.73448 \times 10^9$ heartbeats per 30 years

$57,816,000 \cdot 50 = 2,890,800,000$ or $2.8908 \times 10^9$ heartbeats per 50 years

**8. a)** 960,000 lb.

   **b)** 32,640,000 lb. or $3.264 \times 10^7$ lb.

   Discuss with students the definition of *krill* and/or ask students to find out what it is on their own using the Internet. Share their findings with the class.

**9.**

| a) Order from Least to Greatest Population | b) Standard Notation |
|---|---|
| Jamaica | 2,804,000 |
| New Zealand | 4,173,000 |
| Central African Republic | 4,435,700 |
| Ecuador | 13,928,000 |
| Australia | 20,601,000 |
| Tanzania | 40,213,000 |
| Spain | 40,491,000 |
| Mexico | 109,955,000 |
| United States | 303,825,100 |
| India | 1,147,996,000 |
| China | 1,330,045,000 |

10. A NASA space shuttle travels at approximately 17,500 miles per hour.

   **a)** How far will the shuttle travel in 1 day?

   **b)** How far will the shuttle travel in 1 week?

   **c)** At this rate, how long would it take the shuttle to reach the sun? Write your answer in scientific notation. Do you think this will happen?

11. **Back to the Future!** In order to travel through time, one must travel at the speed of light or very close to it. When things travel at speeds close to the speed of light, time slows down. For example, if you traveled for 10 years in a spaceship at 95% of the speed of light, 32 years would go by for the people who stayed on Earth. So when you arrived back on Earth after your 10-year trip, you could say that you had traveled back to the future.

   **a)** Research the speed of light and write it in scientific notation.

   **b)** How many times faster is the speed of light than the speed of the space shuttle?

**? Hint**
See page 169

---
**Did you know?** An astronaut today would have to travel in a space shuttle for 1 billion years in order to jump 1 year in the future!
Data source: http://curious.astro.cornell.edu/question.php?number=422
---

12. Find three examples of numbers greater 1 million in real-world situations. Write down the situations and write the numbers in standard notation.

**Think Beyond**

13. **a)** If you wanted to create a scale drawing of the solar system with Earth the size of a dime in a poster at the Falling Apple Science Museum in the Newton Discovery Center, how big would Pluto have to be?

   **b)** How big would the sun be?

   **c)** Could you use a wall mural to display the planets and the sun using these proportions? Explain.

11. **a)** Answers may vary slightly, depending on the resource used to obtain the speed of light. Accept answers that are reasonably close.

   The speed of light is approximately $1.86282397 \times 10^5$ miles per second.

   **b)** The space shuttle travels at approximately 4.861 miles per second.

   $1.86282397 \times 10^5 \div 4.861 \approx 3.832182 \times 10^5$

   The speed of light is approximately $3.832182 \times 10^4$ times faster than the space shuttle.

12. Answers will vary.

10. **a)** 420,000 miles

   **b)** 2,940,000 miles

   **c)** $221.42857 = 2.2142857 \times 10^2$ days or $31.633653 = 3.1633653 \times 10^1$ weeks

No, this will not happen. Students' reasons will vary.

Some may suggest the sun's surface is too hot for the shuttle to reach it.

Others may suggest it would not be possible for the spacecraft to carry enough fuel to reach the sun.

**13.** Think Beyond

**a)** The diameter of a dime is approximately 0.6875 inch.

The diameter of Earth is approximately 7,926 miles.

The diameter of Pluto is approximately 1,467 miles.

$\dfrac{0.6875}{7,926} = \dfrac{d}{1,467}, d \approx 0.1272$

Pluto would have a diameter of 0.1272 in. or approximately $\frac{1}{8}$ in.

**b)** The diameter of the sun is approximately 865,000 miles.

$\dfrac{0.6875}{7,926} = \dfrac{d}{865,000}, d \approx 75.03$

The sun would have a diameter of 75.03 inches.

**c)** No, the distance between planets and the sun would be too great to fit on the wall mural using the same scale as the size of the planets.

For example, Uranus is $1.78374 \times 10^9$ miles from the sun.

$\dfrac{0.6875}{7,926} = \dfrac{d}{1.78374} \times 10^9,$
$d \approx 154,700$

The distance from the sun to Uranus is 154,700 inches on the scale drawing. This is equivalent to approximately 12,891.67 feet or approximately 2.44 miles.

 NOTE Due to necessity with limited space, there are usually huge errors in scale on typical models of the solar system.

 Think Back

**14.** Jaden moved the decimal point two places to the left as if he were multiplying by 0.06 instead of dividing. Jaden should have moved the decimal two places to the right, so the correct answer is 1,200,000,000.

---

 Think Back

**14.** Jaden was asked to estimate the quotient of 72,002,003 and 0.06. For his estimate, he ignored all but the 72 million, since 72 divided by 6 is exactly 12. Since there is a two-digit decimal, he said the answer would be 0.12 million or 120,000. What did he do wrong? What is the correct answer?

**15.** What number divided by −3 gives 15 as a result?

**A.** −45     **C.** 5

**B.** −5     **D.** 45

**16.** The area of Bermuda is 21 sq. mi. How many times could you fit the island into the country of Venezuela if its total area is 355,759 sq. mi.?

**17.** Calculate $1.7\overline{)0.37}$ to the nearest thousandth. Show your work.

**18.** Josh, David, Akin and Robert just came off the court at the basketball game. They are going to sit on the bench with the rest of the team. How many different ways can they arrange themselves? Make a list.

**15. A.** −45

**16.** Almost 16,941 times. (16,940.905 is the actual quotient.)

**17.** 0.218 (0.2176471 is the actual quotient.)

**18.** 24 different ways:

| | | | |
|---|---|---|---|
| JRDA | RJAD | AJRD | DJRA |
| JRAD | RJDA | AJDR | DJAR |
| JDRA | RAJD | ADRJ | DAJR |
| JDAR | RADJ | DJR | DARJ |
| JARD | RDAJ | ARDJ | DRAJ |
| JADR | RDJA | ARJD | DRJA |

1. Complete the following place-value table.

|  |  | 10,000,000 |  | 100,000 |  | 1,000 | 100 | 10 | 1 |
|---|---|---|---|---|---|---|---|---|---|
|  | $10^8$ |  | $10^6$ |  |  |  | $10^2$ | $10^1$ | $10^0$ |

2. Write the following numbers in scientific notation.
   Be sure to include the mantissa and the correct power of 10.

   **a)** 400 _____

   **b)** 70 _____

   **c)** 8,000 _____

   **d)** 900,000 _____

   **e)** 30,000 _____

   **f)** 60,000,000 _____

   **g)** 120 _____

   **h)** 2,400 _____

   **i)** 510,000 _____

# Lesson Guide 3.1A *Do You Know the Powers of 10?*
## (Answer Guide)

1. Complete the following place-value table.

| 1,000,000,000 | 100,000,000 | 10,000,000 | 1,000,000 | 100,000 | 10,000 | 1,000 | 100 | 10 | 1 |
|---|---|---|---|---|---|---|---|---|---|
| $10^9$ | $10^8$ | $10^7$ | $10^6$ | $10^5$ | $10^4$ | $10^3$ | $10^2$ | $10^1$ | $10^0$ |

2. Write the following numbers in scientific notation. Be sure to include the mantissa and the correct power of 10.

   Use the place-value table above to help you find the appropriate exponent for the power of ten.

   a) 400          $4.0 \times 10^2 \ (4 \cdot 10 \cdot 10)$

   b) 70          $7.0 \times 10^1 \ (7 \cdot 10)$

   c) 8,000          $8.0 \times 10^3 \ (8 \cdot 10 \cdot 10 \cdot 10)$

   d) 900,000          $9.0 \times 10^5 \ (9 \cdot 10 \cdot 10 \cdot 10 \cdot 10 \cdot 10)$

   e) 30,000          $3.0 \times 10^4 \ (3 \cdot 10 \cdot 10 \cdot 10 \cdot 10)$

   f) 60,000,000          $6.0 \times 10^7 \ (6 \cdot 10 \cdot 10 \cdot 10 \cdot 10 \cdot 10 \cdot 10 \cdot 10)$

   g) 120          $1.2 \times 10^2 \ (1.2 \cdot 10 \cdot 10)$

   h) 2,400          $2.4 \times 10^3 \ (2.4 \cdot 10 \cdot 10 \cdot 10)$

   i) 510,000          $5.1 \times 10^5 \ (5.1 \cdot 10 \cdot 10 \cdot 10 \cdot 10 \cdot 10)$

| | | | | |
|---|---|---|---|---|
| $6.12 \times 10^8$ | $61.2 \times 10^7$ | six million 120 thousand | 6 billion | $6.0 \times 10^8$ |
| 6,416,072,010 | 80 thousand | 800,000 | $8.0 \times 10^5$ | 3.2 trillion |
| 3,000,000,000 | $4.1 \times 10^{10}$ | 4 billion | 41 billion | 6 million |
| $4.102 \times 10^8$ | 4 million | $5.6 \times 10^5$ | $17.635 \times 10^4$ | one hundred seventy-six thousand, three hundred fifty |
| $10^6$ | $10^8$ | 56,000 | 5.6 hundreds | $56 \times 10^4$ |
| 17,700 | one million | one hundred million | ten million | 200 million, six hundred forty-one |
| 10,000,000 | $77 \times 10^7$ | $7.07 \times 10^8$ | $77.7 \times 10^6$ | 100,000 |
| $2.641 \times 10^7$ | $2.00641 \times 10^7$ | 200,000,641 | $1.7635 \times 10^2$ | 177 |

| | | | | |
|---|---|---|---|---|
| **Big Numbers Rule!** | **Big Numbers Rule!** | **Big Numbers Rule!** | **Big Numbers Rule!** | **Big Numbers Rule!** |
| **Big Numbers Rule!** | **Big Numbers Rule!** | **Big Numbers Rule!** | **Big Numbers Rule!** | **Big Numbers Rule!** |
| **Big Numbers Rule!** | **Big Numbers Rule!** | **Big Numbers Rule!** | **Big Numbers Rule!** | **Big Numbers Rule!** |
| **Big Numbers Rule!** | **Big Numbers Rule!** | **Big Numbers Rule!** | **Big Numbers Rule!** | **Big Numbers Rule!** |
| **Big Numbers Rule!** | **Big Numbers Rule!** | **Big Numbers Rule!** | **Big Numbers Rule!** | **Big Numbers Rule!** |
| **Big Numbers Rule!** | **Big Numbers Rule!** | **Big Numbers Rule!** | **Big Numbers Rule!** | **Big Numbers Rule!** |
| **Big Numbers Rule!** | **Big Numbers Rule!** | **Big Numbers Rule!** | **Big Numbers Rule!** | **Big Numbers Rule!** |
| **Big Numbers Rule!** | **Big Numbers Rule!** | **Big Numbers Rule!** | **Big Numbers Rule!** | **Big Numbers Rule!** |

# Using Big Numbers: Exponents to the Rescue

**Suggested Pacing:** 2 Days

In this lesson, students discover shortcut rules for operating with exponents. Students discover that the rules for multiplying numbers with exponents work only when the bases of the numbers are the same.

---

**LESSON OBJECTIVES**

■ Students will explore patterns to discover rules for operating with exponents.

■ Students will generalize rules for operating with exponents using a variety of bases.

---

| DAY 1 | Materials* | ESSENTIAL *ON YOUR OWN* QUESTIONS |
|---|---|---|
| A New Way to Measure Big Distances<br><br>Multiplying Powers of 10 | **In Class**<br>■ Lesson Guide 3.2: *Multiplying Powers of 10*<br>■ Calculators | Questions 1–4, 10–12 |

| DAY 2 | Materials* | ESSENTIAL *ON YOUR OWN* QUESTIONS |
|---|---|---|
| Experimenting with Different Bases | **In Class**<br>■ Calculators<br><br>**On Your Own**<br>■ Calculators | Questions 5–8, 13, 14 |

\* The Think Like a Mathematician Daily Record Sheet should be used daily

---

## MATHEMATICALLY SPEAKING

▶ light-year                    ▶ power

## Start It Off

1. Answers will vary. Accept estimates that are supported with sound reasoning.

   Possible estimate: $25{,}000 \cdot 5{,}000 = 125{,}000{,}000$ feet

   Actual length: $24{,}000 \cdot 5{,}280 = 126{,}720{,}000$ feet in standard notation; $1.2672 \times 10^8$ feet in scientific notation; one hundred twenty-six million, seven hundred twenty thousand feet in words.

2. $1{,}520{,}640{,}000$ inches or $1.52064 \times 10^9$ inches

3. If the dollar bills are placed end-to-end along the 2.5-inch side, two dollar bills make a foot. Therefore, doubling the number of feet in the circumference would make a good estimate of the number of dollar bills needed.

   Approximately 126.5 million feet • 2 dollar bills per foot = 253 million dollar bills are needed.

## DAY 1 TEACHING THE LESSON

### A New Way to Measure Big Distances

 In this lesson, students multiply large numbers written in scientific notation and discover shortcut rules when performing these operations as they work with a new unit of measure, the light-year. Looking for patterns, students recognize that the shortcut rules they discovered also apply to multiplying numbers in other bases beyond the powers of 10. Students realize that the rules for multiplying numbers with exponents work only when the bases of the numbers are the same. They also find out that when adding numbers with exponents, they must evaluate the numbers with exponents first, and then add the resulting numbers together.

 Graphing calculators may be used for this lesson, but are not necessary. Any scientific calculator that has a button that will raise a number to a power will work.

 **Using Big Numbers: Exponents to the Rescue**

### Start It Off

The circumference of Earth is approximately 24 thousand miles. A mile is equal to 5,280 feet.

1. Estimate the circumference in feet. Then, calculate the actual circumference and write the number in standard notation, in scientific notation and in words.

2. What is the circumference of Earth in inches?

3. The dimensions of a dollar bill are approximately 6 inches by 2.5 inches. Estimate how many dollar bills placed end-to-end are needed to wrap around Earth.

In the last lesson, you learned that scientific notation makes reading and writing very large numbers easier. In this lesson, you will see how you can perform operations with large numbers using scientific notation.

## A New Way to Measure Big Distances

As visitors exit the solar system exhibit at the Science Museum, they will see a display of the Milky Way galaxy. The Milky Way is made up of the sun, the planets and much more. It includes billions of distant stars and other solar matter. And, it is only one of many galaxies in the universe!

Distances from planets to the sun are measured in AUs or astronomical units. Astronomers use another unit to measure distances from Earth to stars in the Milky Way galaxy.

> **Did you know?** The phrase *Milky Way* came from the band of white light that can be seen in the sky from Earth. It is literally a path or "way" of light that is white or "milky" in color. The ancient Greek philosopher Democritus is given credit for discovering that the Milky Way existed and was made up of billions of stars. You probably know about another famous Milky Way—made up of chocolate and caramel rather than planets and stars!

Section 3: Exponents and Scientific Notation • Lesson 3.2 **89**

## Light-Years

Introduce students to a new measure, the light-year, as the class reads about the vast size of the Milky Way Galaxy and the need for a more practical unit of measure. Students should read the number 5,865,696,000,000 as five trillion, eight hundred sixty-five billion, six hundred ninety-six million. Have students work independently on Questions 1 and 2 and then share their responses with a partner. Discuss any discrepancies as a class.

1. approximately 5,870,000,000,000 miles or $5.87 \times 10^{12}$ miles

2. diameter • $\pi$ = circumference 100,000 • 3.14 = 314,000 light-years or $3.14 \times 10^5$ light-years

## Multiplying Powers of 10

Explore as a class the example in the text. Partners should recognize that to find the circumference of the Milky Way, you multiply its diameter (100,000) by π. 100,000 • 3.14 = 314,000 light-years or 3.14 × 10⁵ light-years. Students may also write 100,000 as 10⁵ first and then multiply 10⁵ × 3.14. Using the commutative property of multiplication, $10^5 \times 3.14 = 3.14 \times 10^5$. Guide the discussion to help students recognize that the associative and commutative properties of multiplication are helpful when multiplying numbers written in scientific notation. Students may need a review of these properties before completing Question 3.

Have students work independently on Question 3 and then share their responses with the class.

**3.**

| | |
|---|---|
| $3.14 \times 10^5 \cdot 5.87 \times 10^{12} =$ $3.14 \cdot 5.87 \cdot 10^5 \times 10^{12}$ | **Commutative Property of Multiplication** |
| $= (3.14 \cdot 5.87) \cdot (10^5 \times 10^{12})$ | **Associative Property of Multiplication** |
| $= 18.43 \cdot (10^5 \times 10^{12})$ | Combining like terms |

Have students complete Question 4 with a partner using Lesson Guide 3.2: *Multiplying Powers of 10*. Remind students that 10 is the same as 10¹. The table is designed to help students readily identify a pattern among the exponents.

---

### Light-Years

**MATHEMATICALLY SPEAKING**

▶ light-year

The size of the Milky Way galaxy is measured by light-years. A light-year is a way of measuring distance. You are used to measuring distances in inches, feet and miles or in centimeters, meters and kilometers. However, the distances from our planet to stars are huge! Besides the sun, the closest star to Earth, Proxima Centauri, is about 24,000,000,000,000 miles away. Miles and kilometers are not practical units for measuring such extremely large distances. Astronomers use the unit light-years instead. A light-year is the distance that light can travel in a year. Let's find out how many miles this is.

We'll start with the fact that light travels 186,000 miles per second. In other words, a *light-second* is 186,000 miles.

- 186,000 miles per second • 60 seconds/minute = 11,160,000 miles per minute

- 11,160,000 miles per minute • 60 minutes/hour = 669,600,000 miles/hour

- 669,600,000 miles per hour • 24 hours/day = 16,070,400,000 miles/day

- 16,070,400,000 miles per day • 365 days/year = 5,865,696,000,000 miles/year!

How do we read this number?

1. A light-year is 5,865,696,000,000 miles. Round this number to the nearest ten billion, and then write the rounded number in scientific notation.

2. The diameter of the main part of the Milky Way is about 100,000 light-years. What is the circumference of the Milky Way in light years? Write your answer in standard notation and in scientific notation.

### Multiplying Powers of 10

What is the circumference of the main part of the Milky Way in miles? To find out, you need to multiply very large numbers. Once again scientific notation is helpful.

The circumference of the Milky Way = 3.14 × 10⁵ light-years. Talk to your partner and explain how we arrived at this measure.

1 light-year = 5.87 × 10¹² miles

---

**Talk Moves** Discuss the rules derived as a class. Use talk moves, such as agree/disagree and why and adding on, to clarify ideas and extend the discussion. Encourage students to justify their ideas using examples they created when testing their conjectures.

Next, have students complete Questions 5–7 independently. Circulate as students work to informally assess understanding. Use the *Student Snapshot* observation tool to record notes and observations. Note: When multiplying numbers written in scientific notation, students often forget to adjust the product of the mantissas. Address this common error when sharing student responses.

**3.** Fill in the blanks below with the *commutative property of multiplication* or the *associative property of multiplication*.

$$3.14 \times 10^5 \cdot 5.87 \times 10^{12} = 3.14 \cdot 5.87 \cdot 10^5 \cdot 10^{12} \quad \underline{\hspace{3cm}}$$

$$= (3.14 \cdot 5.87) \cdot (10^5 \cdot 10^{12}) \quad \underline{\hspace{3cm}}$$

$$= 18.43 \cdot (10^5 \cdot 10^{12}) \qquad \text{combining like terms}$$

How do we multiply powers of 10? Let's investigate.

**4. a)** Copy and complete the table below.

| Expression | Product in Standard Notation | Product in Scientific Notation |
|---|---|---|
| $10^3 \cdot 10^2$ | $(10 \cdot 10 \cdot 10) \cdot (10 \cdot 10) = 100{,}000$ | $10^5$ |
| $10^4 \cdot 10^3$ | | |
| $10 \times 10^8$ | | |
| $10^5 \cdot 10^3$ | | |

**b)** Look for patterns between the product in standard notation and in scientific notation.

**c)** With your partner, make a conjecture about how to multiply powers of 10 using exponents.

**d)** Each of you make up two more expressions and together test your conjecture on the four expressions.

**e)** Together come up with a rule to multiply powers of 10.

**5. a)** Use your rule to find the circumference of the Milky Way in miles.

**b)** Find the circumference of the Milky Way in kilometers.

**6.** Find the following products. Write your answers first in scientific and then in standard notation.

**a)** $(3.6 \times 10^5)(6.3 \times 10^2)$

**b)** $(423{,}000)(1{,}356{,}024)$

**c)** $(9.84 \times 10^8)(5.20)$

**7.** In the Milky Way display at the Falling Apple Science Museum, there will be several stars featured. One of these is Antares (meaning "Rival of Mars"). This is the brightest star in the constellation Scorpius. It is about 520 light-years from Earth and is 230 times as big as the sun. This incredibly huge old star is the fifteenth brightest in the sky.

**a)** Find the distance in miles from Antares to Earth in scientific notation.

**b)** The sun has a mass of $1.99 \times 10^{30}$ kg. Find the mass of Antares in scientific notation.

Scorpius

**4. a)**

| Expression | Product in Standard Notation | Product in Scientific Notation |
|---|---|---|
| $10^3 \cdot 10^2$ | $(10 \cdot 10 \cdot 10) \cdot (10 \cdot 10) = 100{,}000$ | $10^5$ |
| $10^4 \cdot 10^3$ | $(10 \cdot 10 \cdot 10 \cdot 10) \cdot (10 \cdot 10 \cdot 10)$ | $10^7$ |
| $10 \cdot 10^8$ | $(10) \cdot (10 \cdot 10 \cdot 10 \cdot 10 \cdot 10 \cdot 10 \cdot 10 \cdot 10)$ | $10^9$ |
| $10^5 \cdot 10^3$ | $(10 \cdot 10 \cdot 10 \cdot 10 \cdot 10) \cdot (10 \cdot 10 \cdot 10)$ | $10^8$ |

**b)** The number of times you multiply by 10 equals the exponent in scientific notation.

**c)** When multiplying powers of 10, add the exponents to get the product.

**d)** Answers will vary.

**e)** To multiply powers of 10, add the exponents to get the exponent of the product.

## Experimenting with Different Bases

 **Let's Review**

A base is the number or expression used as a factor in repeated multiplication.

For example, in $4^3$ the base is 4 and the exponent is 3.

$4^3$ means $4 \cdot 4 \cdot 4$, which equals 64.
64 is a power of 4.

8. **a)** Fill in the blanks to continue the pattern.

   2, 4, 8, 16, _____, _____, _____

   **b)** Write each term listed above as a power of 2.

   **c)** If the pattern continues, write a rule to find the $n^{th}$ term.

9. Create a sequence of numbers starting with 3 and using the rule, "Multiply the previous term by 3 to get the next term." Write a rule for the $n^{th}$ term of the sequence.

10. Find the product.

    **a)** $64 \cdot 4$       **d)** $19,683 \cdot 9$

    **b)** $512 \cdot 32$       **e)** $27 \cdot 27$

    **c)** $9 \cdot 243$

11. For each part of Question 10, write the factors and the product as a power of either base 2 or base 3. The first one is done for you.

    **a)** $64 \cdot 4 = 256$. This can be written as:
    $2^6 \cdot 2^2 = (2 \cdot 2 \cdot 2 \cdot 2 \cdot 2 \cdot 2) \cdot (2 \cdot 2) = 2^8$.

12. Work with a partner.

    **a)** Look for patterns in Question 11. How are the patterns similar to those you found in products of powers of 10?

    **b)** Make up a general rule for multiplying powers with the same base.

    **c)** Make up five examples involving products of numbers that can be written as powers with the same base. Use bases other than 2, 3 and 10. (For example, $25 \cdot 125 = 5^2 \cdot 5^3 = 5^5$.)

    **d)** Trade with a partner. Using your partner's examples, apply the rules you wrote for multiplying using exponents. Check your answers by multiplying the numbers as written, without using exponents. Do your answers agree?

    **e)** Share your findings with the class.

---

5. **a)** $(3.14 \times 10^5)(5.87 \times 10^{12}) = (3.14 \cdot 5.87) \cdot (10^5 \times 10^{12})$

   $= 18.4318 \times 10^{17} = 1.843 \times 10^{18}$ miles

   **b)** $1.843 \times 10^{18}$ miles $\div$ 0.6 km/mile $\approx$ $3.0717 \times 10^{18}$ kilometers

6. **a)** $2.268 \times 10^8$ or 226,800,000

   **b)** $5.7359815 \times 10^{11}$ or 573,598,150,000

   **c)** $5.1168 \times 10^9$ or 5,116,800,000

7. **a)** $520 \cdot (5.87 \times 10^{12}) = 3.0524 \times 10^{15}$ miles

   **b)** $230 \cdot (1.99 \times 10^{30}) = 4.577 \times 10^{32}$ kilograms

## Summarize Day 1

As a Wrap It Up discussion for Day 1, have students discuss the following question with a partner and share their responses in a class discussion:

- *Explain to a friend who was absent today how to multiply powers of 10. For example, $10^3 \cdot 10^3$.*

Students should respond that in order to multiply powers of 10, you add the exponents to get the exponent of the product. $10^5 \cdot 10^3 = 10^{5+3} = 10^8$

## Experimenting with Different Bases

 **Talk Moves** Review how to write explicit rules for the $n^{th}$ term in a sequence. Begin by having students examine a simple pattern to identify the explicit rule. Next, have students complete Questions 8 and 9 independently and share responses with a partner. Discuss any unresolved discrepancies. Use talk moves, such as revoicing and agree/disagree and why, to clarify student understanding.

Have students work independently on Questions 10 and 11. Note that by writing the numbers as powers of a base in Question 11, students are finding the prime factorization of each number. When discussing responses to Question 11, help students make a connection to prime factorization, which they studied in grade 6.

Have students complete Questions 12a and 12b with a partner and share their general rules with the class. There should be a class consensus of the rules. Have students work individually on Question 12c, then trade with a partner to complete Question 12d. For Question 12e, have students share their findings in a class discussion.

---

 **NOTE** If, for example, students selected base 4 or base 8, partners may identify the base as 2 instead. This is not incorrect and can lead to an interesting discussion on prime factorization.

---

Have students complete Questions 13 and 14 with a partner. Encourage students to test their conjectures with multiple examples. Discuss responses when students are finished.

Do not rush this discussion. It is important for students to recognize that there are no shortcut rules for these situations. Rather, the numbers with exponents must be evaluated first, then the resulting numbers are multiplied or added. Note, however, that there is an exception. If the two numbers multiplied (whether they are the same base or not) have the same exponent, the bases can be multiplied together and the resulting product is raised to the same exponent. For example, $2^2 \cdot 5^2 = (2 \cdot 5)^2 = 10^2 = 100$. These questions are designed to draw attention to common errors students make when performing operations with exponents.

8. **a)** 2, 4, 8, 16, **32, 64, 128**

   **b)** $2^1, 2^2, 2^3, 2^4, 2^5, 2^6, 2^7$

   **c)** $2^n$

9. 3, 9, 27, 81, 243, 729, . . . $3^n$    The rule is $3^n$.

10. **a)** 256

   **b)** 16,384

   **c)** 2,187

   **d)** 177,147

   **e)** 729

**11. a)** $2^6 \cdot 2^2 = (2 \cdot 2 \cdot 2 \cdot 2 \cdot 2 \cdot 2) \cdot (2 \cdot 2) = 2^8$

**b)** $2^9 \cdot 2^5 = (2 \cdot 2 \cdot 2 \cdot 2 \cdot 2 \cdot 2 \cdot 2 \cdot 2 \cdot 2) \cdot$ $(2 \cdot 2 \cdot 2 \cdot 2 \cdot 2) = 2^{14}$

**c)** $3^2 \cdot 3^5 = (3 \cdot 3) \cdot (3 \cdot 3 \cdot 3 \cdot 3 \cdot 3) = 3^7$

**d)** $3^9 \cdot 3^2 = (3 \cdot 3 \cdot 3 \cdot 3 \cdot 3 \cdot 3 \cdot 3 \cdot 3 \cdot 3) \cdot$ $(3 \cdot 3) = 3^{11}$

**e)** $3^3 \cdot 3^3 = (3 \cdot 3 \cdot 3) \cdot (3 \cdot 3 \cdot 3) = 3^6$

**12. a)** When you multiply numbers that have the same bases, the exponents of the bases are added together the same way as when you multiply powers of 10.

**b)** When you multiply numbers with the same bases, keep the base the same and add the exponents.

**c)** Answers will vary. Possible responses:
125 • 625    49 • 2,401    25 • 3,125

**d)** Answers will vary. Possible responses:

$125 \cdot 625 = 5^3 \cdot 5^4 = 5^7$
$125 \cdot 625 = 78,125$ ✓

$49 \cdot 2,401 = 7^2 \cdot 7^4 = 7^6$
$49 \cdot 2,401 = 117,649$ ✓

$25 \cdot 3,125 = 5^2 \cdot 5^5 = 5^7$
$25 \cdot 3,125 = 78,125$ ✓

**e)** Answers will vary.

**13.** There is no shortcut rule. The exponents must be evaluated first. Then multiply the resulting numbers.

Example:  $2^2 \cdot 3^4 \neq 6^{(2 + 4)}$
$4 \cdot 81 \neq 6^6$
$324 \neq 46,656$

**14.** There is no shortcut rule. Evaluate the exponents first. Then, add the resulting numbers.

Example:  $3^2 + 3^3 \neq 3^{(2 + 3)}$
$9 + 27 \neq 3^5$
$36 \neq 243$

13. Skyler wondered if there is a rule for multiplying exponents when the bases are different, for example, $2^2 \cdot 3^4$. Explore this with your partner and respond to Skyler.

14. Sung Hee wondered if there is a rule for adding exponents with the same base, for example, $3^2 + 3^3$. Explore this with your partner and respond to Sung Hee.

## ⬆W rap It Up

Jenna and Janine were discussing rules for using exponents. Do you agree with either Jenna or Janine? Discuss why or why not.

**MATHEMATICALLY SPEAKING**

▶ light-year
▶ powers

*When multiplying two numbers with exponents, keep the base the same and multiply the exponents.*

*When multiplying two numbers with exponents, multiply the bases together and add the exponents.*

• Janine was incorrect about multiplying the bases. If the bases of both numbers are the same, the base should be kept the same and the exponents should be added together.

• If the bases and the exponents of the numbers being multiplied are different, there is no shortcut rule for multiplying the numbers together. The exponents must be evaluated first, and then the resulting numbers are multiplied.

 Some students may state that if the bases of the numbers being multiplied are different, but the exponents are the same, then the bases can be multiplied together and the resulting product is then raised to the same exponent.

## ⬆W rap It Up

Answers will vary. Student responses should include the following key ideas:

• Neither Jenna nor Janine is entirely correct.

• Assuming the bases are the same for both numbers, Jenna was correct about keeping the base the same. However, instead of multiplying the exponents, she should have added the exponents together.

## Reflect

Use these questions to help you reflect on the lesson and plan for future instruction.

• How skillfully are students able to multiply and divide numbers with exponents?

• What are some lingering misconceptions about the rules for operating with exponents that need to be addressed in future instruction?

LESSON
3.2
SECTION 3

On Your Own

MATERIALS LIST
▶ Calculators

 Write About It

1. Explain how to multiply two numbers that are written as powers of 10. Give two examples.

2. Simplify the following using scientific notation and exponent rules.

   a) $15{,}000{,}000 \times 10^6$

   d) $120{,}000{,}000{,}000 \times (6.4 \times 10^{20})$

   b) $(5 \times 10^{10})(3 \times 10^{17})$

   e) $(2.45 \times 10^4)(3.864 \times 10^2)$

   c) $(8 \times 10^{20})(7.1 \times 10^6)$

3. The most distant space probe, *Voyager I*, was about 14 light-*hours* away from Earth in the week ending March 9, 2007. How many miles is this? (It took *Voyager I* 30 years to cover that distance!)

4. Arcturus is a star that will be featured in the Milky Way galaxy display. It is the brightest star in the constellation Boötes and the fourth brightest star in the sky. Arcturus is 34 light-years from Earth. How many miles is that? Write your answer in scientific notation.

5. Evaluate the following. Write your answer as a power of a base and in standard notation.

   a) $2^5 \cdot 2^3 \cdot 2^9$

   b) $6^2 \cdot 6 \cdot 6^3$

   c) $10 \cdot 100 \cdot 10^3$

## On Your Own

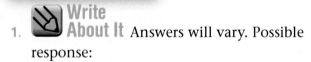 Write About It

1. **Answers will vary. Possible response:**

   To multiply powers of 10, keep the same base and add the exponents. For example,

   $10^3 \cdot 10^2 = 10^5$

   $10^4 \cdot 10^5 = 10^9$

2. a) $1.5 \times 10^{13}$

   b) $1.5 \times 10^{28}$

   c) $5.68 \times 10^{27}$

   d) $7.68 \times 10^{31}$

   e) $9.4668 \times 10^6$

3. 186,000 miles/sec. • 60 sec./min. • 60 min./hr. • 14 hours = 9,374,400,000 miles

4. $5.87 \times 10^{12}$ • 34 = $1.9958 \times 10^{14}$ miles

5. a) $2^{17}$ or 131,072

   b) $6^6$ or 46,656

   c) $10^6$ or 1,000,000

6.  a) Fill in the table with numbers as powers of 2 so that each row, column and diagonal has the same product.

| $2^8$ | $2$ | $2^6$ |
|---|---|---|
|  |  | $2^7$ |
| $2^4$ |  |  |

b) Find the product and write it in standard and scientific notation.

7.  a) Write a sequence of numbers for the powers of 5, starting with 5. Write each number without an exponent.

b) Write each number as a power of 5 and write a rule for the $n^{th}$ term.

c) Is 1,025 a number in the sequence? Explain your answer.

8.  When Mario was born, his grandmother set up a bank account for him. On his first birthday, she put $2 in the account. On his next birthday, she put $4 in the account. On his next birthday, she put in $8. She continued this doubling pattern until Mario turned 25.

Carla's grandmother started a bank account for Carla and put in $1,000,000 a year, starting at her first birthday, for 25 years!

a) Predict who will have more money at age 25.

b) Now, calculate who will have more money, Carla or Mario.

c) Round each amount to the nearest hundred thousand and write it in scientific notation.

**Think Beyond**

9.  a) List powers of 10 starting with $10^1$ up to $10^{10}$.

b) Which of the following sets share numbers with the powers of 10? Explain.

  i) powers of 5    ii) powers of 100    iii) powers of 200

c) Name three sets of powers that will share numbers with the powers of 2. How do you know without writing each sequence?

6.  a)

| $2^8$ | $2$ | $2^6$ |
|---|---|---|
| $2^3$ | $2^5$ | $2^7$ |
| $2^4$ | $2^9$ | $2^2$ |

b) $2^{15} = 32,768$ or $3.2768 \times 10^4$

7.  a) 5, 25, 125, 625, 3,125, 15,625, 78,125 . . .

b) $5^1, 5^2, 5^3, 5^4, 5^5, 5^6, 5^7$ . . . ; rule is $5^n$

c) No, when using the explicit rule $5^n$, there is no value for $n$ that would result in 1,025.

8.  a) Answers will vary. Students will most often choose Carla since the grandmother put more money in the account on the first birthday.

b) Mario: $2 + 2^2 + 2^3 + 2^4 + \ldots + 2^{24} + 2^{25}$
$= 2 + 4 + 8 + 16 + \ldots + 33,554,432 =$ $67,108,862

Carla: $1,000,000 \cdot 25 =$ $25,000,000

Mario will receive more money.

c) Mario: $67,100,000 = 6.71 \times 10^7$
Carla: $25,000,000 = 2.5 \times 10^7$

**Think Beyond**

9.

a) $10^1, 10^2, 10^3, 10^4, 10^5, 10^6, 10^7, 10^8, 10^9, 10^{10}$

b) ii) 100, 10,000, 1,000,000 are some of the powers of 100 that are also powers of 10. Every power of 10 that has an even exponent will also be a power of 100.

c) Answers will vary. Possible response: The powers of 4, 8 and 16 will share numbers with the powers of 2 since 4, 8 and 16 are themselves powers of 2.

Think
Back

10. $(1.3)^2 - (0.3)^2 =$

   **A.** 1            **C.** 1.6

   **B.** 1.06        **D.** 2

11. Melanie bought a rug in New Hampshire, where there is no sales tax. She paid $50. Her friend Patrice lives in Massachusetts, where there is a 5% sales tax. She found the same rug on sale for 5% off but had to pay the 5% sales tax. She was surprised when she did not pay the same as Melanie. Who paid more? Why did they not pay the same amount?

12. It was estimated that it will cost NASA $104 billion to send a team to the moon in 2018. If the 300 million people in the United States had to equally share the cost of this flight, how much would each person pay? (This may be why the mission has been recently scrapped!)

13. Give the additive inverse and absolute value for each of the following:

   **a)** −1.4           **d)** 0.001

   **b)** 0.052         **e)** −200

   **c)** −35

14. Jason is adding a railing to the porch. The slats are 1 inch wide, and he wants to put them an inch and a half apart, including between the posts and the first slats. If there are 64 inches between the posts, how many slats will he need to have? Show your reasoning.

---

 **Think
Back**

10. **C.** 1.6

11. Melanie paid more for the rug.
The 5% sales tax was 5% of the sale price of $47.50 (95% of $50). 0.05 • 47.50 = 2.375, which rounds to $2.38. $2.38 = The amount Patrice paid was $47.50 + $49.88.

12. $346.67 per person

13. Additive Inverse    Absolute Value

   **a)** 1.4               1.4

   **b)** −0.052          0.052

   **c)** 35               35

   **d)** −0.001          0.001

   **e)** 200             200

**NOTE** Students studied absolute value in Grade 7 and may need a review of its meaning.

---

14. The space between the post or slat plus the slat itself equals 2.5 inches for every slat used. There is an additional space of 1.5 inches between the last slat used and the post at the opposite end.
64 − 1.5 = 62.5; 62.5 ÷ 2.5 = 25 slats
A total of 25 slats are needed for the railing.

**4.** **a)** Fill in the table below.

| Expression | Product in Standard Notation | Product in Scientific Notation |
|---|---|---|
| $10^3 \cdot 10^2$ | $(10 \cdot 10 \cdot 10) \cdot (10 \cdot 10) = 100{,}000$ | $10^5$ |
| $10^4 \cdot 10^3$ | | |
| $10 \cdot 10^8$ | | |
| $10^5 \cdot 10^3$ | | |

    **b)** Look for patterns between the product in standard notation and in scientific notation.

    **c)** With your partner, make a conjecture about how to multiply powers of 10 using exponents.

    **d)** Each of you make up two more expressions and together test your conjecture on the four expressions.

    **e)** Together come up with a rule to multiply powers of 10 using exponents.

## LESSON 3.3 Dividing with Exponents

**Suggested Pacing:** 1 Day

In this lesson, by looking at patterns, students form a generalization for dividing numbers written in scientific notation.

---

**LESSON OBJECTIVES**
- Students will use ratios to compare numbers written in standard notation to determine how many times as great one number is than another.
- Students will discover a rule or shortcut method for dividing numbers written in scientific notation.

---

| DAY 1 | Materials* | ESSENTIAL *ON YOUR OWN* QUESTIONS |
|---|---|---|
| How Big Are the Planets?<br><br>Using Scientific Notation: A Shortcut for Simplifying Expressions | **In Class**<br>■ Calculators<br><br>**On Your Own**<br>■ Calculators<br>■ Internet access or encyclopedia | Questions 1–6, 9, 10–13 |

\* The Think Like a Mathematician Daily Record Sheet should be used daily

## Dividing with Exponents

###  Start It Off

1. Make a number line that includes zero. Then put the following numbers on it. (Think about your scale!) Label the numbers using numerals.

   **a)** one hundred thousand       **d)** five hundred million

   **b)** one million                 **e)** one billion

   **c)** two million

## How Big Are the Planets?

In the new solar system exhibit in the Falling Apple Science Museum, you would like the masses of the model planets to be proportional to the masses of the actual planets. First, you want to compare the masses of the planets to each other. The table below lists the masses of some of the planets.

| Planet | Mass in kg |
|--------|------------|
| Earth | $5.98 \times 10^{24}$ |
| Mars | $6.42 \times 10^{23}$ |
| Mercury | $3.3 \times 10^{23}$ |
| Neptune | $1.03 \times 10^{26}$ |
| Saturn | $5.69 \times 10^{26}$ |
| Venus | $4.87 \times 10^{24}$ |

**MATHEMATICALLY SPEAKING**

► ratio

 **Let's Review**

We often use a ratio in the form of $\frac{a}{b}$ to compare two quantities. For example, to determine how many times as tall the Empire State Building (1,250 feet) is as the Pentagon (77 feet), we can set up a ratio: $\frac{1,250}{77}$ and then simplify. What is the answer to the nearest whole number?

Pentagon          Empire State Building

###  Start It Off

This exercise is designed to draw attention to the effect of scale when working with very large numbers. When discussing student responses, focus on the idea that, although one million and two million are considered large numbers, they appear almost on top of one another and are close to zero when they are placed in scale on the number line that stretches to one billion. One hundred thousand is almost touching zero.

1. The numbers are:

   **a)** 100,000

   **b)** 1,000,000

   **c)** 2,000,000

   **d)** 500,000,000

   **e)** 1,000,000,000

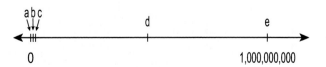

# DAY 1 TEACHING THE LESSON

In this lesson, students explore how to divide numbers written in scientific notation as they compare the mass of various planets using ratios. By looking for patterns in the lesson exercises, students form a generalization about a shortcut method for dividing numbers written in scientific notation. They discover that dividing the mantissa of the given numbers and then subtracting the exponents of the powers of ten is an easy method for arriving at a quotient.

## How Big Are the Planets?

Discuss the meaning of the term *ratio* with students and the given example. Students should find that the answer to the nearest whole number is 16. Have students complete Question 1 with a partner. Discuss responses and guide students to recognize that one way to simplify the ratio in Question 1b is to eliminate zeros by dividing the numerator and denominator by the same power of 10. Students may state that they "cancel" the zeros but not have a clear conceptual understanding. Discuss this idea to build deeper understanding.

1. How many times the mass of Mercury is the mass of Mars?

   a) Write the mass of Mercury and the mass of Mars in standard notation.

   Mercury          Mars

   b) Set up a ratio to find out how many times the mass of Mercury the mass of Mars is.

   c) Simplify the expression to get an answer to the nearest whole number.

When you compared the masses in standard notation, you had to deal with a lot of zeros! You can eliminate many of the zeros by dividing the numerator and denominator by a power of 10. You are left with $\frac{642}{330}$, which is 2 when rounded to the nearest whole number.

## Using Scientific Notation: A Shortcut for Simplifying Expressions

The masses of the planets are much easier to compare if you write them in scientific notation.

**Step 1.** First, write the numbers in scientific notation and as a ratio.
$$\frac{\text{Mass of Mars}}{\text{Mass of Mercury}} = \frac{6.42 \times 10^{23}}{3.3 \times 10^{23}}$$

**Step 2.** Rewrite this as:
$$\frac{6.42}{3.3} \times \frac{10^{23}}{10^{23}}.$$

**Step 3.** Any number divided by itself (or multiplied by its reciprocal) equals 1, so substitute 1 for $\frac{10^{23}}{10^{23}} = 1$ to get $\frac{6.42}{3.3} \cdot 1$.

**Step 4.** $\frac{6.42}{3.3} \cdot 1 = \frac{6.42}{3.3}$. (What property of multiplication are we using here?)

**Step 5.** $\frac{6.42}{3.3} = 1.95$, which is close to 2.

So, the mass of Mars is about twice the mass of Mercury.

1. a) Mass of Mars:
   642,000,000,000,000,000,000,000

   Mass of Mercury:
   330,000,000,000,000,000,000,000

   b) $\dfrac{\text{Mass of Mars}}{\text{Mass of Mercury}}$

   $\dfrac{642{,}000{,}000{,}000{,}000{,}000{,}000{,}000}{330{,}000{,}000{,}000{,}000{,}000{,}000{,}000}$

   c) $\dfrac{642}{330} \approx 2$ when rounded to the nearest whole number

## Using Scientific Notation: A Shortcut for Simplifying Expressions

Explore the model in the student text as a class. Guide students to recognize that when a number is multiplied by an equivalent form of 1, the product will always be that number. This is known as the identity property of multiplication.

 **Talk Moves** Have students complete Questions 2–4 independently and compare their responses with a partner. Have partners discuss Question 5 and share their conjectures in a class discussion. Use talk moves, such as agree/disagree and why, to build consensus on how to compare two numbers with ratios using scientific notation. Have students complete Question 6 independently and then discuss Question 7 with a partner. Have partners share their rules for dividing numbers that are powers of 10 with the class.

Students should complete Questions 8 and 9a independently. Have students share their reasoning for Question 9a with a partner and then with the class. Spend time discussing the idea that mathematicians have defined any number to the zero power to be 1. This definition is in agreement with the rules for dividing exponents and the fact that any number divided by itself equals 1. For example, $\frac{10^6}{10^6} = 1 = 10^{6-6} = 10^0$.

 **Differentiation**

**Think Differently:** For students having difficulty understanding the notion that $10^0 = 1$, have them examine the following examples and determine a pattern to arrive at the value for a number to the zero power.

| | |
|---|---|
| $10^4 = 10,000$ | As the exponent decreases by 1 in the column on the left, |
| $10^3 = 1,000$ | the number on the right is divided by 10. So following this pattern, |
| $10^2 = 100$ | since $10^1$ equals $100 \div 10$ or 10, $10^0$ is equal to $10 \div 10$, which is 1. |
| $10^1 = 10$ | |
| $10^0 = ?$ | (1) |
| $5^4 = 625$ | As the exponent decreases by 1 in the column on the left, the |
| $5^3 = 125$ | number on the right is divided by 5 (the base). |
| $5^2 = 25$ | Since $5^1$ equals 5, $5^0$ is equal to $5 \div 5$, which is 1. |
| $5^1 = 5$ | |
| $5^0 = ?$ | (1) |

Have students complete Question 10 independently and share their responses with the class. Students should recognize that the shortcut rule for dividing powers of 10 works for all bases.

**2. a)** Mass of Saturn: $5.69 \times 10^{26}$

Mass of Neptune: $1.03 \times 10^{26}$

$\dfrac{5.69 \times 10^{26}}{1.03 \times 10^{26}} = \dfrac{5.69}{1.03} \times \dfrac{10^{26}}{10^{26}} = \dfrac{5.69}{1.03} \cdot 1 \approx 5.52$

Saturn's mass is about 5.5 times greater than the mass of Neptune.

**b)** Mass of Earth: $5.98 \times 10^{24}$

Mass of Venus: $4.87 \times 10^{24}$

$\dfrac{5.98 \times 10^{24}}{4.87 \times 10^{24}} = \dfrac{5.98}{4.87} \times \dfrac{10^{24}}{10^{24}} = \dfrac{5.98}{4.87} \cdot 1 \approx 1.2$

Earth's mass is about 1.2 times greater than the mass of Venus.

**3. a)** 100

**b)** 20,000

**c)** 300

**4. b)** $\dfrac{6 \times 10^6}{3 \times 10^2} = 2 \times 10^4$

**c)** $\dfrac{3.6 \times 10^5}{1.2 \times 10^3} = 3 \times 10^2$

**5. a)** Divide the mantissa of the numerator by the mantissa of the denominator.

**b)** Next, subtract the exponent of the power of ten in the denominator from the exponent of the power of ten in the numerator.

**6. a)** $2 \times 10^3 \div 1 \times 10^2 = (2 \div 1) \times 10^{(3-2)} = 2 \times 10^1$

**b)** $\dfrac{6 \times 10^4}{3 \times 10^2} = \dfrac{6}{3} \times \dfrac{10^4}{10^2} = 2 \times 10^{(4-2)} = 2 \times 10^2$

**c)** $\dfrac{5.2 \times 10^6}{1 \times 10^5} = \dfrac{5.2}{1} \times \dfrac{10^6}{10^5} = 5.2 \times 10^{(6-5)} = 5.2 \times 10^1$

**d)** $\dfrac{4 \times 10^4}{4 \times 10^1} = \dfrac{4}{4} \times \dfrac{10^4}{10^1} = 1 \times 10^{(4-1)} = 1 \times 10^3$

**e) a)** 20    **b)** 200    **c)** 52    **d)** 1,000

2. Use the table that lists the masses of the planets to compare the following. Use scientific notation to help you get the answer.

a) How many times the mass of Neptune is the mass of Saturn?

b) How many times the mass of Venus is the mass of Earth?

Notice that not all planet masses have the same power of 10 when written in scientific notation. We can still evaluate these ratios using scientific notation. Let's investigate further.

3. Simplify the following expressions using standard notation.

a) $\dfrac{10,000}{100}$  b) $\dfrac{6,000,000}{300}$  c) $\dfrac{360,000}{1,200}$

The expressions in Question 3 can be simplified by writing the numerator and denominator in scientific notation. For example, here's how you would simplify the expression in Part a.

$$\dfrac{10,000}{100} = \dfrac{1 \times 10^4}{1 \times 10^2} = 1 \times 10^2$$

4. Simplify the expressions in Parts b and c of Question 3 using scientific notation.

5. Look at the exponents of 10 in each example in Question 4. Do you see any patterns? Talk to your partner and come up with an easy way for simplifying ratios using scientific notation.

a) What do you do with the mantissas of the two numbers?

b) What do you do with the exponents of the powers of 10?

6. Write the dividend and divisor in scientific notation and then divide using your rule.

a) $2,000 \div 100$

b) $\dfrac{60,000}{300}$

c) $\dfrac{5,200,000}{100,000}$

d) $\dfrac{40,000}{40}$

e) Check your answers by dividing the standard forms of the numbers and compare results with your partner.

7. a) Compare Saturn's mass with Mercury's mass using the table and scientific notation.

b) Compare Earth's mass to Mercury's mass using the table and scientific notation.

7. a) $\dfrac{\text{Saturn's Mass}}{\text{Mercury's Mass}} = \dfrac{5.69 \times 10^{26}}{3.3 \times 10^{23}} \approx 1.724 \times 10^3$

b) $\dfrac{\text{Earth's Mass}}{\text{Mercury's Mass}} = \dfrac{5.98 \times 10^{24}}{3.3 \times 10^{23}} \approx 1.812 \times 10^1$

8. a) To divide numbers that are powers of 10, subtract the exponents.

b) Using our new rule for dividing numbers that are powers of 10 with exponents, $\dfrac{10^{23}}{10^{23}} = 10^{(23-23)} = 10^0 = 1.$

c) Students should state that any number divided by itself is 1 and that when we divide numbers with the same base, we keep the base the same and subtract the exponents. So, using both rules gives us any number raised to the zero power is one. Students will probably give an example to illustrate.

**9.** Yes, the shortcut rule does work for other bases.

**a)** $\frac{2^4}{2^2} = 2^{(4-2)} = 2^2$ or 4

$16 \div 4 = 4$ ✓

**b)** $\frac{3^3}{3} = 3^{(3-1)} = 3^2$ or 9

$27 \div 3 = 9$ ✓

**c)** $\frac{6^3}{6^3} = 6^{(3-3)} = 6^0$ or 1

$216 \div 216 = 1$ ✓

**d)** $\frac{2^8}{2^0} = 2^{(8-0)} = 2^8$ or 256

$256 \div 1 = 256$ ✓

rap It Up

Answers will vary. Student responses should include the following key ideas:

- Use a ratio to compare the two numbers.

- Divide the mantissa of the numerator by the mantissa of the denominator.

- Subtract the exponent of the power of 10 in the denominator from the exponent of the power of 10 in the numerator.

- Adjust the quotient of the mantissa division so that it is expressed as a number greater than or equal to 1, but less than 10.

- Increase or decrease the value of the exponent of the remaining power of 10 the number of places used to adjust the mantissa appropriately.

- This is a shortcut method because it is easier to divide the mantissas and to subtract the exponents of the powers of 10 than to divide very large numbers.

---

**8.** Mathematicians have defined any number (other than zero) raised to the zero power to be 1. For example, $100^0 = 1$. Let's see why. Look back at the ratio comparing Mars to Mercury. We used the fact that $\frac{10^{23}}{10^{23}} = 1$.

**a)** From your work in Questions 5–7, write a rule for dividing powers of 10.

**b)** Use your rule for dividing numbers that are powers of 10 to explain why mathematicians define any number raised to the zero power to be equal to 1.

**c)** Share your thoughts with a partner and then with the class.

**9.** Does your rule for dividing powers of 10 work for different bases? Test your rule with the following examples. Use your rule first, then write each expression without exponents and find the answer. Compare answers to see if they are equivalent.

**a)** $\frac{2^4}{2^2}$

**c)** $\frac{6^3}{6^3}$

**b)** $\frac{3^3}{3}$

**d)** $\frac{2^8}{2^0}$

rap It Up

**MATHEMATICALLY SPEAKING**

▸ ratio

Explain how to divide numbers that are different powers of 10 using scientific notation. Why do we call using scientific notation "a shortcut" method for simplifying expressions?

## Reflect

Use these questions to help you reflect on the lesson and plan for future instruction.

- How efficient are students at using the shortcut method for dividing numbers written in scientific notation?

- Do students have a strong conceptual understanding of what it means to "cancel" the zeros when simplifying a ratio or division problem that involves very large numbers?

MATERIALS LIST

▶ Calculators

On Your Own

**Write About It**

1. Imagine you are writing the entry for "The Rules of Exponents" for an online mathematics encyclopedia. Write a concise, clear set of rules based on what you have learned in Lessons 3.2 and 3.3. Explain why each rule works.

2. Simplify the following using scientific notation and rules for exponents.

   a) $\dfrac{24 \times 10^{18}}{1.3 \times 10^6}$

   b) $\dfrac{73.2 \times 10^{17}}{0.25 \times 10^{17}}$

   c) $\dfrac{20 \text{ trillion}}{1.4 \text{ million}}$

   d) $\dfrac{850,000}{2.500}$

   e) $241,532,005 \div (8.2 \times 10^4)$

3. Find how many times as great the mass of each planet listed below is as the mass of Mars using scientific notation. (the mass of Mars is $6.42 \times 10^{23}$)

| Planet | Mass |
|--------|------|
| Jupiter | $1.90 \times 10^{27}$ |
| Uranus | $8.68 \times 10^{25}$ |
| Venus | $4.87 \times 10^{24}$ |

4. Is it possible for the exhibitors to make a real-life scale model of the planets based on their mass? If so, recommend how they would do this. If not, explain why not.

JUPITER            URANUS            VENUS

---

Example: $3^9 \div 3^5 = 3^{(9-5)} = 3^4 = 81$
$3^9 \div 3^5 = 19{,}683 \div 243$
$= 81$

When multiplying or dividing two numbers that do not have the same base or exponent, evaluate the powers first, and then multiply or divide the numbers accordingly.

Example: $5^3 \cdot 2^4 = 125 \div 16 = 7.8125$

 **NOTE** Discuss these rules with the class to build consensus after students have had a chance to write about them.

2. a) $1.8461538 \times 10^{13}$

   b) $2.928 \times 10^2$

   c) $1.4285714 \times 10^7$

   d) $3.4 \times 10^5$ 3

   e) $2.945512 \times 10^3$

3. Mars has a mass of $6.42 \times 10^{23}$ kg.
   Jupiter's mass is $2.959502 \times 10^3$ times as great.
   Uranus's mass is $1.3520249 \times 10^2$ times as great.
   Venus's mass is $7.58567 \times 10^1$ or 7.58567 times as great.

4. No, it is not possible. Earth's mass is approximately $5.98 \times 10^{24}$ kg, which is 9 times the mass of Mars, and Jupiter's mass is almost 300 times the mass of Mars. Many of the other planets have masses that are greater than the mass of Earth. It would not be possible to make a model for these large masses.

---

 **NOTE** This is the purpose of the activity in this lesson. Make sure students complete this question and discuss student answers in class.

---

## On Your Own

**Write About It**

1. Answers will vary. Possible response:

When multiplying exponential numbers or terms that have the same base, add the exponents together and leave the base the same. (Product Rule)

Example: $2^4 \cdot 2^5 = 2^{(4+5)}$
$2^4 \cdot 2^5 = 16 \cdot 32 = 2^9$
$512 = 512$

When dividing two numbers that have the same base, subtract the exponents and leave the base the same. (Quotient Rule)

5. The populations of the countries from which people came to visit the Discovery Center are given below.

| Country | Population |
|---|---|
| Jamaica | $2.804 \times 10^6$ |
| United States | 303,825,100 |
| Australia | twenty million, 601 thousand |
| India | one billion, one hundred forty-seven million, nine hundred ninety-six thousand |
| China | 1,330,045,000 |
| Ecuador | $1.3928 \times 10^7$ |
| Mexico | $1.09955 \times 10^8$ |
| Spain | forty million, four hundred ninety-one thousand |
| Tanzania | 40,213,000 |
| Central African Republic | $4.4357 \times 10^6$ |
| New Zealand | 4,173,000 |

a) Using scientific notation, find how many times as great the population of India is as the population of the United States.

b) How many times the population of Australia is the population of the United States?

c) Name two countries for which the population of one country is about twice that of the other.

d) Name two countries for which the population of one country is about three times that of the other.

e) Name two countries for which the population of one country is about 10 times that of the other.

f) Name two countries for which the population of one country is about 100 times that of the other.

6. Evaluate the following expressions. Give your answer as a power of a base and also in standard notation.

a) $\frac{5^{17}}{5^{10}}$

b) $10^{20} \div 10^{14}$

c) $\frac{4^7}{4^0}$

d) $\frac{2^{22}}{2^{22}}$

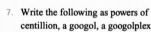
Think Beyond

7. Write the following as powers of 10: 1 quadrillion, 1 septillion, 1 centillion, a googol, a googolplex. Use the Internet or a mathematics dictionary.

5. a) $\frac{\text{India's Population: } 1.147996 \times 10^9}{\text{U.S. Population: } 3.038251 \times 10^8} \approx$ $0.37784765 \times 10^1$ or $3.7784765$ times as great

b) $\frac{\text{U.S. Population: } 3.038251 \times 10^8}{\text{Australia's Population: } 2.0601 \times 10^7} \approx$ $1.47481 \times 10^1$ or $1.47481$ times as great

c) Spain's population is about twice the population of Australia.

d) The United States's population is about three times the population of Mexico. Spain's population is about three times the population of Ecuador.

e) Tanzania's population is about 10 times the population of Central African Republic. Spain's population is about 10 times the population of New Zealand. India's population is about 10 times the population of Mexico.

f) China's population is about 100 times the population of Ecuador.

6. a) $5^7$ or $78,125$

b) $10^6$ or $1,000,000$

c) $4^7$ or $16,384$

d) $2^0 = 1$

**Think Beyond**

8. The Egyptians used the symbol of an astonished man to represent one million and anything greater than that. You often hear people use the word *zillions*. Do some research and determine if this represents a specific number.

Astonished Man

 **Think Back**

9. Solve for $x$. Show your work. $3x - 7 > 5 - 6x$

10. It cost Trey $140 to make a set of T-shirts to support the track team. He plans to sell them for $8 each. If $p$ represents his profit and $x$ represents the number of T-shirts he sells, write a formula that represents his income. How many shirts does he have to sell to make a profit?

11. The ratio of wins to games played for a baseball team is 3 to 5. If the team played 45 games, how many did the team win?

    A. 18

    B. 15

    C. 36

    D. 27

12. The Nile River in Egypt is 4,160 miles long. How many feet is this? How many inches?

13. Solve for $x$: $2 - 6(-4 + {}^-8) = 2x$

---

7.  **Think Beyond**

1 quadrillion $= 10^{15}$

1 septillion $= 10^{24}$

1 centillion $= 10^{303}$

1 googol $= 10^{100}$

1 googolplex $= 10^{10,100}$

8. **Think Beyond** *Zillion* is a generic term meaning a very large number. It has no specific definition. The term *zillion* is used just as the astonished man was used by the ancient Egyptians.

 **Think Back**

9. $x > \frac{4}{3}$ or $x > 1.\overline{3}$

10. $p = 8x - 140$  He will begin to make a profit with the 18th T-shirt he sells. ($140 \div 8 = 17.5$)

11. **D.** 27

12. 21,964,800 feet  or  263,577,600 inches

13. $x = 37$

# LESSON 3.4 It's a Very, Very Small World

**Suggested Pacing:** 3 Days

In this lesson, students learn how to use scientific notation to write and work with small numbers. Students will represent numbers with negative exponents as equivalent fractions and decimals.

---

**LESSON OBJECTIVES**

■ Students will represent and interpret very small numbers between 0 and 1 using scientific notation.

■ Students will translate very small numbers written with negative exponents to equivalent fractions and decimal forms.

■ Students will discover that the rules for multiplying and dividing numbers with exponents apply to numbers with negative exponents as well.

---

| DAY 1 | Materials* | ESSENTIAL *ON YOUR OWN* QUESTIONS |
|---|---|---|
| The Number Line between 0 and 0.01 | **In Class**<br>■ Calculators<br>■ Lesson Guide 3.4: *Patterns with Powers of 10*<br>■ Lesson Guide 3.4: *Comparing Different Bases: Looking for Patterns with Negative Exponents*<br>■ Internet access (optional) | Questions 2, 3, 10, 11 |

| DAY 2 | Materials* | ESSENTIAL *ON YOUR OWN* QUESTIONS |
|---|---|---|
| Scientific Notation with Really Small Numbers<br><br>Scaling Down in a Nano-World | **In Class**<br>■ Calculators<br>■ Lesson Guide 3.4A: *Dividing by Powers of 10*<br>■ Internet access (optional) | Questions 1, 4, 5, 12, 13 |

| DAY 3 | Materials* | ESSENTIAL *ON YOUR OWN* QUESTIONS |
|---|---|---|
| Using the Negative Exponents and the Rules of Exponents | **In Class**<br>■ Calculators<br>■ Internet access (optional for Think Beyond questions) | Questions 6, 7, 14 |

\* The Think Like a Mathematician Daily Record Sheet should be used daily

---

## MATHEMATICALLY SPEAKING

▶ micrometer   ▶ micron   ▶ nanometer   ▶ nanotechnology

## Start It Off

Students have been working with large numbers in previous lessons of this section. This exercise is designed for students to begin thinking about the relative size of numbers that are very, very small.

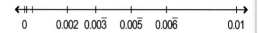

The first tick mark to the right of zero is actually $\frac{1}{150}$ of the way to 0.01 or approximately 0.00007. The next is $\frac{1}{30}$ of the way or approximately 0.0003. The third mark is $\frac{30}{150}$ or $\frac{1}{5}$ of the way or approximately 0.002. Students might not get close to these estimations, but they should at least realize that the first two spaces are remarkably different in size and use this observation to help determine the value of the other points.

### DAY 1 TEACHING THE LESSON

In this lesson, students learn how to use scientific notation to write and work with very small numbers. As students explore nanotechnology, they discover that the rules for multiplying and dividing numbers with exponents learned in previous lessons also apply to numbers with negative exponents. Students investigate how to represent numbers with negative exponents as equivalent fractions and decimals.

---

### LESSON 3.4 It's a Very, Very Small World

## Start It Off

Note the labeled points on this number line. Using what you know about scale, estimate what the value of the other points would be. Explain your reasoning to your partner.

### The Number Line Between 0 and 0.01

A new exhibit, Life in a Nano-World, has just opened in the Newton Discovery Center. To enter the nano-world, you need to know that the prefix *nano* means $10^{-9}$.

1. To learn about $10^{-9}$, complete the following table and look for a pattern. Write numbers less than 1 as fractions.

| Power of 10 | Value |
|---|---|
| $10^4$ | 10,000 |
| $10^3$ | 1,000 |
| $10^2$ | 100 |
| $10^1$ | 10 |
| $10^0$ | |
| $10^{-1}$ | |
| $10^{-2}$ | |
| $10^{-3}$ | |
| $10^{-4}$ | |
| $10^{-5}$ | |
| $10^{-6}$ | |
| $10^{-7}$ | |
| $10^{-8}$ | |
| $10^{-9}$ | |

Check your answers with a calculator.

You can see that the nano-world involves very, very, very small numbers!

---

### The Number Line between 0 and 0.01

Read together about what the prefix *nano* means. Ask students what might be included in the Life in a Nano-World exhibit.

- *Why might you need a measurement so small?*

- *What types of objects would you be measuring?*

Distribute a copy of Lesson Guide 3.4: *Patterns with Powers of Ten*. Have students complete Questions 1 and 2 with a partner to determine the value of $10^{-9}$.

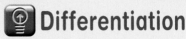

## Differentiation

**Think Differently:** For those students who are experiencing difficulty completing the table in Question 1, encourage them to look for a pattern as the powers of 10 decrease by 1. Ask:

- *When the power of 10 decreases by 1 from $10^4$ to $10^3$, does this change represent a multiplication or division by 10?*
- *When the power of 10 decreases by 1 from $10^3$ to $10^2$, does this change represent a multiplication or division by 10?*
- *When a power of 10 decreases by 1, what is the change?*

Discuss student responses as a class when finished. For Question 2, focus students' attention on the fact that a negative power of 10 can be written in another format using a positive power. For example, $10^{-n} = \frac{1}{10^n}$.

Next, distribute a copy of Lesson Guide 3.4: *Comparing Different Bases: Looking for Patterns with Negative Exponents*. Have students complete Question 3 with a partner. Encourage pairs to share their generalizations in a class discussion.

Have students discuss Question 4 with their partners before sharing their ideas with the class. Encourage them to support their ideas with examples. Next, have students complete Question 5 independently.

1.

| Power of 10 | Value |
|---|---|
| $10^4$ | 10,000 |
| $10^3$ | 1,000 |
| $10^2$ | 100 |
| $10^1$ | 10 |
| $10^0$ | 1 |
| $10^{-1}$ | $\frac{1}{10}$ |
| $10^{-2}$ | $\frac{1}{100}$ |
| $10^{-3}$ | $\frac{1}{1,000}$ |
| $10^{-4}$ | $\frac{1}{10,000}$ |
| $10^{-5}$ | $\frac{1}{100,000}$ |
| $10^{-6}$ | $\frac{1}{1,000,000}$ |
| $10^{-7}$ | $\frac{1}{10,000,000}$ |
| $10^{-8}$ | $\frac{1}{100,000,000}$ |
| $10^{-9}$ | $\frac{1}{1,000,000,000}$ |

**2. a)** As the power of 10 decreases by 1, the number's value is divided by 10.

**b)** $\frac{1}{10^2}$

**c)** The value of 10 raised to a negative exponent is the reciprocal of 10 raised to the absolute value of that exponent.

| Power of 10 | Standard Notation | |
|---|---|---|
| $10^{-1}$ | $\frac{1}{10}$ | $\frac{1}{10^1}$ |
| $10^{-2}$ | $\frac{1}{100}$ | $\frac{1}{10^2}$ |
| $10^{-3}$ | $\frac{1}{1,000}$ | $\frac{1}{10^3}$ |
| $10^{-4}$ | $\frac{1}{10,000}$ | $\frac{1}{10^4}$ |
| $10^{-5}$ | $\frac{1}{100,000}$ | $\frac{1}{10^5}$ |
| $10^{-6}$ | $\frac{1}{1,000,000}$ | $\frac{1}{10^6}$ |
| $10^{-7}$ | $\frac{1}{10,0000,000}$ | $\frac{1}{10^7}$ |
| $10^{-8}$ | $\frac{1}{100,000,000}$ | $\frac{1}{10^8}$ |
| $10^{-9}$ | $\frac{1}{1,000,000,000}$ | $\frac{1}{10^9}$ |

**d)** Represent negative powers of 10 by using a unit fraction with a denominator of 10 to the opposite of the original power.
$10^{-7} = \frac{1}{10^7}$

**3. a)** Answers will vary. See the table in Question 6 as a possible example.

**b)** Any number raised to a negative power is equivalent to a unit fraction with the number raised to the opposite of the power in the denominator. The value of any positive number raised to a negative exponent will be less than 1.

**4.** Answers will vary. Students may reason that when different bases are raised to the same power (except for the zero power), the resulting values are different for each base. For example, $2^2 = 4$, $5^2 = 25$ and $10^2 = 100$. Therefore, when different bases are raised to the zero power, it would seem reasonable to assume that the resulting values should also be different.

**5.** Crystal is correct when she states that $3^4 = 81$. However, $3^{-4}$ is not equivalent to $-81$. The correct value for $3^{-4}$ is $\frac{1}{3^4} = \frac{1}{81}$. Students can produce a table starting with $3^3$ and going down to $3^{-4}$ to justify their response.

2. **a)** What pattern did you observe in the table?

   **b)** Represent the value of $10^{-2}$ as a fraction with the denominator written as a power of 10.

   **c)** Represent the rest of the negative powers of 10 in the table as fractions with denominators written as powers of 10.

   **d)** Talk to your partner and make a generalization about representing negative powers of 10 as fractions.

3. Work with a partner.

   **a)** Each partner should fill in a new table with three columns, similar to the table for base 10 above. Each partner should use a base other than 10 and different from each other. Use integer exponents from 4 down to $-9$ like the table on the previous page. Example: $2^{-3} = \frac{1}{8} = \frac{1}{2^3}$.

   **b)** Compare your results and make a generalization about the value of any number raised to a negative power.

In order for the patterns in the tables to continue, you should have found that raising a base to the zero power must give a result of 1. In fact, *any* number, other than zero, raised to the zero power is 1. You learned this earlier when you were using rules for dividing with exponents. The patterns in your tables are another justification for this rule!

4. Why do you think the fact that a nonzero number raised to the 0 power equals 1 surprises some people? How would you explain this rule?

5. Crystal thinks that $3^{-4}$ is $-81$ since $3^4$ is positive 81. Explain to her why she is wrong.

## Summarize Day 1

As a wrap up discussion for Day 1, have students share their responses to Question 5 in a class discussion. This question represents a common student misconception. To help students understand why Crystal's thinking is incorrect, encourage them to justify their ideas by using patterns and creating a table of values to support their thinking.

You already learned that scientific notation involves powers of 10.

6. Fill in the table below using *decimals* to see how powers of 10 with negative exponents can be represented.

| Power of 10 | Standard Notation |
|---|---|
| $10^4$ | 10,000 |
| $10^3$ | 1,000 |
| $10^2$ | 100 |
| $10^1$ | 10 |
| $10^0$ | |
| $10^{-1}$ | |
| $10^{-2}$ | |
| $10^{-3}$ | |
| $10^{-4}$ | |
| $10^{-5}$ | |
| $10^{-6}$ | |
| $10^{-7}$ | |
| $10^{-8}$ | |
| $10^{-9}$ | |

The form of scientific notation is the same for very small numbers as it is for very large numbers.

 times

| a number greater than or equal to 1 and less than 10 | × | 10 raised to a power (using an exponent) |

However, the exponent is a *negative* number rather than a positive number.

**Example**

From the table above, you see that $10^{-2}$ can be written as 0.01. So, in scientific notation, 0.01 is written as $1 \times 10^{-2}$.

**NOTE** Notice that the number of decimal places you moved to the right to get a mantissa greater than 1 is the absolute value of the exponent.

So, $0.0005 = 5 \cdot 0.0001 = 5 \times 10^{-4}$.

Notice that you move the decimal point **four** places to the right in the number 0.0005, which is the absolute value of the exponent.

## DAY 2 TEACHING THE LESSON

## Scientific Notation with Very Small Numbers

Have students refer to the table they completed in Question 1 and complete Question 6 independently. Then, have students share responses with the class. Discuss how to write very small numbers using scientific notation and the example given.

 **Differentiation**

**Think Differently:** For students having difficulties dividing by powers of 10, offer Lesson Guide 3.4A: *Dividing by Powers of 10*.

Have students complete Questions 7 and 8 independently and compare their answers with a partner. Then, have partners complete Question 9 together and share their responses with the class. The examples in Question 9 may be counterintuitive for students because small numbers have mantissas with greater values. It may be helpful for students to write the numbers in standard notation in order to compare values.

6.

| Power of 10 | Standard Notation |
|---|---|
| $10^4$ | 10,000 |
| $10^3$ | 1,000 |
| $10^2$ | 100 |
| $10^1$ | 10 |
| $10^0$ | 1 |
| $10^{-1}$ | 0.1 |
| $10^{-2}$ | 0.01 |
| $10^{-3}$ | 0.001 |
| $10^{-4}$ | 0.0001 |
| $10^{-5}$ | 0.00001 |
| $10^{-6}$ | 0.000001 |
| $10^{-7}$ | 0.0000001 |
| $10^{-8}$ | 0.00000001 |
| $10^{-9}$ | 0.000000001 |

7. Write the following numbers in scientific notation.

   a) 0.006

   b) 0.00000003

   c) 0.00000000009

   d) 0.167

Now let's look at the reverse process.

---
**Example**

Write $5 \times 10^{-4}$ in standard notation.
You can write this as $5 \cdot 0.0001$ and then multiply to get 0.0005.

Or

You can begin with the mantissa, which in this case is 5. Move the decimal point (which is understood to be after the number) the same number of places to the left as the absolute value of the exponent.
You will get 0.0005.

---

8. Write the following numbers in standard notation.

   a) $8 \times 10^{-6}$

   b) $3.2 \times 10^{-3}$

   c) $5.6709 \times 10^{0}$

   d) $34 \times 10^{-4}$

   e) $267 \times 10^{-5}$

   f) Which of the numbers in Parts a through e are not written in scientific notation? Explain. Write each of them in scientific notation.

9. a) Talk to your partner and decide which is greater: $4 \times 10^{-5}$ or $8 \times 10^{-6}$. Explain.

   b) Order these numbers from least to greatest.

   $5 \times 10^{-8}, 12 \times 10^{-10}, 5 \times 10^{-4}, 12 \times 10^{0}$

---

7. a) $6 \times 10^{-3}$   c) $9 \times 10^{-11}$

   b) $3 \times 10^{-8}$   d) $1.67 \times 10^{-1}$

8. a) 0.000008

   b) 0.0032

   c) 5.6709

   d) 0.0034

   e) 0.00267

   f) Parts d and e are not written in scientific notation, since their mantissas do not represent a number greater than or equal to 1 and less than 10.

   d) $3.4 \times 10^{-3}$

   e) $2.67 \times 10^{-3}$

9. a) $4 \times 10^{-5}$ is greater. Its power of 10 is ten times the power of 10 in $8 \times 10^{-6}$.
   $4 \times 10^{-5} = 0.00005$ or 5 hundred thousandths;
   $8 \times 10^{-6} = 0.000008$ or 8 millionths

   b) Order from least to greatest: $12 \times 10^{-10}$, $5 \times 10^{-8}$, $5 \times 10^{-4}$, $12 \times 10^{0}$

## Scaling Down in a Nano-World

**Nanotechnology** is about working with things that are a few nanometers long. A **nanometer** is one millionth of a millimeter. (By the way, that is how much your fingernails grow each second!) The new exhibit, Life in a Nano-World, will showcase how nanotechnology is used in computer science, medicine, cosmetics, aerospace and even criminology.

10. *Nano* means $10^{-9}$. Explain why it makes sense that a nanometer is one millionth of a millimeter.

> **? Hint**
> See page 169

11. Nanometers (abbreviated nm) are in use today. If you take apart a laptop computer, you will discover a small computer chip that does all the processing. This chip is made up of wires that are less than 200 nanometers long. Write this number in scientific notation.

12. A news bulletin released by Intel Corporation in January 2007 shows how rapidly computer technology is changing.

   Write this new size mentioned in the bulletin in meters using scientific notation.

**Breaking**
**NEWS**
**Bulletin!**

Intel's Transistor
Technology Breakthrough
Represents Biggest Change to
Computer Chips in 40 Years

**EXTRA! EXTRA!**

Intel Producing First
Processor Prototypes with
New, Tiny 45-Nanometer
Transistors, Accelerating
Era of Multi-Core Computing

---

## Scaling Down in a Nano-World

Have students work with a partner to complete Questions 10–12. Circulate to observe solution methods and assess understanding. Encourage partners who used different solution strategies to share their answers and problem-solving methods with the class. Ask a few student volunteers to present their work on the board or interactive white board. Encourage students to share their thinking and reasoning. Do not rush the discussion.

10. A millimeter is equal to 0.001 meter. Since a nanometer is 1 millionth of a meter, divide 0.001 by 1,000,000 to get a quotient of 0.000000001. Using scientific notation,

    $1 \times 10^{-3} \div 1 \times 10^{6} = 1 = 10^{(-3-6)} = 1 \times 10^{-9}$.

11. $2 \times 10^{-7}$ (Note: One way to solve this problem is to think of 200 nm as $200 \times 10^{-9}$. Since this number is not in scientific notation, the mantissa must be adjusted. $200 = 2 \times 10^{2}$

    Therefore, $(2 \times 10^{2}) \times 10^{-9} = 2 \times 10^{(2 + -9)} = 2 \times 10^{-7}$.)

12. $4.5 \times 10^{-8}$

## Summarize Day 2

Have students share their answers to the following question in a class discussion. Encourage students to explain their reasoning.

  • *Why is $6.2 \times 10^{-5}$ greater than $9.8 \times 10^{-8}$?*

When written in standard notation, $6.2 \times 10^{-5} = 0.000062$

$9.8 \times 10^{-8} = 0.000000098$

$0.000062 > 0.000000098$

## Using Negative Exponents and the Rules of Exponents

Do the rules of exponents also hold true for negative exponents?

**13. a)** Make up two multiplication examples and two division examples using negative exponents. Try out the rules and see if they work. An example is given below.

$$3^{-2} \cdot 3^{-2} = \frac{1}{3^2} \cdot \frac{1}{3^2} = \frac{1}{9} \cdot \frac{1}{9} = \frac{1}{81} = \frac{1}{3^4} = 3^{-4}$$

In this case the rules for multiplying exponents work!

**b)** Compare your results with your partner. Make a conjecture about the rules for negative exponents. Then discuss as a class.

**14.** Simplify the following expressions and write your answer without exponents. If the answer is less than 1, write it as a fraction.

**a)** $10^{-3}$          **e)** $1.4 \times 10^{-5}$

**b)** $14^{-2}$          **f)** $5^{-2} \cdot 5^2$

**c)** $4^{-3} \cdot 4^{-4}$          **g)** $8.901 \times 10^9$

**d)** $\frac{2^{-7}}{2}$

**15.** Larry he says he can always write an expression without negative exponents that is equivalent to an expression using negative exponents. Larissa didn't believe him, so he gave her the following example: $2^3 \cdot 2^{-2}$ can be written as $\frac{2^3}{2^2}$. Explain why Larry's idea makes sense.

**16.** Write the following expressions using only positive exponents.

**a)** $9^{-4}$          **c)** $2^{-5} \cdot 2^{-3}$

**b)** $10^{-6} \cdot 10$          **d)** $3^{-10} \div 3^{-7}$

## TEACHING THE LESSON

### Using Negative Exponents and the Rules of Exponents

Ask students to predict whether the rules they discovered for multiplying and dividing with positive exponents will hold true for negative exponents. Explain to them that they will investigate problems to see whether the predictions they made hold true.

Have students work independently on Question 13a and then compare their answers with a partner to help make the conjecture for Question 13b. Encourage student pairs to share their conjectures with the class. Using examples to support their thinking, guide the discussion so that students come to a consensus that the rules they discovered for positive exponents also hold true for negative exponents. Ask for student volunteers to share the examples they created on the board or overhead to help clarify and deepen student understanding of these rules.

Next, have students complete Questions 14–17 and compare their answers with a partner. Circulate among pairs to informally assess student understanding. Use the *Student Snapshot* observation tool to record observations and anecdotal notes. Encourage students to discuss any discrepancies as a class. For Question 17, students may have written their answers as decimals or as fractions without exponents. Discuss both equivalent forms.

**13. a)** Answers will vary. One possible example is listed for each:

Multiplying with negative exponents:
$5^{-2} \bullet 5^{-1} = \frac{1}{25} \bullet \frac{1}{5} = \frac{1}{125} = 5^{-3}$

In this example, the multiplication rule works. $5^{-2} \bullet 5^{-1} = 5^{(-2 + -1)} = 5^{-3}$

Dividing with negative exponents:
$5^{-2} \div 5^{-1} = \frac{1}{25} \div \frac{1}{5} = \frac{5}{25} = \frac{1}{5} = 5^{-1}$

In this example, the division rule works. $5^{-2} \div 5^{-1} = 5^{(-2 - -1)} = 5^{(-2 + 1)} = 5^{-1}$

**b)** The rules hold true for negative exponents.

**14.** **a)** $\frac{1}{1,000}$

**b)** $\frac{1}{196}$

**c)** $\frac{1}{16,384}$

**d)** $\frac{1}{256}$

**e)** $\frac{14}{1,000,000}$

**f)** 1

**g)** 8,901,000,000

**15.** Larry's idea makes sense, since it is always possible to rewrite exponents without using negative values.
$23 \cdot 2^{-2} = \frac{2^3}{1} \cdot \frac{1}{2^2} = \frac{2^3}{2^2}$

**16.** **a)** $\frac{1}{9^4}$

**b)** $\frac{1}{10^5}$

**c)** $\frac{1}{2^8}$

**d)** $\frac{1}{3^3}$

**17.** **a)** 0.00001 or $\frac{1}{100,000}$

**b)** $0.\overline{3}$ or $\frac{1}{3}$

**c)** 216

**d)** 625

**e)** 0.25 or $\frac{1}{4}$

**f)** 27

**18.** The 200 nm length chip is $4.\overline{4}$ times larger than the new Intel computer chip.

## Wrap It Up

Student responses should include the following key ideas:

- As long as $a$ does not equal zero and $b$ represents any integer, $a^{-b} = \left(\frac{1}{a}\right)^b$ holds true.

In this lesson, we discovered that $a^{-b} = \frac{1}{a^b}$. Since 1 raised to any power is always 1, $\frac{1}{a^b} = \frac{1^b}{a^b}$. Therefore, $\frac{1}{a^b} = \left(\frac{1}{a}\right)^b$.

We can show this by substituting values for the variables. Let $a = 3$ and $b = 4$.

---

**17.** Simplify the following expressions. Write your answers without exponents.

**a)** $10^{-2} \cdot 10^{-3}$

**b)** $3^{-5} \cdot 3^4$

**c)** $\frac{6^2}{6^{-1}}$

**d)** $25 \div 5^{-2}$

**e)** $4^0 \cdot 4^{-1}$

**f)** $\frac{3^{-3}}{3^{-6}}$

**18.** How many times larger is the 200 nm chip found in laptops than Intel's new computer chip advertised in the news bulletin?

## Wrap It Up

For any number $a$ not equal to 0 and any integer $b$, $a^{-b} = \left(\frac{1}{a}\right)^b$. Explain what this means using words and examples.

**MATHEMATICALLY SPEAKING**

- micrometer
- micron
- nanometer
- nanotechnology

$3^{-4} = \frac{1}{3^4} = \frac{1}{3} \cdot \frac{1}{3} \cdot \frac{1}{3} \cdot \frac{1}{3} = \frac{1}{81}$, which is equal to $\left(\frac{1}{3}\right)^4$.

### Reflect

Use these questions to help you reflect on the lesson and plan for future instruction.

- How successful are students in representing and interpreting very small numbers using scientific notation?

- Are students able to relate the rules for exponents to numbers with negative exponents?

See corresponding assessments in Assessment Resources.

Write About It

1. How do you write numbers between 0 and 1 in scientific notation? Explain in words and give some examples.

2. Brian thinks that $6^{-2}$ has the value of $-36$. He argues that since the exponent is negative, the answer should be negative as well. Explain to him why this is not true. Find the real value of $6^{-2}$ and explain why your answer makes sense.

3. Kim says that the value of any number to the zero power has to be 0. Explain to her why she is incorrect. Tell her the correct answer and show why your answer makes sense in two different ways.

4. Evaluate the following expressions using the rules of exponents. Do not use a calculator. Write all answers in standard notation.

   a) $4^0$

   b) $-8^{-2}$

   c) $5.68 \times 10^{-3}$

   d) $10^{-4} \times 10^8$

   e) $2^{-6} \cdot 2^3$

   f) $\frac{9^2}{9^{-1}}$

   g) $(-1)^5$

   h) $4.329^0$

   i) $\left(\frac{2}{3}\right)^5$

   j) $(-10)^4$

   k) $\frac{8.24 \times 10^{-6}}{4.12 \times 10^{-2}}$

5. Put these numbers in order from least to greatest.
   $8 \times 10^{-6}, 3.2 \times 10^{-3}, 5.6709 \times 10^0, 34 \times 10^{-4}, 267 \times 10^{-5}$

6. At your exhibit, Life in a Nano-World, you will have a display called *Cracking Down on Crime* that shows how nanotechnology can stop counterfeiters.

Section 3: Exponents and Scientific Notation • Lesson 3.4  **111**

---

## On Your Own

Write About It

1. Numbers between 0 and 1 can be written in scientific notation as two factors—a mantissa that is a number greater than or equal to 1 and less than 10, and a power of 10 that has a negative exponent. The absolute value of the exponent for the negative power of 10 represents the number of places the decimal was moved to the right in order to create an appropriate mantissa.

Possible example: 0.0134 written in scientific notation is $1.34 \times 10^{-2}$.

2. $6^{-2}$ has a value of $\frac{1}{36}$. Numbers with negative exponents are represented as a fraction with 1 in the numerator, and the denominator is the same base raised to the absolute value of the negative power.

3. The value of any number raised to the zero power is 1, not zero. One way to explain this is to consider the idea that any number divided by itself equals 1. For example, $3^2 \div 3^2 = 1$. Using the rule for dividing numbers with exponents, $3^2 \div 3^2 = 3^{(2-2)} = 3^0 = 1$.

Another way to explain this is by studying patterns and evaluating numbers as the values of the exponents decrease within a given base. For example,
$4^4 = 256$

$4^3 = 64$

$4^2 = 16$

$4^1 = 4$

$4^0 = 1$

As the value of the exponent decreases by 1, the value of the previous number is divided by 4. Since $4^1$ has a value of 4, $4^0$ has a value of $4 \div 4$, which is equal to 1. Examining patterns in other bases shows the same result. Any base raised to the zero power is always equal to 1.

4. a) 1

   b) $-\frac{1}{64}$

   c) 0.00568

   d) 10,000

   e) $\frac{1}{8}$

   f) 729

   g) $-1$

   h) 1

   i) $\frac{32}{243}$

   j) 10,000

   k) 0.0002

**Did you know?** The federal government can create complex codes using nano-sized particles called quantum dots. Forgers would have a very difficult time recreating these. These codes can be hidden on dollar bills, credit cards and gift vouchers to protect against counterfeit documents. As part of the Nano-World exhibit, you want visitors to get an idea of the very small size of quantum dots. You plan to create two posters for the exhibit. The information on the first poster is written below.

Small quantum dots, such as nanocrystals, can be as small as 2 to 10 nanometers. Self-assembled quantum dots are typically between 10 and 50 nanometers in size. Some quantum dots can have diameters exceeding 100 nanometers. At 10 nanometers in diameter, a line of nearly 3 million quantum dots could fit within the width of a human thumb.

a) The second poster will contain the same information but with all the numbers written in scientific notation. Write the information for the second poster.

b) Compare the size of the dots mentioned in the posters. How many times as large is the largest dot as the smallest?

5. $8 \times 10^{-6}$, $267 \times 10^{-5}$, $3.2 \times 10^{-3}$, $34 \times 10^{-4}$, $5.6709 \times 10^{0}$

or 0.000008, 0.00267, 0.0032, 0.0034, 5.6709

6. **a)** Small quantum dots, such as nanocrystals, can be as small as $2 \times 10^{-9}$ to $1 \times 10^{-8}$ meters. Self-assembled quantum dots are typically between $1 \times 10^{-8}$ and $5 \times 10^{-8}$ meters in size. Some quantum dots can have diameters exceeding $1 \times 10^{-7}$ meters. At $1 \times 10^{-8}$ meters in diameter, nearly $3 \times 10^{6}$ quantum dots could be lined up end to end and fit within the width of a human thumb.

**b)** $\frac{1 \times 10^{-7}}{2 \times 10^{-9}} = 0.5 \times 10^{(-7 - -9)} = 0.5 \times 10^{2} = $ 50 times larger

**7.** When discussing nanotechnology, scientists often mention microelectromechanical systems (MEMS). MEMS use micrometers, also called microns, which are one thousand times larger than nanometers.

Using MEMS, scientists have created very tiny robots. They hope that someday these robots can be inserted into a human body to perform complex surgeries or deliver medication to isolated infected cells.

Nanobots alongside dust particles

**a)** Write the size of 1 micrometer in scientific notation.

**b)** The diameter of a human hair is approximately 100 micrometers. Write this number in scientific notation and standard notation.

**c)** What is the diameter of a human hair in nanometers? Do you think you would be able to see something that is 1 nanometer in diameter?

**Think Beyond**

**8.** There are many possibilities for the use of nanotechnology in the world of the future. Using the Internet, investigate some of these and share your findings with the class in a PowerPoint presentation.

**Think Beyond**

**9.** There are serious ethical issues involved in using nanotechnology that scientists are grappling with. Using the Internet, investigate some of these issues and share your findings in a class presentation.

better design and synthesis of pharmaceuticals, the development of improved medical equipment to monitor patients, and the ability to treat diseases such as cancer more directly. Perhaps even miniature robots and other nanomachines could be used to perform microscopic surgeries on the human body. Benefits to the environment may also be possible with nanotechnology. Nanomachines could be used to clean up toxins, recycle garbage and eliminate the need for landfills. (adapted from *www.actionbioscience.org/ newfrontiers/chen.html*)

**9.** **Think Beyond** Answers will vary. Possible answer: Self-replicating nanomachines could malfunction and multiply endlessly like a virus. Nanotechnologies could be used to erode our freedom and privacy by misusing molecular-sized microphones, cameras and homing beacons to track and monitor people. (adapted from *www.actionbioscience. org/newfrontiers/chen.html*)

**7.** **a)** $1 \times 10^{-6}$ m

**b)** $1 \times 10^{-4}$ m or 0.0001 m

**c)** 100,000 nm. Since a human hair is 100,000 nm in diameter, it is unlikely that you would be able to see something that is only 1 nm in diameter.

**8.** **Think Beyond** Answers will vary. Possible answer: Some possible uses for nanotechnology in the future include many manufacturing applications, such as helping to design and develop electronics and other goods in more miniature sizes that require less consumption of energy. There are also many potential medical benefits, such as

## Think Back

10. $y = -10x + 6$ is a steeper line, since the absolute value of the slope (coefficient of $x$) is greater. $|-10| > |3|$ or $10 > 3$

11. Answers will vary.

    Accept any linear equation where the coefficient of $x$ is 0, so $x$ does not appear in the equation.

    Possible equation: $y = 2$. This is a horizontal line, two units above the $x$-axis. Any line in the form $y = b$ will be a horizontal line $b$ units above the $x$-axis when $b$ is positive, or $|b|$ units below the $x$-axis when $b$ is negative.

12. Jodi is correct. $y = -6.4x$ is the same as $y = -6.4x + 0$. This line will cross the $y$-axis at the point $(0, 0)$, so the $y$-intercept is 0.

13. Yes. The rate of change between points is constant. For every 1-unit increase in $x$-values, there is a 1.5-unit increase in $y$-values.

14. **a)** $3c - 9d$

    **b)** $3x - 3.5$

    **c)** $9(2 - x)$

    **d)** $-15y + 21$

## Optional Technology Lesson for this section available at www.mymathinnovations.com

---

## LESSON 3.4 — SECTION 3 — On Your Own

## Think Back

10. Which line will be steeper when graphed, $y = -10x + 6$ or $y = 3x + 40$? Explain.

11. Write the equation of a line that has a slope of 0. Explain how you know that the slope is 0. Describe what the line will look like on a graph.

12. Joanna says that the line $y = -6.4x$ has no $y$-intercept. Jodi disagrees and says this line has a $y$-intercept of 0. Who is correct? Explain your answer.

13. Will the ordered pairs in the table below form a straight line? Explain how you can find the answer without graphing the values.

| x | y |
|---|---|
| 1 | 4.5 |
| 2 | 6 |
| 3 | 7.5 |
| 4 | 9 |
| 5 | 11.5 |

14. Write an equivalent expression for each of the following:

    **a)** $3(c - 3d)$

    **b)** $\frac{1}{2}(6x - 7)$

    **c)** $18 - 9x$

    **d)** $-3(5y - 7)$

## Optional Technology Lesson for this section available at www.mymathinnovations.com

**114**    Course 3: Solve It: Focusing on Equations, Inequalities and Exponents

1. Think like a mathematician. Look for a pattern as you fill in the table below.

| Power of 10 | Standard |
|---|---|
| $10^4$ | 10,000 |
| $10^3$ | 1,000 |
| $10^2$ | 100 |
| $10^1$ | 10 |
| $10^0$ | |
| $10^{-1}$ | |
| $10^{-2}$ | |
| $10^{-3}$ | |
| $10^{-4}$ | |
| $10^{-5}$ | |
| $10^{-6}$ | |
| $10^{-7}$ | |
| $10^{-8}$ | |
| $10^{-9}$ | |

2. c) Represent the values of the negative powers of 10 as fractions with denominators written using powers of 10.

| Negative Powers of 10 as a Fraction with the Denominator Written Using Powers of 10 |
|---|
| $10^{-1}$ |
| $10^{-2}$ |
| $10^{-3}$ |
| $10^{-4}$ |
| $10^{-5}$ |
| $10^{-6}$ |
| $10^{-7}$ |
| $10^{-8}$ |
| $10^{-9}$ |

**3.** Work with a partner.

**a)** Each partner should fill in a new table with three columns similar to the table for base 10 above. Each partner should use a base other than 10 and different from each other. Make sure you include negative exponents. Example: $2^{-3} = \frac{1}{8} = \frac{1}{2^3}$.

**c)** Compare your results and make a generalization about the value of any number raised to a negative exponent.

| Base with Power | Standard Notation | Fractions with Denominators Written Using Exponents for Numbers with Negative Powers |
|---|---|---|
|  |  |  |
|  |  |  |
|  |  |  |
|  |  |  |
|  |  |  |
|  |  |  |
|  |  |  |
|  |  |  |

**1.** When you divide by 10, the decimal point moves one place to the left.

$300 \div 10 = 30$ $\qquad$ $125 \div 10 = 12.5$ $\qquad$ $4.3 \div 10 = 0.43$ $\qquad$ $200.3 \div 10 = 20.03$

Solve the following problems:

**a)** $34 \div 10 =$ _____

**b)** $14{,}681 \div 10 =$ _____

**c)** $2.67 \div 10 =$ _____

**d)** $0.174 \div 10 =$ _____

**2.** When you divide by 100, the decimal point moves two places to the left.

$600 \div 100 = 6$ $\qquad$ $346 \div 100 = 3.46$ $\qquad$ $7{,}892 \div 100 = 78.92$ $\qquad$ $1.436 \div 100 = 0.01436$

Solve the following problems:

**a)** $790 \div 100 =$ _____

**b)** $12.3 \div 100 =$ _____

**c)** $89{,}400 \div 100 =$ _____

**d)** $6.27 \div 100 =$ _____

**e)** $0.0917 \div 100 =$ _____

When you divide by 1,000, the decimal point moves three places to the left.

$3{,}075 \div 1{,}000 = 3.075$ $\qquad$ $86{,}400 \div 1{,}000 = 86.4$
$286 \div 1{,}000 = 0.286$ $\qquad$ $5.9 \div 1{,}000 = 0.0059$

Solve the following problems:

**a)** $1{,}234{,}000 \div 1{,}000 =$ _____

**b)** $300 \div 1{,}000 =$ _____

**c)** $24{,}070 \div 1{,}000 =$ _____

**d)** $7.488 \div 1{,}000 =$ _____

**e)** $13.99 \div 1{,}000 =$ _____

**f)** $600.4 \div 1{,}000 =$ _____

**4.** When you divide by 10,000, how many places is the decimal point moved to the left?

_____

**5.** Complete the following:

**a)** $4{,}207.3 \div 10 = $ _____

**b)** $4{,}207.3 \div 100 = $ _____

**c)** $4{,}207.3 \div 1{,}000 = $ _____

**d)** $4{,}207.3 \div 10{,}000 = $ _____

**e)** $4{,}207.3 \div 100{,}000 = $ _____

**f)** $4{,}207.3 \div 1{,}000{,}000 = $ _____

Solve:

**6.** $147 \div 10 = $ _____

**7.** $2{,}359 \div 100 = $ _____

**8.** $78.49 \div 100 = $ _____

**9.** $333.56 \div 10 = $ _____

**10.** $54{,}205 \div 1{,}000 = $ _____

**11.** $306{,}071 \div 10{,}000 = $ _____

**12.** $9.14 \div 1{,}000 = $ _____

**13.** $47.203 \div 10 = $ _____

**14.** $8.35 \div 10{,}000 = $ _____

**15.** $34{,}050{,}339 \div 100{,}000 = $ _____

1. When you divide by 10, the decimal point moves one place to the left.

   $300 \div 10 = 30$     $125 \div 10 = 12.5$     $4.3 \div 10 = 0.43$     $200.3 \div 10 = 20.03$

   Solve the following problems:

   a) $34 \div 10 =$ __**3.4**__

   b) $14,681 \div 10 =$ __**1,468.1**__

   c) $2.67 \div 10 =$ __**0.267**__

   d) $0.174 \div 10 =$ __**0.0174**__

2. When you divide by 100, the decimal point moves two places to the left.

   $600 \div 100 = 6$                $346 \div 100 = 3.46$
   $7,892 \div 100 = 78.92$        $1.436 \div 100 = 0.01436$

   Solve the following problems:

   a) $790 \div 100 =$ __**7.90**__

   b) $12.3 \div 100 =$ __**0.123**__

   c) $89,400 \div 100 =$ __**894**__

   d) $6.27 \div 100 =$ __**0.0627**__

   e) $0.0917 \div 100 =$ __**0.000917**__

3. When you divide by 1,000, the decimal point moves three places to the left.

   $3,075 \div 1,000 = 3.075$        $86,400 \div 1,000 = 86.4$
   $286 \div 1,000 = 0.286$          $5.9 \div 1,000 = 0.005$

   Solve the following problems:

   a) $1,234,000 \div 1,000 =$ __**1,234**__

   b) $300 \div 1,000 =$ __**0.3**__

   c) $24,070 \div 1,000 =$ __**24.07**__

   d) $7.488 \div 1,000 =$ __**0.007488**__

   e) $13.99 \div 1,000 =$ __**0.01399**__

   f) $600.4 \div 1,000 =$ __**0.6004**__

4. When you divide by 10,000, how many places is the decimal point moved to the left?
   **The decimal point moves 4 places to the left.**

© Kendall Hunt Publishing Company

5. Complete the following:

   a) $4{,}207.3 \div 10 =$ __420.73__

   b) $4{,}207.3 \div 100 =$ __42.073__

   c) $4{,}207.3 \div 1{,}000 =$ __4.2073__

   d) $4{,}207.3 \div 10{,}000 =$ __0.42073__

   e) $4{,}207.3 \div 100{,}000 =$ __0.042073__

   f) $4{,}207.3 \div 1{,}000{,}000 =$ __0.0042073__

   Solve:

6. $147 \div 10 =$ __14.7__

7. $2{,}359 \div 100 =$ __23.59__

8. $78.49 \div 100 =$ __0.7849__

9. $333.56 \div 10 =$ __33.356__

10. $54{,}205 \div 1{,}000 =$ __54.205__

11. $306{,}071 \div 10{,}000 =$ __30.6071__

12. $9.14 \div 1{,}000 =$ __0.00914__

13. $47.203 \div 10 =$ __4.7203__

14. $8.35 \div 10{,}000 =$ __0.000835__

# Sum It Up

In this section, you learned how to use exponents with scientific notation to write very large and very small numbers. You saw how applied mathematics is very useful in the world of science. You discovered rules for multiplying and dividing expressions with exponents. These rules provide efficient ways to compare very large and very small numbers.

The following are important new ideas that you learned in this section:

■ A number written in scientific notation is always in the following form:

**times**

| a number greater than or equal to 1 and less than 10 | × | 10 raised to a power (using an exponent) |

Example: 123,000,000 is written as $1.23 \times 10^8$
0.0000123 is written as $1.23 \times 10^{-5}$.

■ Multiplying by 10 results in the decimal point moving one place to the right.

Examples: $2.4 \cdot 10 = 24$
$3.26 \cdot 1,000$ or $3.26 \times 10^3 = 3,260$

■ Dividing by 10 (or multiplying by $10^{-1}$) results in the decimal point moving one place to the left.

Examples: $2.4 \times 10^{-1} = 0.24$
$3.26 \times 10^{-3} = 0.00326$

■ When multiplying two numbers or variables with the same base, keep the base the same and add the exponents.

Examples: $10^{13} \cdot 10^5 = 10^{18}$
$2^6 \cdot 2^4 = 2^{10}$
$(5.1 \times 10^{10})(1.23 \times 10^7) = 6.273 \times 10^{17}$
$2^{-4} \cdot 2^{-3} = 2^{-7}$

The Sum It Up summarizes the important mathematics students should have learned in this section. Encourage students to use this Sum It Up as they complete the Study Guide and prepare for quizzes and tests.

- When dividing two numbers or variables with the same base, keep the base the same and subtract exponents.

  Examples: $10^{13} \div 10^5 = 10^8$

  $\qquad\quad 3^{10} \div 3^2 = 3^8$

  $\qquad\quad (4.4 \times 10^6) \div (2.2 \times 10^3) = 2 \times 10^3$

  $\qquad\quad \dfrac{3^{-8}}{3^3} = 3^{-11}$

- Mathematicians have defined any number, except 0, raised to the zero power as 1:

  Examples: $10^0 = 1$

  $\qquad\quad 100^0 = 1$

  $\qquad\quad$ Why? $\quad \dfrac{10^5}{10^5} = 10^{5-5} = 10^0 = 1$

- A number or variable raised to a negative power can be expressed as the reciprocal of the number or variable raised to the absolute value of the power.

  Example: $2^{-3} = \dfrac{1}{2^3} = \left(\dfrac{1}{2}\right)^3 = \dfrac{1}{8}$

---

## MATHEMATICALLY SPEAKING

Do you know what these mathematical terms mean?

| | | |
|---|---|---|
| ▶ astronomical unit (AU) | ▶ micrometer | ▶ powers |
| ▶ base | ▶ micron | ▶ ratio |
| ▶ exponent | ▶ nanometer | ▶ scientific notation |
| ▶ light-year | ▶ nanotechnology | ▶ standard notation |
| ▶ mantissa | | |

# Study Guide

Solve It: Focusing on Equations,
Inequalities and Exponents

## Part 1. What did you learn?

1. A typical dust mite is 420 micrometers in length.

   a. Write this length in scientific notation.

   b. Given that 1 micrometer equals one-millionth of a meter, write the length of a dust mite in meters using scientific notation.

2. The United States consumes approximately 20 million barrels of gasoline each day. Write this number using scientific notation.

3. Write each number in scientific notation.

   a. 7.5 trillion

   b. 63,060,080

4. Order the following numbers from least to greatest: $7.8995 \times 10^8$, $7.9 \times 10^9$, 705,900,080.

5. Simplify the following using scientific notation and rules for exponents. Show your work and write your answers in standard notation.

   a. $(6 \times 10^7) \div (3 \times 10^4)$

   b. $\dfrac{28,600,000}{1.43 \times 10^4}$

   c. $450,000,000 \div (1.5 \times 10^6)$

6. Simplify the following using scientific notation and rules for exponents. Show your work and write your answers in scientific notation.

   a. $(8 \times 10^{14})(2.5 \times 10^6)$

   b. $(2.5 \times 10^3)(5 \times 10^7)$

7. Evaluate the following expressions using the rules of exponents.

   a. $\dfrac{12 \times 10^{-2}}{2 \times 10^2}$

   b. $\dfrac{3.2 \times 10^{-2}}{8}$

   c. $\dfrac{2.4 \times 10^3}{8 \times 10^{-2}}$

Section 3: Exponents and Scientific Notation • Study Guide    **117**

# Study Guide

1. a. $4.2 \times 10^2$

   b. $4.2 \times 10^{-4}$

2. $2.0 \times 10^7$

3. a. $7.5 \times 10^{12}$

   b. $6.306008 \times 10^7$

4. 705,900,080, $7.8995 \times 10^8$, $7.9 \times 10^9$

5. a. 2,000

   b. 2,000

   c. 300

6. a. $2.0 \times 10^{21}$

   b. $1.25 \times 10^{11}$

7. a. $6.0 \times 10^{-4}$

   b. $4.0 \times 10^{-3}$

   c. $3.0 \times 10^4$

8. Determine whether each statement is true or false.

   a. $4^{-2} = -4^2$

   b. $5^{-2} = -25$

   c. $17^0 = 0$

   d. $6^{-2} = \frac{1}{36}$

## Part 2. What went wrong?

9. Elliott was asked the following true/false question on a recent quiz:

   > True or false: The expressions $(-5)^2$ and $-5^2$ are equivalent.

   Elliott wrote that the statement was true but his answer was marked wrong. Why?

10. Sofia's teacher asked her to find the value of the following expression: $4^0 \cdot 4^4 \cdot 4^{-2}$. Sofia said, "The value of that expression is 0. $4^0 = 0$ and any number times 0 is 0." Jose disagrees. He wrote that the value of the expression is 16. Who do you agree with? Why?

8. a. false

   b. false

   c. false

   d. true

9. Answers will vary. Possible answer: The expressions are not equivalent. $(-5)^2 = -5 \cdot -5 = 25$. But $-5^2 = -(5 \cdot 5) = -25$, and $25 \neq -25$.

10. Answers will vary. Possible answer: I agree with Jose. $4^0 = 1$ not 0. So, the expression can be rewritten as $1 \cdot 4^4 \cdot 4^{-2}$ and its value of 16.

# SECTION 4

# Functions with Exponents and the Curves They Make

## LESSON 4.1 Equations with Exponents

**Suggested Pacing: 1 Day**

In this lesson, students explore solving equations by using square roots. Students work with area formulas in real-life situations.

---

**LESSON OBJECTIVES**

■ Students will determine the square root of a given number.

■ Students will solve equations in which the variable is squared by taking the square root of a number.

---

| DAY 1 | Materials* | | ESSENTIAL *ON YOUR OWN* QUESTIONS |
|---|---|---|---|
| Creating a Seal Pool | ■ Calculators | | Questions 1–3, 5–8, 10–14 |
| Evaluating Equations with Exponents | *On Your Own*<br>■ Calculators | | |

*\* The Think Like a Mathematician Daily Record Sheet should be used daily*

---

## MATHEMATICALLY SPEAKING

▶ radical sign    ▶ square root    ▶ symbol "$\sqrt{\phantom{x}}$"

# Functions with Exponents and the Curves They Make

In this section, you will explore and solve equations with exponents, and discover the interesting graphs that they make. This will open up a whole new way of solving problems and using graphs as you think like a mathematician. You will continue to explore these ideas in your study of algebra.

**LESSON 4.1** Equations with Exponents

 **Start It Off**

Make a table for $y = x^2$ for $0 \le x \le 5$, where $x$ is an integer. Graph the $y$-values from the table on a number line. What do you notice about the spacing between the numbers on your graph? Talk about it with your partner.

## Creating a Seal Pool

You are creating a new pool for a seal family that will live at the Magellan Aquarium. The total area for this rectangular pool will be 2,880 square feet. There will be a shallow end and a deep end, similar to the dolphin pool. Your pool designer has said that the ideal ratio for the area of the shallow section to the area of the deep section is 1:4 and that the shallow section should be square in shape. You need to find the dimensions for the pool.

Section 4: Functions with Exponents and the Curves They Make • Lesson 4.1 **119**

 **Start It Off**

| $x$ | 0 | 1 | 2 | 3 | 4 | 5 |
|---|---|---|---|---|---|---|
| $y$ | 0 | 1 | 4 | 9 | 16 | 25 |

0 1 2 3 4 5 6 7 8 9 10 11 12 13 14 15 16 17 18 19 20 21 22 23 24 25

Students should mention that the distance between the numbers keeps increasing. Specifically, the distance between consecutive points is the next odd number.

$(0 + \underline{1} = 1; 1 + \underline{3} = 4; 4 + \underline{5} = 9$, etc.)

In this lesson, students explore solving equations with exponents, which involves taking the square root of numbers. As they consider the design of a variety of new pools at the Magellan Aquarium, students will use area formulas to solve problems in a real-life context.

## Creating a Seal Pool

Read together about the design of the seal pool. Have students discuss the unknown quantities with a partner for Question 1 and share their responses in a class discussion. Have students complete Questions 2 and 3 independently and share their answers in a class discussion. Note that there is more than one way to write the formula for the area of the entire pool. Discuss these equivalent formulas and encourage students to combine like terms to arrive at a final formula of $A = 5x^2$.

Next, have students complete Questions 4 and 5 and compare their answers with a partner. Discuss any discrepancies as a class.

In order to solve for $x$ in Question 5, students will have to take the square root of 576. Discuss the Let's Review on finding the square root of a number. Have students discuss Question 6 with a partner and share their thoughts with the class. Talk about why the solution $-24$ does not make sense in the context of the problem. Help students recognize that a dimension of the side of the pool cannot be a negative number.

Use the formula for area to help figure out the dimensions. There are three unknown quantities in this situation that we can represent with variables.

1. Talk to your partner and figure out what these quantities are.

2. A lot of information is based on the length of the shallow section. We are going to use $x$ to represent the length of the shallow section. Other values can be written in terms of $x$. Fill in the blanks with expressions that show the other lengths in terms of $x$.

3. Write the formula for the area of the entire pool using the variables in the diagram.

4. Maya wrote the formula for the area this way:

$A = \text{length} \cdot \text{width}$
$A = 5x \cdot x$
$A = 6x$

Jonas wrote it this way:

$A = \text{length} \cdot \text{width}$
$A = 5x \cdot x$
$A = 5x^2$

Talk to your partner. Who is correct? What mistake did the other student make?

5. If we substitute 2,880 for area in the formula $A = 5x^2$, we get $2{,}880 = 5x^2$.

Fill in the cells in the table to justify the steps used to solve the equation.

| Equivalent Equations | Justification |
|---|---|
| $2{,}880 = 5x^2$ | |
| $\frac{1}{5}(2{,}880) = \frac{1}{5}(5x^2)$ | |
| $576 = (\frac{1}{5} \cdot 5) \cdot x^2$ | |
| $576 = 1 \cdot x^2$ | |
| $576 = x^2$ | |

120    Course 3: Solve It: Focusing on Equations, Inequalities and Exponents

---

NOTE The principal (nonnegative) square root of a number is indicated by a radical symbol: $\sqrt{\ }$.

1. The three unknown quantities are: the length of the shallow end, the width of the shallow end and the length of the deep end.

2.

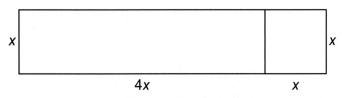

3. Answers will vary. Possible equations: $A = 4x(x) + x(x)$; $A = x(4x + x)$; $A = 4x^2 + x^2$. These equations simplify to the equation $A = 5x^2$.

4. Jonas is correct. Maya added like terms instead of multiplying them.

$5x + x = 6x$
$5x \cdot x = 5x^2$

5. $\frac{1}{5}(2{,}880) = \frac{1}{5}(5x^2)$ — multiplication property of equality

$576 = (\frac{1}{5} \cdot 5) \cdot x^2$ — associative property of multiplication

$576 = 1 \cdot x^2$ — inverse property of multiplication

$576 = x^2$ — identity property of multiplication

$\sqrt{576} = \sqrt{x^2}$ — Taking the square root of both sides of an equation does not change the equality.

$24 = |x|$ — evaluating the square root

**MATHEMATICALLY SPEAKING**

▶ square root
▶ radical sign
▶ symbol "$\sqrt{\ }$"

$576 = x^2$ means that $x \cdot x = 576$. We need to find a number that, when multiplied by itself, is equal to 576. This value is the **square root** of the number. For example, if $x^2 = 9$, then $x$ is the square root of 9. You can see that $x = 3$ or $-3$, since $3^2 = 9$ and $(-3)^2 = 9$.

The **radical sign**, $\sqrt{\ }$ , indicates the positive, or principal, square root of the number beneath it, so $\sqrt{49} = 7$.

Continuing the solution to the equation:

$$576 = x^2$$
$$\pm\sqrt{576} = \pm\sqrt{x^2} \qquad \text{Taking the square root of both sides of an equation does not change the equality.}$$
$$\pm 24 = x \qquad \text{Evaluate the square root.}$$

So, the width of the pool is 24 feet.

**6. a)** It is also true that $-24 \cdot -24 = 576$. Why do you think we used the positive square root for our solution?

   **b)** Find all the dimensions of the pool.

## Evaluating Equations with Exponents

If the design of the pool changes so that the width is 28 feet and the area of the deep end is still four times the area of the shallow end, what is the area of the entire pool?

• Start with $A = 5x^2$.

• Substitute 28 for $x$. $A = 5 \cdot 28^2$

• Solve for $A$.

But how? Do we multiply $5 \cdot 28$ first and then square the answer? Or do we square 28 and then multiply by 5?

In other words, where does squaring fit in the order of operations?

 **Let's Review**

Remember Please Excuse My Dear Aunt Sally. The **E** in **E**xcuse is for exponents. We evaluate exponents after we perform operations inside grouping symbols, but before we perform multiplication and division.

So, we square 28 first and then multiply by 5.

$A = 5 \cdot 784$ or $A = 3,920$ ft.$^2$

---

**6. a)** Students should indicate that $x$ represents the length of a side of the pool and, therefore, cannot be a negative number since a length always has a positive value.

   **b)** The width is 24 feet, the length of the shallow section is also 24 feet and the length of the deeper section is 96 feet. The total length of the pool is 120 feet.

## Evaluating Equations with Exponents

Discuss the Let's Review, making sure students recognize that they must evaluate exponents first, and then multiply.

Have students complete Question 7 independently and compare answers with a partner. Circulate as students work to informally assess understanding. Use the *Student Snapshot* observation tool to record notes. Discuss any unresolved discrepancies as a class to clarify understanding and address misconceptions.

Have students complete Questions 8–10 with a partner.

7. Substitute the value for the variable, and then use the correct order of operations to solve the equation.

   a) Solve for $A$ when $x = 9$: $A = 4x^2$.

   b) Solve for $y$ when $x = 4$: $y = \frac{1}{3}x^2$.

   c) Solve for $y$ when $x = 2$: $y = -7x^4$.

   d) Solve for $y$ when $x = 3$: $y = 2x^2 - 4$.

   e) Solve for $y$ when $x = -\frac{1}{2}$: $y = -4x^2$.

   f) Solve for $A$ when $r = 0.02$: $A = \pi r^2$.

    **Hint**
   See page 169

8. If the designer of the seal pool changes the area to 3,125 square feet and the ratio of the length of the square-shaped shallow end to the length of deep end to 1 : 4, what are the dimensions of each end?

    **Hint**
   See page 169

9. a) If the area of the pool is 3,125 square feet, but the designer changes the width to 20 feet and the length of the deep end to twice the length of the shallow end, find the dimensions of the pool.

   b) How is this equation different than the earlier equations for the area of the pool?

   c) Can the shallow end of this pool be square-shaped? Explain.

10. The pool designer suggests a different pool in which the deep end is square and the shallow end is rectangular. The length of the deep end will be twice the length of the shallow end. Draw a diagram and label the dimensions. Find the dimensions if the area of the entire pool is 2,904 square feet.

## Differentiation

**Think Differently:** For students experiencing difficulty, encourage them to draw a diagram of the pool and label the dimensions. Ask the following guiding questions:

- *What can you use to label the width of the shallow end of the pool if you don't know its measure?* Use a variable, perhaps *x*.

- *How can we use that label to determine the label for the length of the deep end?* (4*x*)

- *How do we find the area of a rectangle?* Multiply the entire length (4*x* + *x*) by the width (*x*).

 **Talk Moves**    Ask a few volunteers to share their solution strategies on the board or interactive white board. Encourage them to explain their reasoning. Discuss why the area formula is different in Question 9 and why the shallow end of the pool is not square. Use talk moves, such as agree/disagree and why, to clarify and deepen understanding. Learn more about the "talk moves" in the Teaching and Learning Strategies on p. ix.

In Question 10, students may overlook that it is the deep end that is square in shape, rather than the shallow end. This is a good opportunity to remind students that they must read each problem carefully and identify key information before rushing to solve it.

7. **a)** $A = 324$

   **b)** $y = \frac{16}{3}$ or $5\frac{1}{3}$

   **c)** $y = -112$

   **d)** $y = 14$

   **e)** $y = -1$

   **f)** $A = 0.001256$

**8.** $3,125 = 5x^2$; $x = 25$, where $x$ is the length of the shallow end.

The length and width of the shallow end each measure 25 feet, and the length of the deep end is 100 feet and the width is 25 feet.

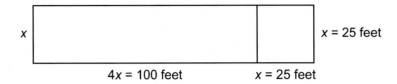

$x$                                            $x = 25$ feet

         $4x = 100$ feet          $x = 25$ feet

**9. a)** $3,125 = 20 \cdot 3x$; $x = 52.08\overline{3}$, where $x$ is the length of the shallow end.
The width of the pool is 20 feet and the overall length is 156.25 feet.
The length of the shallow end is $52.08\overline{3}$ feet.

20 ft.                                         20 ft.

      $2x = 104.16$ ft.         $x = 52.08\overline{3}$ ft.

**b)** In Question 9a, the width of the shallow end is given, so you do not need to take the square root to determine the value of $x$. It cannot be assumed that the shallow end is a square, so $x$ represents the length of the shallow end and $2x$ represents the length of the deep end. The equation for the area of this pool is $A = 20 \cdot 3x$.

In Question 8, the shallow end was a square. If $x$ represented the length of the shallow end, it also represented the width since the sides of a square are congruent. To find the area of the entire pool, $x$ was multiplied by the overall length ($5x$), so the formula is $A = 5x^2$.

**c)** No. The length and width of the shallow end are different. If the shallow end was square, it would be 20 ft. × 20 ft. and then the deep end could not be twice as long and still have an area of 3,125 square feet.

**10.** $2{,}904 = 6x^2$; $x = 22$, where $x$ is the length of the shallow end.

The overall length of the pool is 66 feet and the width is 44 feet. The length of the deep end is 44 feet and the length of the shallow end is 22 feet.

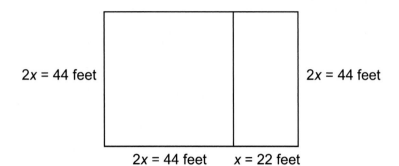

2x = 44 feet

2x = 44 feet

2x = 44 feet     x = 22 feet

## rap It Up

**MATHEMATICALLY SPEAKING**
▸ radical sign
▸ square root
▸ symbol "√"

Seokhee showed Tomas how she solved $3x^2 = 27$.
Here are her steps:

$$3x^2 = 27$$

$$\frac{1}{3}(3x^2) = \frac{1}{3}(27) \quad \text{Multiply by the reciprocal of 3, which is } \frac{1}{3}.$$

$$x^2 = 9$$

$$\frac{x^2}{2} = \frac{9}{4.5} \quad \text{Next, divide by 2.}$$

$$x = 4.5$$

Tomas is confused. When he checks this answer, it doesn't work.

$$3(4.5^2) = 3(20.25) = 60.75, \text{ not } 27!$$

Discuss with your partner what went wrong.

## rap It Up

Responses should include the following key ideas:

- Seeokhee correctly multiplied both expressions on either side of the equation by $\frac{1}{3}$ to isolate the variable.

- Instead of dividing by 2, Seeokhee should have taken the square root of 9.

- When taking the square root of a number, you are trying to find a number that, when multiplied by itself, will result in a product equal to the given number.

- The square roots of 9 are 3 and $-3$, and so $x = 3$ or $-3$.

- $3(-3)^2 = 27$ and $3(3)^2 = 27$

### Reflect

Use these questions to help you reflect on the lesson and plan for future instruction.

- What evidence did you observe that indicates that students conceptually understand taking the square root of a number?

- How successful are students at using the rules for the order of operations to solve equations with exponents?

## On Your Own

 **Write About It**

1. **a)** In solving $V = 4x^3$ for $V$ (volume) when $x = 7$, why do we start by finding $7^3$ rather than $4 \cdot 7$?

   **b)** Find $V$ when $x = 7$.

2. Solve.

   **a)** Solve for $y$ when $x = 3$: $y = \frac{1}{2}x^2 + 6$.

   **b)** Solve for $s$ when $t = \frac{1}{2}$: $s = -\frac{1}{8}t^2$.

   **c)** Solve for $A$ when $r = 0.36$: $A = \pi r^2$.

    **Hint** See page 169

   **d)** Solve for $A$ when $x = -1$: $A = -2x^2 + 5$.

3. Evaluate.

   **a)** $\sqrt{81}$

   **b)** $\sqrt{196}$

   **c)** $4\sqrt{900}$

   **d)** $6\sqrt{225} - \sqrt{676}$

   **e)** $\sqrt{100} - \frac{1}{2}\sqrt{64}$

**Think Beyond**

4. Simplify.

   **a)** $\sqrt{625x^4}$     **c)** $\sqrt{324c^2d^{10}}$

   **b)** $\sqrt{36z^8}$     **d)** $\sqrt[4]{16}$

5. If the ratio of the square shallow end's area to the deep end's area in the rectangular seal pool is changed to $1:3$, find the dimensions of the pool if its total area is 2,500 square feet.

6. The solar system exhibit is circular and has a radius of 20.5 feet.

   **a)** Write an equation that represents the total amount of floor space the exhibit occupies, or the area of the exhibit.

   **b)** What is the area of the exhibit?

---

## On Your Own

 **Write About It**

1. **a)** Answers will vary. Responses should include that according to the rules for the order of operations, numbers with exponents are evaluated first, and then the resulting number can be multiplied.

   **b)** $V = 1,372$

2. **a)** $y = 10.5$

   **b)** $s = -\frac{1}{32}$

   **c)** $A = 0.406944$

   **d)** $A = 3$

3. **a)** 9

   **b)** 14

   **c)** 120

   **d)** 64

   **e)** 6

**Think Beyond**

4. **a)** $25x^2$

   **b)** $6z^4$

   **c)** $324c^2d^{10}$

   **d)** 2

5. $2,500 = 4x^2$; $x = 25$

   The width of the pool is 25 feet and the overall length is 100 feet. The length of the shallow end is 25 feet and the length of the deep end is 75 feet.

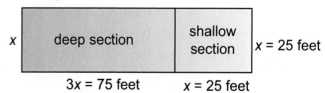

6. **a)** $A = \pi \cdot 20.5^2$

   **b)** Area $\approx 1,319.585$ square feet (using 3.14 for $\pi$)

**7.** The railing around the exhibit is 8 feet away from its edge.

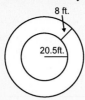

8 ft.

20.5ft.

An equation that represents the area between the exhibit and the railing is $A = \pi(28.5)^2 - \pi(20.5)^2$.

**a)** Explain what 28.5 represents.

**b)** Why is subtraction used in this formula?

**c)** Find this area.

**8. a)** Write an equation for the total area the entire exhibit inside the railing in Question 7 will occupy.

**b)** What is the area of the entire exhibit?

**Think Beyond**

9. There are also two rectangular polar bear pools at the Magellan Aquarium that are separated by a rectangular 6-foot-wide platform for the bears to sit and soak up the sun. The pools on either side are congruent and square-shaped.

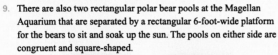
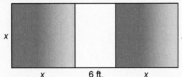

x          x

x          6 ft.          x

Find the dimensions of each pool if the area of the entire polar bear exhibit is 260 sq. ft.

---

**7. a)** 28.5 represents the length of the radius from the center of the exhibit to the railing.

**b)** To determine the area of the floor space between the exhibit and the railing, you must subtract the area of the exhibit from the total area of the floor space of the exhibit and railing.

**c)** The area of the floor space between the exhibit and the railing is 2,550.465 − 1,319.585 = 1,230.88 square feet.

**8. a)** $A = \pi(28.5)^2$

**b)** 2,550.465 square feet

**Think Beyond**

9.

$A = 2x^2 + 6x$; so $260 = 2x^2 + 6x$. $x = 10$ feet

The dimensions of the square pool on either end are 10 feet by 10 feet.

The dimensions of the rectangular platform are 6 feet by 10 feet.

**Think Back**

10. Trey saved $1,400 on the carpet for his house. His final cost was 40% lower than the original price. How much was the carpet originally?

11. Of the following numbers, which best approximates 2,093 − 107.3?

   **A.** 20

   **B.** 200

   **C.** 2,000

   **D.** 20,000

12. The temperature is 5°F, but the 15-mph wind makes it feel 18° colder. How cold does it feel? This is called the windchill.

13. What two numbers are 8 units away from −4 on a number line? Write this as an equation with an absolute value sign in it.

14. Find a number $x$, so that

   **a)** $1,000,999 < x < 1,100,000$

   **b)** $x$ is not less than one million, five hundred thousand and not greater than one million, five hundred one thousand

   **c)** $x$ is between 1,111,111 and 1,111,112 (Be careful!)

**Think Back**

10. $1,400 = 0.4x$, so the original price was $3,500.

11. **C.** 2,000

12. −13°F

13. $|x - (-4)| = 8$ The two numbers are −12 and 4.

14. **a)** Answers will vary. Accept any number between 1,000,999 and 1,100,000.

   **b)** Answers will vary. Accept any number from 1,500,000 to 1,501,000.

   **c)** Answers will vary. Accept any number that has 1,111,111 and a decimal part or common fraction.

# LESSON 4.2 What a Difference an Exponent Makes!

**Suggested Pacing:** 2 Days

In this lesson, students are introduced to quadratic functions. They will compare these new functions to linear functions.

---

**LESSON OBJECTIVES**

- Students will compare linear and quadratic functions.
- Students will create a table of values for a variety of quadratic functions and graph the functions.
- Students will compare a variety of quadratic functions and be able to make predictions about their graphs.

---

| DAY 1 | Materials* | ESSENTIAL *ON YOUR OWN* QUESTIONS |
|---|---|---|
| Quadratic Functions | **In Class**<br>■ Graphing calculators<br>■ Graph paper | Questions 12–16 |

| DAY 2 | Materials* | ESSENTIAL *ON YOUR OWN* QUESTIONS |
|---|---|---|
| **Comparing** Quadratic Functions | **In Class**<br>■ Graphing calculators<br>■ Graph paper<br>■ Lesson Guide 4.2A: *Tables for Quadratic Functions*<br><br>**On Your Own**<br>■ Graphing calculators<br>■ Graph paper | Questions 1–8 |

\* The Think Like a Mathematician Daily Record Sheet should be used daily

---

## MATHEMATICALLY SPEAKING

| ▶ function | ▶ parabola | ▶ quadratic function |
|---|---|---|
| ▶ line of symmetry | ▶ quadratic equation | ▶ vertex |

## ➡ Start It Off

1. E

2. C

3. A

4. F

5. D

6. B

This exercise is designed to help students review linear functions written in the slope-intercept form ($y = mx + b$). Read the review section as a class and then discuss student responses. When discussing student responses, emphasize the strategies they used to help them match the graphs with the appropriate linear equations. Focus on the coefficient of $x$ ($m$) and have students explain what this represents (the slope). Ask students to explain what the constant, $b$, represents (the $y$-intercept) and how they can use this information to help them match the equations to the graphs. Students will build on their knowledge of linear functions as they begin to explore nonlinear functions in the coming lessons.

## LESSON 4.2

# What a Difference an Exponent Makes!

 **Start It Off**

Match each equation to the correct graph. (Pay attention to the scale!)

1. $y = x + 1$
2. $y = 2x$
3. $y = 2x - 1$

4. $y = x$
5. $y = \frac{x}{3} + 2$
6. $y = -x + 7$

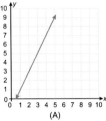

(A)

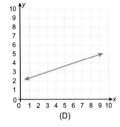

(D)

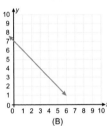

(B)

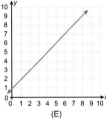

(E)

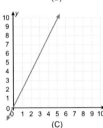

(C)

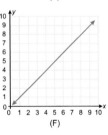

(F)

Section 4: Functions with Exponents and the Curves They Make • Lesson 4.2    **127**

## DAY 1 TEACHING THE LESSON

In this lesson, students are introduced to quadratic functions as they compare them to linear functions. They discover that there is more to graphing than straight lines in algebra! Students create a table of values for a variety of quadratic equations as they look for patterns and make predictions to determine how the graphs of quadratic equations behave.

## Quadratic Functions

Introduce the terms *quadratic equation* and *quadratic function*. A quadratic equation has one variable and the greatest exponent of that variable is 2. Examples are $32 = 2x^2$ and $10 = x^2 + 3x$ and any equation that can be written in the form $0 = ax^2 + bx + c$. Emphasize that a function represents a relationship between two variables. A function in which one of the variables is raised to the second power, the highest power of the function, is known as a quadratic function. Examples include $A = 2x^2$ or $P = x^2 + 3x$ or any function of the form $y = ax^2 + bx + c$.

Have students complete Question 1 with a partner. Encourage them to graph the quadratic function on grid paper. Discuss student responses as a class. Introduce the term *parabola*. Also, discuss the vertex and line of symmetry as they relate to the graph of a quadratic function.

Next, have students complete Questions 2–3 and compare their responses with a partner. Have students use grid paper to graph the functions in Question 2, and a graphing calculator for Questions 3 and 4. When discussing responses, guide students to recognize that the coefficient of $x^2$ determines the width of the curve of the parabola. The greater the absolute value of the coefficient, the narrower the curve will be.

1.  a) $y = x^2$

| x | y |
|------|------|
| −3 | 9 |
| −2.5 | 6.25 |
| −2 | 4 |
| −1.5 | 2.25 |
| −1 | 1 |
| −0.5 | 0.25 |
| 0 | 0 |
| 0.5 | 0.25 |
| 1 | 1 |
| 1.5 | 2.25 |
| 2 | 4 |
| 2.5 | 6.25 |
| 3 | 9 |

b) Answers will vary. Students should predict that the graph will not be a straight line, since the *y*-values repeat for different *x*-values.

---

MATHEMATICALLY SPEAKING
▶ function

Let's Review

The equations and graphs in the Start it Off represent linear functions where *x* and *y* can be any number. Remember, a function is a relationship in which there is exactly one *y*-value for each *x*-value. In the graphs above, you will notice that this is the case.

## Quadratic Functions

MATHEMATICALLY SPEAKING
▶ quadratic equation
▶ quadratic function

An equation with one variable in which the greatest exponent of the variable is 2, such as $2,880 = 5x^2$, is called a **quadratic equation**. If we relate two variables, and one of the variables has an exponent of 2 and this is the highest power in the function (for example, $A = 5x^2$), this is called a **quadratic function**.

The simplest quadratic function is $y = x^2$. Let's see what the graph of this function looks like.

1.  $y = x^2$

    a)  Fill in this table of values.

| x | y |
|------|------|
| −3 | |
| −2.5 | |
| −2 | |
| −1.5 | |
| −1 | |
| −0.5 | |
| 0 | |
| 0.5 | |
| 1 | |
| 1.5 | |
| 2 | |
| 2.5 | |
| 3 | |

    b)  Predict what the graph will look like. Will it be a straight line?

    c)  Graph the function, connect the points with a smooth curve and describe its shape.

c)

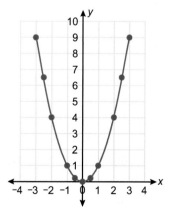

The graph is a curve. It looks like the letter U.

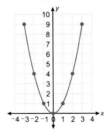
You should have discovered that the graph is a curve, not a line! So, this is not a linear function. But, for every $x$-value there is exactly one $y$-value. So it is a function. It is also symmetrical. If you fold the graph along the $y$-axis, the two sides of the curve match up perfectly. For this function, the $y$-axis is the line of symmetry. Remember that the equation for the $y$-axis is $x = 0$. (The value for $x$ is always zero, no matter what the value of $y$ is.)

This curve has a special name. It is called a parabola. The turning point of the graph—the point where it changes direction—is called the vertex.

**2. a)** What point is the vertex of the graph above?

   **b)** What will the graph look like if we add values for $x$ that are greater than 3?

   **c)** What if we add values for $x$ that are less than $-3$?

**3.** The equation for the area of the seal pool in Lesson 4.1 was $A = 5x^2$. To graph this equation, let $y$ represent the area and rewrite it as $y = 5x^2$.

   **a)** What does $x$ represent in this situation?

   **b)** List three points on the graph.

   **c)** Find $y$ if $x = 5$.

   **d)** Find $x$ if $y = 500$.

   **e)** Graph the function on your graphing calculator. What are the coordinates of the vertex?

   **f)** What is the equation of the line of symmetry?

   **g)** When the area of the pool is 2,880, the width of the pool is 24. Find the point (24, 2,880) on your graph. You will need to readjust your scales on the $x$- and $y$-axes to do so.

**4.** Graph the equation $y = x^2$ on the same axes as $y = 5x^2$. How are the two graphs alike? How are they different?

**3. a)** $x$ represents the width of the pool.

   **b)** Answers will vary. Possible points: (1, 5), ($-1$, 5), (2, 20), ($-2$, 20)

   **c)** $y = 125$

   **d)** $x = 10$

   **e)** (0, 0)

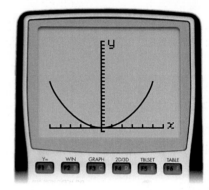

   **f)** $x = 0$

   **g)** Note that the integer trace function on the graphing calculator will give students the exact value for $y$ when $x$ is equal to 24. However, using the normal trace key will only give students approximate points.

**2. a)** (0, 0)

   **b)** The curve on the right will extend upward more steeply. For example, the graph will intersect the points (5, 25) and (6, 36).

   **c)** The curve on the left will extend upwards more steeply. For example, the graph will intersect the points ($-5$, 25) and ($-6$, 36).

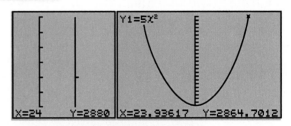

**4.** They are both parabolas and have a vertex at $(0, 0)$. Their axis of symmetry is the $y$-axis. However, $y = 5x^2$ has a more narrow curve than $y = x^2$.

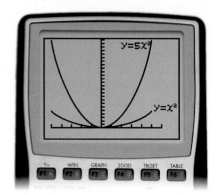

## Summarize Day 1

Have students discuss the following question with a partner and share their responses in a class discussion.

- *Explain to a friend who was absent what a quadratic equation is and describe to them what the graph of a quadratic function looks like.*

The discussion should include the following key ideas:

- A quadratic equation is an equation of one variable in which the largest exponent of the variable is 2, for example, $27 = 3x^2$.

- The graph of a quadratic function is called a parabola. Students might also suggest that the graph is U-shaped.

## Comparing Quadratic Functions

Have students complete Question 5 independently and then compare answers with a partner. Encourage students to use grid paper to graph each set of equations on the same axes by hand.

 **Differentiation**

**Think Differently:** For students who may need support organizing tables of values for the various equations, offer Lesson Guide 4.2A: *Tables for Quadratic Functions*. The tables have values for $x$ included to guide students.

 **Talk Moves**  Discuss as a class how the shapes of the three equations compare. Focus on how the coefficient of $x^2$ and the constant being added to the $x^2$ term ($y$-intercept) affect the graph of the functions. Students should notice the pattern that a positive coefficient of $x^2$ means that the parabola will open upward and a negative coefficient of $x^2$ means that the parabola will open downward. The greater the absolute value of the coefficient of $x^2$, the narrower the curve of the parabola. The constant is the $y$-intercept and determines the vertex of the parabola. Use talk moves, such as adding on and agree/disagree and why, to clarify ideas and deepen student understanding.

Next, have students complete Question 6, using a graphing calculator to check their predictions.

 **Differentiation**

**Think Differently:** For students who may need additional practice graphing quadratic functions, encourage them to graph the equations in Question 6 on grid paper first, and then use the graphing calculator to verify their graphs.

**5. a)**

| $y = x^2$ | |
|---|---|
| x | y |
| −3 | 9 |
| −2 | 4 |
| −1 | 1 |
| 0 | 0 |
| 1 | 1 |
| 2 | 4 |
| 3 | 9 |

| $y = 2x^2$ | |
|---|---|
| x | y |
| −3 | 18 |
| −2 | 8 |
| −1 | 2 |
| 0 | 0 |
| 1 | 2 |
| 2 | 8 |
| 3 | 18 |

| $y = \frac{1}{2}x^2$ | |
|---|---|
| x | y |
| −3 | 4.5 |
| −2 | 2 |
| −1 | 0.5 |
| 0 | 0 |
| 1 | 0.5 |
| 2 | 2 |
| 3 | 4.5 |

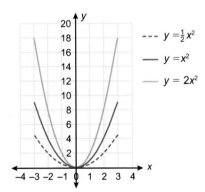

The vertex for each graph is (0, 0). The line of symmetry for each graph is the y-axis, x = 0.

All the graphs open upward. However, the graph of $y = 2x^2$ is the most narrow, followed by $y = x^2$, and the graph of $y = \frac{1}{2}x^2$ is the widest.

**b)**

| $y = x^2$ | |
|---|---|
| x | y |
| −3 | 9 |
| −2 | 4 |
| −1 | 1 |
| 0 | 0 |
| 1 | 1 |
| 2 | 4 |
| 3 | 9 |

| $y = -x^2$ | |
|---|---|
| x | y |
| −3 | −9 |
| −2 | −4 |
| −1 | −1 |
| 0 | 0 |
| 1 | −1 |
| 2 | −4 |
| 3 | −9 |

| $y = -3x^2$ | |
|---|---|
| x | y |
| −3 | −27 |
| −2 | −12 |
| −1 | −3 |
| 0 | 0 |
| 1 | −3 |
| 2 | −12 |
| 3 | −27 |

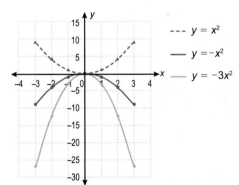

The vertex for each equation is (0, 0) and the line of symmetry is the y-axis, x = 0.

The equation $y = x^2$ is the only graph that opens upward. The equations $y = -x^2$ and $y = -3x^2$ open downward. The equations $y = x^2$ and $y = -x^2$ have graphs that are mirror images, or reflections of each other, about the x-axis. They have the same shape, but they open in opposite directions. The equation $y = -3x^2$ is the most narrow of the three graphs.

**c)**

| $y = x^2$ | |
|---|---|
| **x** | **y** |
| −3 | 9 |
| −2 | 4 |
| −1 | 1 |
| 0 | 0 |
| 1 | 1 |
| 2 | 4 |
| 3 | 9 |

| $y = x^2 + 2$ | |
|---|---|
| **x** | **y** |
| −3 | 11 |
| −2 | 6 |
| −1 | 3 |
| 0 | 2 |
| 1 | 3 |
| 2 | 6 |
| 3 | 11 |

| $y = x^2 - 1$ | |
|---|---|
| **x** | **y** |
| −3 | 8 |
| −2 | 3 |
| −1 | 0 |
| 0 | −1 |
| 1 | 0 |
| 2 | 3 |
| 3 | 8 |

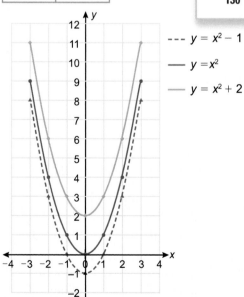

$- - -$ $y = x^2 - 1$

$—$ $y = x^2$

$—$ $y = x^2 + 2$

All the equations have the same line of symmetry: the $y$-axis, $x = 0$.

## Comparing Quadratic Functions

5. For each set of quadratic functions:

 • Make a table of values with values of $x$ from −3 to +3 as in Question 1a.

 • Without using a graphing calculator, graph each equation on the same set of axes.

 • Find the vertex and line of symmetry for each equation.

 • Compare the shapes of all three equations. How are they alike? How are they different?

 **a)** $y = x^2, y = 2x^2, y = \frac{1}{2} \cdot x^2$

 **b)** $y = x^2, y = -x^2, y = -3x^2$

 **c)** $y = x^2, y = x^2 + 2, y = x^2 - 1$

6. Now, make some predictions about each of the following:

 • What will its graph look like?

 • What will the vertex be?

 • What will the line of symmetry be?

 • Check your predictions by graphing the functions on a graphing calculator.

 **a)** $y = 4x^2$          **d)** $y = x^2 - 6$

 **b)** $y = 2x^2$          **e)** $y = x^2 - 2$

 **c)** $y = x^2 + 3$

### ⬆ Wrap It Up

Discuss with your partner how the coefficient of $x$ in a quadratic equation affects the shape of the graph. Explain how a constant value added to or subtracted from a quadratic equation affects the placement and shape of the graph.

**MATHEMATICALLY SPEAKING**

▸ function
▸ line of symmetry
▸ parabola
▸ quadratic equation
▸ quadratic function
▸ vertex

The vertex for each equation is different. The equation $y = x^2$ has a vertex at (0, 0). The equation $y = x^2 + 2$ has a vertex at (0, 2). The equation $y = x^2 - 1$ has a vertex at (0, −1).

All the equations are parabolas that open upward. The graphs have the same width but are shifted along the $y$-axis so their vertices are at different locations. The graph $y = x^2 + 2$ is located above the other graphs, $y = x^2$ is in the middle and $y = x^2 - 1$ is located below the other graphs.

**6. a)** $y = 4x^2$; This graph will open upward and have a fairly narrow curve. It will have a vertex at (0, 0) and the line of symmetry is the $y$-axis, $x = 0$.

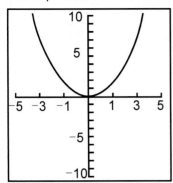

**b)** $y = 2x^2$; This graph will open upward. It will have a vertex at (0, 0) and the line of symmetry is the $y$-axis, $x = 0$. The graph will have a curve that is wider than $y = 4x^2$.

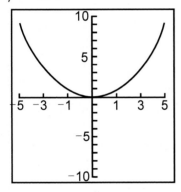

**c)** $y = x^2 + 3$; This graph will open upward. It will have a vertex at (0, 3) and the line of symmetry is the $y$-axis, $x = 0$. This graph will be wider than the first two graphs above.

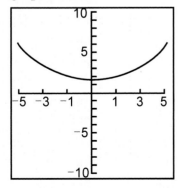

**d)** $y = x^2 - 6$; This graph will open upward. It will have a vertex at (0, −6) and a line of symmetry about the $y$-axis, $x = 0$. This graph will have the same width as the graph in Part c.

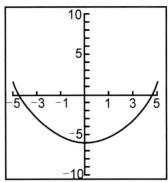

**e)** $y = x^2 - 2$; This graph will open upward. It will have a vertex at (0, −2) and the line of symmetry is the $y$-axis, or $x = 0$. The graph will have the same width as the graph in Part d.

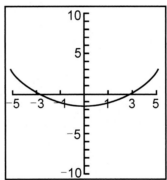

## Wrap It Up

Responses will vary. The discussion should include the following key ideas:

- The coefficient of $x$ in a quadratic equation determines the width of the parabola. The greater the absolute value of the coefficient, the narrower the parabola.

- When the coefficient is a positive value, the graph of the parabola will open upward. When the coefficient is a negative value, the graph of the parabola will open downward.

- The constant value determines the location along the $y$-axis where the vertex will be located.

### Reflect

Use these questions to help you reflect on the lesson and plan for future instruction.

- What key characteristics do students use to compare linear and quadratic functions?

- How successful are students at predicting features of the graphs of quadratic functions?

- What lingering misconceptions need to be addressed in future instruction?

1. **Write About It** Answers will vary. Responses should include the following key ideas:

- An equation of a linear function represents a relationship between two variables, each raised to the first power. Example: $y = 2x + 1$

- An equation of a quadratic function also represents a relationship between two variables; however, one variable in the equation is raised to the second power. Example: $y = 2x^2 + 1$

- The graph of a linear function is a straight line. The steepness of the line is determined by the value of $m$ or the coefficient of $x$ when the equation is written in the slope-intercept form, $y = mx + b$. A greater absolute value of $m$ indicates a steeper line. A positive value for $m$ will result in a graph that is a line that rises from left to right. A negative value for $m$ will result in a graph that is a line that falls from left to right. $b$ represents the second coordinate of the $y$-intercept; $(0, b)$ is the point at which the line will cross the $y$-axis.

- The graph of a quadratic function is a parabola. The parabolas studied in this lesson can be written in the form $y = ax^2 + b$. The curve of the parabola is symmetrical. The line of symmetry for each parabola in this lesson is the $y$-axis. The shape of the curve is determined by the coefficient of $x^2$; the greater the absolute value of the coefficient, the narrower the curve. A positive value of the coefficient of $x^2$ will result in a curve that will open upward; a negative value will result in a curve that opens downward. The constant added to the $x^2$ term ($b$) or $y$-intercept represents the vertex of the parabola. It is the turning point of the curve.

Write
About It

1. Explain the difference between the equations and graphs of a quadratic function and a linear function.

2. Represent the function $y = -4x^2 + 1$ using a table of values and a graph.

3. Without actually graphing, tell how the graphs of $y = x^2$ and $y = -\frac{1}{2} \cdot x^2 \quad \frac{-1}{2x^2}$ compare.

4. Without graphing, tell how the graphs of $y = 3x^2$, $y = 3x^2 - 2$ and $y = 3x^2 + 2$ compare. State the vertex of each graph.

5. Without graphing, describe the general shape of each of the following graphs. List the vertex and equation for the axis of symmetry.

   a) $y = \frac{1}{2} \cdot x^2$

   b) $y = -6x^2$

   c) $y = x^2 - 5$

   d) $y = x^2 + \frac{1}{2}$

2. Possible table:

| $y = -4x^2 + 1$ | |
|---|---|
| **x** | **y** |
| 3 | −35 |
| 2 | −15 |
| 1 | −3 |
| 0 | 1 |
| −1 | −3 |
| −2 | −15 |
| −3 | −35 |

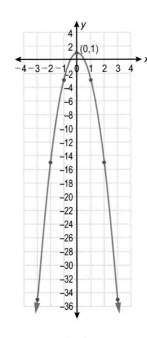

3. Possible response: The graphs will be parabolas that have a line of symmetry at the $y$-axis ($x = 0$). Both graphs have a vertex at the point (0, 0). The graph of $y = x^2$ will open upward and the curve will be narrower than the graph of $y = -\frac{1}{2}x^2$. The graph of $y = -\frac{1}{2}x^2$ will open downward.

4. Possible response: The graphs of all three quadratic functions will be parabolas that have a line of symmetry at the $y$-axis, $x = 0$. The curves will have the same width and will all open upward. All three functions will have different vertices. The graph of $y = 3x^2 + 2$ has a vertex at point (0, 2) and will be located above the other two graphs. The graph of $y = 3x^2$ has a vertex at point (0, 0) and will be located in the middle of the other two graphs. The graph of $y = 3x^2 - 2$ has a vertex at (0, −2) and will be located below the other two graphs along the $y$-axis.

5. a) The graph will be a parabola that opens upward. The vertex will be at point (0, 0) and the axis of symmetry is the $y$-axis, $x = 0$.

   b) The graph will be a parabola that opens downward. The vertex will be at point (0, 0) and the axis of symmetry is the $y$-axis, $x = 0$.

   c) The graph will be a parabola that opens upward. The vertex will be at point (0, −5) and the axis of symmetry is the $y$-axis, $x = 0$.

   d) The graph will be a parabola that opens upward. The vertex will be at point (0, $\frac{1}{2}$) and the axis of symmetry is the $y$-axis, $x = 0$.

6. Match each equation to its graph.

a) $y = -x$       d) $y = x + 4$

b) $y = -x^2 + 4$      e) $y = x^2$

c) $y = x^2 - 4$      f) $y = 4$

1.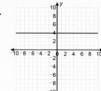

4.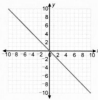

2.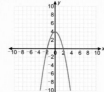

5.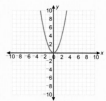

3.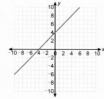

6.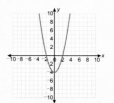

7. One of the new attractions at the Discovery Center is Virtual Skateboarding, where visitors learn about the effects of gravity and physics on skateboarding. The half-pipe (a skateboard track) on the computer screen is in the shape of a parabola.

6. a) 4

b) 2

c) 6

d) 3

e) 5

f) 1

7. a) 5.3 feet

b) 24 feet

c) Make the coefficient of $x^2$ less in value. Possible equation: $y = \frac{1}{20}x^2$

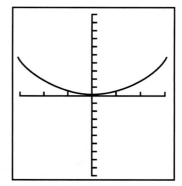

The equation to create this half-pipe is $y = \frac{1}{12} \cdot x^2$, where $y$ is the height and $x$ is one-half the horizontal distance across the half-pipe.

a) When the width of the half-pipe is 16 feet, how high is the half-pipe to the nearest tenth of a foot?

b) When the height of the half-pipe is 12 feet off the ground, how wide is the half-pipe?

c) Discuss with your partner what changes should be made to the equation to make the half-pipe wider. Together, make up one equation that would work. Show that you are correct using your graphing calculator.

8. Design engineers at the Discovery Center are building a new attraction. It is a wave pool scale model that will show the effects of an underground earthquake in the ocean. They used the equation $y = \frac{-1}{200}x^2 + 50$ for the size of a wave created by the simulated earthquake, where $y$ represents the height of the wave and $x$ represents half the width of the wave. This equation is graphed below.

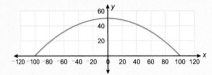

For the scale model, they used a ratio of 1 ft. : 100 ft.

a) What is the equation of the line of symmetry for this function?

b) Give the coordinates of the vertex.

c) For this function, the vertex is also the $y$-intercept. Explain why this is true.

d) Explain what the coordinates of the vertex indicate about of the size of the wave.

e) If the maximum height of the parabola is 50 feet, how tall and wide should your scale model of this wave be?

 **Think Beyond**

9. a) Predict what the graph of $x = y^2$ will look like. How will this be different from $y = x^2$?

b) Graph both equations on the same axes and compare. Write the vertex and line of symmetry for each function.

b) The graphs have curves with the same width.

Both graphs have a vertex at (0, 0). The graph of $y = x^2$ is a parabola and the line of symmetry is the $y$-axis and opens upward. The line of symmetry of $x = y^2$ is the $x$-axis and opens to the right. (Note that $x = y^2$ is not a function since there is more than $y$ value for many of the $x$ values.)

| $y = x^2$ | |
|---|---|
| x | y |
| 3 | 9 |
| 2 | 4 |
| 1 | 1 |
| 0 | 0 |
| −1 | 1 |
| −2 | 4 |
| −3 | 9 |

| $x = y^2$ | |
|---|---|
| x | y |
| 9 | 3 |
| 4 | 2 |
| 1 | 1 |
| 0 | 0 |
| 1 | −1 |
| 4 | −2 |
| 9 | −3 |

**8.** **a)** The line of symmetry is the $y$-axis, $x = 0$.

**b)** The vertex is (0, 50).

**c)** The vertex is the point of turn for the curve of the parabola. It is also the point at which the curve will cross the $y$-axis.

**d)** The vertex represents the maximum height of the wave.

**e)** The maximum height of the wave is 0.5 foot and the overall width is 2 feet.

 **Think Beyond**

9.

**a)** Predictions will vary. The graph is the parabola $y = x^2$ on its side, facing right, with the $x$-axis as the line of symmetry.

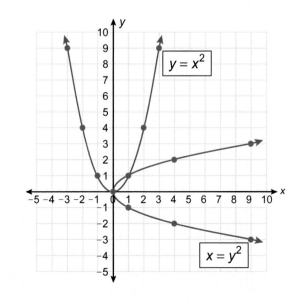

**Think Beyond**

10. **a)** Make a table of values for $y = (x - 1)^2$ and graph the function.

   **b)** How does this function compare to $y = x^2$?

   **c)** Predict what the graph of $y = (x + 1)^2$ will look like.

   **d)** Graph and compare to your prediction.

 **Think Beyond**

11. **a)** Make a table of values for the function $y = x^3$. Include positive, negative and zero values for $x$.

   **b)** This is called a cubic function. Why do you think mathematicians use this term?

   **c)** Predict what the graph of this function will look like.

   **d)** Graph and compare to your prediction.

**Think Back**

12. If $y = 7 - 4x$, find $y$ if $x = -12$. Show your work.

13. Use the same equation, $y = 7 - 4x$, but now solve for $x$ if $y = -12$. Show your work.

14. $-3[(-4)(-2) + 7] =$

   **A.** 45     **B.** 3     **C.** -3     **D.** -45

15. Simplify $7 - (7 - (7 - (-8) - 8) - 8)$. Be careful with the signs!

16. Carrie is taking care of her neighbors' Irish setter, Mimi. She charges $7 per walk and $15 to watch Mimi overnight. Write an expression for her fee, using $x$ for the number of walks and $y$ for the number of nights she watched Mimi. When her neighbors went away for a weekend, Carrie walked Mimi four times on Saturday, four times on Sunday and once on Friday and Monday. She stayed over on Friday, Saturday and Sunday nights. What is Carrie's fee for this?

---

10.  **Think Beyond**

**a)**

| $y = (x - 1)^2$ | |
|:---:|:---:|
| $x$ | $y$ |
| 5 | 16 |
| 4 | 9 |
| 3 | 4 |
| 2 | 1 |
| 1 | 0 |
| 0 | 1 |
| -1 | 4 |
| -2 | 9 |
| -3 | 16 |

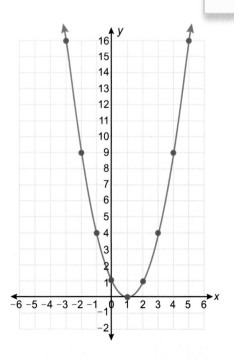

**b)** The function $y = (x - 1)^2$ and the function $y = x^2$ are parabolas that have the same width and open upward. However, they have different vertices and lines of symmetry. The graph of $y = x^2$ has a vertex at (0, 0) and the $y$-axis ($x = 0$) as a line of symmetry. The graph of $y = (x - 1)^2$ has a vertex that is one unit to the right at (0, 1) and $x = 1$ is the line of symmetry.

**c)** Predictions will vary. The graph of $y = (x + 1)^2$ will be a parabola that has the same width as the graphs of $y = (x - 1)^2$ and $y = x^2$ and will also open upward. However, the vertex of the graph of $y = (x + 1)^2$ will be at $(0, -1)$ and will have at line of symmetry at $x = -1$.

**d)**

| $y = (x + 1)^2$ | |
|:---:|:---:|
| **x** | **y** |
| 3 | 16 |
| 2 | 9 |
| 1 | 4 |
| 0 | 1 |
| −1 | 0 |
| −2 | 1 |
| −3 | 4 |
| −4 | 9 |
| −5 | 16 |

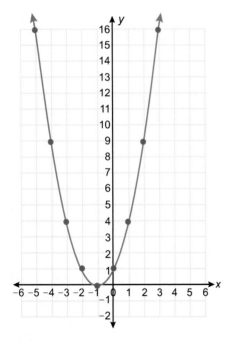

Responses comparing to predictions will vary.

**a)**

| $y = x^3$ | |
|:---:|:---:|
| **x** | **y** |
| 3 | 27 |
| 2 | 8 |
| 1 | 1 |
| 0 | 0 |
| −1 | −1 |
| −2 | −8 |
| −3 | −27 |

**b)** Answers will vary. Possible response: This is called a cubic function because the greatest value of any exponent for a variable in the function is 3. An exponent of 3 is often read "cubed" as in $x^3$ ("x cubed") because the volume of a cube with each edge of length $x$ is $x^3$.

**c)** Predictions will vary. Students should indicate that the graph is curved.

**d)** Answers comparing graph to predictions will vary.

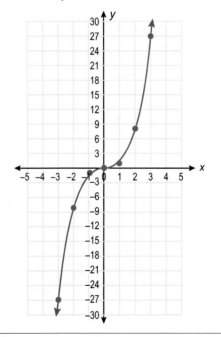

 **NOTE** For students who are interested in pursuing other functions, have them try $y = x^4$ and $y = x^6$ and compare these to quadratic and cubic functions.

**Think Back**

**12.** $y = 7 - 4x$
$= 7 - 4(-12)$
$= 7 + 48$
$= 55$

**13.**
$y = 7 - 4x$
$-12 = 7 - 4x$
$-12 - 7 = 7 - 7 - 4x$
$-19 = -4x$
$-\frac{1}{4}(-19) = -\frac{1}{4}(-4x)$
$\frac{19}{4} = x$
$4\frac{3}{4} = x$

**14. D.** $-45$

**15.** 15

**16.** Carrie's fee $= 7x + 15y$
$\$7(10) + \$15(3) = \$70 + \$45 = \$115$

| x | y |
|---|---|
| −3 | |
| −2 | |
| −1 | |
| 0 | |
| 1 | |
| 2 | |
| 3 | |

| x | y |
|---|---|
| −3 | |
| −2 | |
| −1 | |
| 0 | |
| 1 | |
| 2 | |
| 3 | |

| x | y |
|---|---|
| −3 | |
| −2 | |
| −1 | |
| 0 | |
| 1 | |
| 2 | |
| 3 | |

| x | y |
|---|---|
| −3 | |
| −2 | |
| −1 | |
| 0 | |
| 1 | |
| 2 | |
| 3 | |

| x | y |
|---|---|
| −3 | |
| −2 | |
| −1 | |
| 0 | |
| 1 | |
| 2 | |
| 3 | |

| x | y |
|---|---|
| −3 | |
| −2 | |
| −1 | |
| 0 | |
| 1 | |
| 2 | |
| 3 | |

| x | y |
|---|---|
| −3 | |
| −2 | |
| −1 | |
| 0 | |
| 1 | |
| 2 | |
| 3 | |

| x | y |
|---|---|
| −3 | |
| −2 | |
| −1 | |
| 0 | |
| 1 | |
| 2 | |
| 3 | |

| x | y |
|---|---|
| −3 | |
| −2 | |
| −1 | |
| 0 | |
| 1 | |
| 2 | |
| 3 | |

# Variables as Exponents

**Suggested Pacing:** 2 Days

In this lesson, students explore exponential functions. They will use the variable $x$ as an exponent in these equations. They will discover that their graphs are curves rather than lines and do not cross the $x$-axis. Students explore real-life situations that represent two types of exponential functions: exponential growth and exponential decay. They play the Function Game, in which they identify and match linear, quadratic and exponential functions using their graphs, equations and tables of values.

---

**LESSON OBJECTIVES**

- Students will learn to identify exponential functions.
- Students will identify and compare exponential growth and exponential decay functions, using equations, graphs and tables.
- Students will match linear, quadratic and exponential functions using graphs, equations and tables.

---

| DAY 1 | Materials* | ESSENTIAL *ON YOUR OWN* QUESTIONS |
|---|---|---|
| Getting the Word Out<br><br>Exponential Functions | *In Class*<br>■ Graphing calculators<br>■ Graph paper<br>■ Plain copy paper<br>■ Lesson Guide 4.3: *Paper Folding* | Questions 1, 4, 12–16 |
| **DAY 2** | **Materials*** | **ESSENTIAL *ON YOUR OWN* QUESTIONS** |
| Exponential Decay Functions<br><br>Heat 'Em Up! | *In Class*<br>■ Food thermometer<br>■ Cup of boiling water<br>■ Graphing calculators<br>■ Graph paper<br>■ Plain copy paper<br>■ Lesson Guide 4.3: *Paper Folding*<br>■ Lesson Guide 4.3A: *Heat 'Em Up!*<br>■ Lesson Guide 4.3: *Function Game Cards*<br><br>*On Your Own*<br>■ Graphing calculators<br>■ Graph paper<br>■ Internet access<br>■ Lesson Guide 4.3A: *Babysitting Job Earnings* | Questions 2, 3, 5–9 |

\* The Think Like a Mathematician Daily Record Sheet should be used daily

---

## MATHEMATICALLY SPEAKING

▶ explicit rule　　　▶ exponential function　　　▶ recursive rule

▶ exponential decay　　　▶ exponential growth

## Variables as Exponents

### Start It Off

**MATHEMATICALLY SPEAKING**

▸ recursive rule
▸ explicit rule

Fill in the blanks to evaluate each sequence. Write two rules: a recursive rule that shows how you can find the next value using the previous value, and an explicit rule that shows how you can find the value given the number of the term.

1.

| Number of Term | 1 | 2 | 3 | 4 | 5 | 6 | 10 | 15 | $n$ |
|---|---|---|---|---|---|---|---|---|---|
| Value | 2 | 4 | 8 | 16 | | | | | |
| | $2^1$ | $2^2$ | $2^3$ | $2^4$ | | | | | |

2. 3, 9, 27, 81, _____, _____, _____

3. 10, 100, 1,000, _____, _____, _____

4. $\frac{1}{4}, \frac{1}{16}, \frac{1}{64}$, _____, _____, _____

### Getting the Word Out

As Director of the Newton Discovery Center, you will advertise special admission rates for school vacation in the local newspaper. You have the costs for a full-page ad, a half-page ad and a quarter-page ad in the following table.

---

### Start It Off

1.

| Number of Term | 1 | 2 | 3 | 4 | 5 | 6 | 10 | 15 | $n$ |
|---|---|---|---|---|---|---|---|---|---|
| Value | 2 | 4 | 8 | 16 | **32** | **64** | **1,024** | **32,768** | **$2^n$** |
| | $2^1$ | $2^2$ | $2^3$ | $2^4$ | **$2^5$** | **$2^6$** | **$2^{10}$** | **$2^{15}$** | **$2^n$** |

The recursive rule is: *next = previous* • 2
The explicit rule is: $2^n$, $n = 1, 2, 3, \ldots$

2. 3, 9, 27, 81, **243, 729, 2,187**
   Recursive rule is: next = previous • 3
   Explicit rule is: $3^n$, $n = 1, 2, 3, \ldots$

3. 10, 100, 1,000, **10,000, 100,000, 1,000,000**
   Recursive rule is: *next = previous* • 10
   Explicit rule is: $10^n$, $n = 0, 1, 2, \ldots$

4. $\frac{1}{4}, \frac{1}{16}, \frac{1}{64}, \frac{1}{256}, \frac{1}{1,024}, \frac{1}{4,096}$
   Recursive rule is: *next = previous* • $(\frac{1}{4})$   Explicit rule is: $(\frac{1}{4})^n$, $n = 0, 1, 2, \ldots$

### DAY 1 TEACHING THE LESSON

In this lesson, students explore a new type of nonlinear function: exponential functions. They discover that the variable $x$ is an exponent in these equations and their graphs are curves. Students explore situations that represent exponential growth and exponential decay. As a culminating activity, they identify and match linear, quadratic and exponential functions using their graphs, equations and tables of values.

### Getting the Word Out

Introduce the newspaper ad scenario to the class. Have students work with a partner to complete Question 1. Discuss and compare the rules pairs wrote. Next, distribute a copy of Lesson Guide 4.3: *Paper Folding* to each student. Have students conduct the experiment in Question 2 with a partner and record their data in the table. Then, have partners complete Question 3. Encourage students to share how they arrived at the rules for Questions 3a and 3b. Focus on the patterns they noticed in the tables that helped them make a generalization. Highlight for students that there is more than one correct rule for each question.

**Cost of Advertising**

| Size of Ad | Cost of Advertising |
|---|---|
| Full-Page Ad | $2,696.10 |
| Half-Page Ad | $1,348.05 |
| Quarter-Page Ad | $674.03 |
| Eighth-Page Ad | |
| Sixteenth-Page Ad | |

1. **a)** If these rates continue, what would you expect an eighth-page advertisement to cost?

   **b)** What about a sixteenth-page ad?

   **c)** Write a rule to find the cost of advertising using this table.

What will happen if a process like this goes on indefinitely? Perform the following activity with a partner to help you see this process.

Fold a piece of unlined paper in half as many times as you can. Then answer Questions 2–6.

2. **a)** Each time you fold the paper in half, what happens to the number of sections formed by the folds?

   **b)** If the area of the entire piece of paper is 1 square unit, what happens to the area of each section formed by the folds? Fill in the table below.

**Paper Folding**

| Number of Folds | Number of Sections | Area (square units) of the Smallest Section |
|---|---|---|
| 0 | 1 | 1 |
| 1 | 2 | $\frac{1}{2}$ |
| 2 | | |
| 3 | | |
| 4 | | |
| $n$ | | |

Next, have partners complete Questions 4–6. Circulate as pairs work to informally assess their understanding. When discussing responses as a class, encourage students to justify whether the functions are linear or quadratic by the relationship between variables on the graph in addition to the shape of the graph. Use talk moves, such as repeat/rephrase and agree/disagree and why, to extend the discussion and deepen understanding.

1. **a) b)**

| Size of Ad | Cost of Advertising |
|---|---|
| Full-Page Ad | $2,696.10 |
| Half-Page Ad | $1,348.05 |
| Quarter-Page Ad | $674.03 |
| Eighth-Page Ad | **$337.01 a)** |
| Sixteenth-Page Ad | **$168.51 b)** |

**c)** The rule is multiplying the previous ad cost by $\frac{1}{2}$ or dividing the previous ad cost by 2 to get the next term's ad cost: next = previous • $(\frac{1}{2})$ or *next = previous ÷ 2.*

2. **a)** The number of sections is doubled, or multiplied by a factor of 2.

   **b)** The area of the smallest section formed by the fold is divided by 2 or multiplied by a factor of $\frac{1}{2}$ each time the paper is folded.

| Number of Folds | Number of Sections Formed | Area of the Smallest Section |
|---|---|---|
| 0 | 1 | 1 |
| 1 | 2 | $\frac{1}{2}$ |
| 2 | 4 | $\frac{1}{4}$ |
| 3 | 8 | $\frac{1}{8}$ |
| 4 | 16 | $\frac{1}{16}$ |
| $n$ | $2^n$ | $\frac{1}{2^n}$ |

**3 a)** Write a recursive rule in words for the number of sections formed based on the previous number of sections. Write the explicit rule as an equation where *n* is the number of folds and *S* is the number of sections.

**Hint**
See page 169

**b)** Write a recursive rule in words for the area of the smallest section based on the previous area. Write the explicit rule as an equation where *n* is the number of folds and *A* is the area of the smallest section.

**c)** Approximately how many folds would be needed to make 1,000,000 sections?

**4.** Using *x* for the number of folds ($0 \leq x \leq 6$) and *y* for the number of sections formed, graph this relationship and connect the points by drawing a smooth curve.

**a)** Which variable is the independent variable?

**b)** Which variable is the dependent variable?

**c)** Describe the graph of this function

**d)** Is it a linear function? Explain.

**e)** Is it a quadratic function? Explain.

**5.** Using *x* for the number of folds ($0 \leq x \leq 6$) and *y* for the area of the smallest section, graph this relationship and connect the points.

**a)** Which variable is the independent variable?

**b)** Which variable is the dependent variable?

**c)** Describe the graph of this function.

**d)** Is it a linear function? Is it a quadratic function? Explain.

**6.** With your partner, compare the graphs you made in Questions 4 and 5. How are they alike? How are they different? Share with the class.

**3. a)** The recursive rule for the number of sections formed by each new fold is two times the number of sections from the previous fold: *next = previous* • 2. The explicit rule for the number of sections formed by each new fold is 2 raised to the power represented by the number of folds or $S = 2^n$.

**b)** The recursive rule for the area of the smallest section formed by each new fold is $\frac{1}{2}$ the area of one section formed by the previous fold. The explicit rule for the area of the smallest section is $\frac{1}{2}$ raised to the power represented by the number of folds or $A = \left(\frac{1}{2}\right)^n$.

**c)** It would take 20 folds to make approximately 1,000,000 sections. (20 folds actually make 1,048,576 sections.)

**4.**

| x | y |
|---|---|
| 0 | 1 |
| 1 | 2 |
| 2 | 4 |
| 3 | 8 |
| 4 | 16 |
| 5 | 32 |
| 6 | 64 |

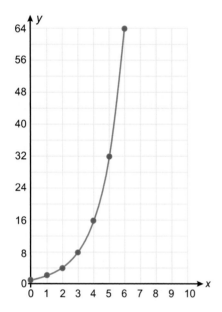

**a)** The independent variable is the number of folds, $x$.

**b)** The dependent variable is the number of sections formed, $y$.

**c)** The function is a curve that begins at (0, 1) and rises slowly initially and then more steeply as the $x$-values increase. The function is increasing. (See Part e below to discuss.)

**d)** No. The graph is not a straight line. Looking at the relationship between variables, there isn't a constant rate of change. As the $x$-values increase by 1, the $y$-values do not increase or decrease by a constant interval.

**e)** No. The graph is not a parabola. It is not symmetric around an axis.

**5.** $x$ represents the number of folds; $y$ represents the area of the smallest section formed.

| x | y |
|---|---|
| 0 | 1 |
| 1 | $\frac{1}{2}$ |
| 2 | $\frac{1}{4}$ |
| 3 | $\frac{1}{8}$ |
| 4 | $\frac{1}{16}$ |
| 5 | $\frac{1}{32}$ |
| 6 | $\frac{1}{64}$ |

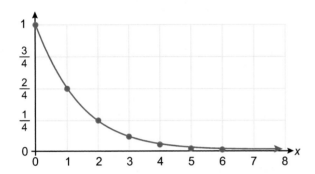

**a)** The independent variable is the number of folds, $x$.

**b)** The dependent variable is the area of the smallest section formed, $y$.

**c)** The graph consists of points that lie on a curve that begins at (0, 1). The curve declines rapidly toward 0 initially and then becomes less steep as the $x$-values increase. The function is decreasing. The $y$-values are always positive and the graph does not cross the $x$-axis.

**d)** No, this function is not linear. The points do not lie on a straight line. Looking at the relationship between variables in the table of values, there is no constant rate of change. As the $x$-values increase by 1, the $y$-values do not decrease by a constant interval.

No, this function is not a quadratic function. This function's graph does not seem symmetrical.

**6.** Both graphs have points that lie on curves that begin at the point (0, 1) or have a $y$-intercept at (0, 1). There is a varying rate of change between the variables. The curve in the graph for Question 3 rises slowly initially and then more rapidly as the $x$-values increase, moving from left to right. This function is an increasing function. The curve in Question 4 falls more rapidly initially and then more slowly as the $x$-values increase, moving left to right. This function is a decreasing function.

## Exponential Functions

Introduce the term *exponential function*. Explain that the equation $y = 2^x$ in the ad scenario modeling the number of new sections created with each new fold is an example of an exponential growth function. Draw students' attention to the graph of this function. Discuss why mathematicians call this function an exponential growth function. This is because the curve rises slowly initially, and then more rapidly as the values of $x$ increase by 1.

Have students complete Questions 7–9 with a partner and share their responses with the class. Discuss why the value of $y$ will never be zero for Question 7b. It is important for students to recognize that the values will approach zero but never reach a value of zero.

 **Differentiation**

**Think Differently:** If students are having difficulty visualizing the graphs in Question 9, have them use graphing calculators.

## Exponential Functions

MATHEMATICALLY SPEAKING

▸ exponential function

▸ exponential growth

A function of the form $y = a^x$, where $a$ is a constant greater than zero and not equal to 1, is called an **exponential function**. The exponential function $y = 2^x$ is an example of **exponential growth**. It is graphed below. Why do you think mathematicians call this an exponential *growth* curve?

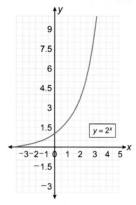

7. **a)** From the graph, find the values of $y$ when $x = -1$, $-2$ and $-3$. Explain why these values make sense based on what you have learned about negative exponents.

   **b)** Can the value of $y$ ever equal zero? Explain your reasoning.

   **c)** Does this function have a constant rate of change like a linear function? Explain your answer using the graph.

   **d)** Which paper-folding activity does this equation represent?

8. Talk to your partner and compare the graph and table of values for $y = 2^x$ to the graph and table of values for $y = x^2$ in Lesson 4.2.

   **a)** How are they different?

   **b)** Discuss the rate of change of both functions.

9. How does the graph of $y = 2^x$ compare to the graph of $y = 2x$? Discuss the rate of change in both functions.

## Summarize Day 1

Have students discuss the following question with a partner and share their responses in a class discussion.

- *What is similar and what is different about exponential, quadratic and linear functions?*

The discussion should include the following key ideas:

- An equation of a linear function represents a relationship between two variables; both variables in the equation are raised to the first power. Example: $y = 2x + 1$

- An equation of a quadratic function also represents a relationship between two variables; however, the variable $x$ in the equation is raised to the second power. Example: $y = 2x^2 + 1$

- An equation of an exponential function also represents a relationship between two variables; however, a base is raised to a variable power. Example: $y = 2^x$

- The graph of a linear function is a straight line.

- The graph of a quadratic function is a parabola.

- The graph of an exponential function is a curve that increases steeply in one direction.

**7. a)**

| x | y |
|---|---|
| -1 | $\frac{1}{2}$ |
| -2 | $\frac{1}{4}$ |
| -3 | $\frac{1}{8}$ |

A number raised to a negative exponent is equal to a fraction that has 1 as the numerator and a denominator that consists of the given number raised to the absolute value of that exponent. Therefore, $2^{-1} = \frac{1}{2}$, $2^{-2} = \frac{1}{2^2} = \frac{1}{4}$, etc.

**b)** No, it will get increasingly close to zero but will never be equal to zero. A base raised to a negative exponent will always be equal to a fraction that has 1 as the numerator and a denominator that consists of the base raised to the absolute value of that exponent.

**c)** No, the relationship between variables in this function does not represent a constant rate of change like a linear function. As the negative values of $x$ increase, the $y$-values begin to increase very slightly. Then as the positive values for $x$ increase, the $y$-values increase more rapidly. The $y$-values do not increase at a constant interval.

**d)** This represents the paper-folding function that determines the number of sections that result given a number of folds. However, this scenario only makes sense for $x$-values greater than or equal to 0.

**8. a)** $y = 2^x$

| x | y |
|---|---|
| 0 | 1 |
| 2 | 4 |
| 3 | 8 |
| 4 | 16 |
| 5 | 32 |
| 6 | 64 |

$y = x^2$

| x | y |
|---|---|
| 0 | 0 |
| 1 | 1 |
| 2 | 4 |
| 3 | 9 |

The graph of $y = 2^x$ is an exponential growth curve; the $y$-values increase slowly initially and then more rapidly as the $x$-values increase. It has a $y$-intercept of (0, 1). The graph of $y = x^2$ is a parabola that opens upward whose line of symmetry is the $y$-axis, $x = 0$. It has a vertex at (0, 0). This is also the $y$-intercept.

**b)** Both functions have a varying rate of change. For $y = 2^x$, as the $x$-values increase by 1, the $y$-values increase at a varying rate. The $y$-values increase slowly initially and then more rapidly as the $x$-values increase by 1. For $y = x^2$, the $y$-value is determined by squaring the $x$-value. Therefore, the increase or decrease in $y$-values is not consistent. The same positive and negative values for $x$ have the same $y$-value. For example, -3 and 3 have a $y$-value of 9.

**9.** The graph of $y = 2^x$ is an exponential growth curve, not a straight line. The $y$-values increase slowly initially and then more rapidly as the $x$-values increase. It has a $y$-intercept of (0, 1). It never crosses the $x$-axis. The graph of $y = 2x$ is a line with a $y$-intercept of (0, 0). For $y = 2^x$, the rate of change varies; as the $x$-values increase, the $y$-values increase at a varying rate, first slowly, then more rapidly. For $y = 2x$, the graph is a straight line. The rate of change is constant; as the $x$-values increase by 1, the $y$-values increase by 2.

## Exponential Decay Functions

Discuss the term *exponential decay*. Mathematicians call the function $y = \left(\frac{1}{2}\right)^x$ an exponential decay function because the curve decreases or decays as the value of *x* increases. Students have encountered this type of function in the paper-folding activity when they graphed the relationship between the number of folds and the area of the smallest section.

## Heat 'Em Up

As a class, complete Question 11. Note that you will need a food thermometer and a cup of boiling water. (The water could be heated in the teacher's lounge prior to the lesson.) Make sure students make predictions before conducting the experiment. As you read the temperature every 30 seconds, have students record the time and temperature in a table. You may want to model this using the chalkboard or interactive white board. Once the five minutes is over, have students complete Question 11c.

### Differentiation

**Think Differently:** For students having difficulty organizing their work and creating a table, offer Lesson Guide 4.3A: *Heat 'Em Up!*

Next, have student pairs complete Questions 12 and 13. Emphasize that it is important to make predictions first and then graph the exponential functions using a graphing calculator.

### Differentiation

**Think Differently:** For those who may benefit from more experience with hands-on graphing, offer the opportunity to graph the functions on grid paper first, and then compare these to the ones on the graphing calculator.

Have a class discussion comparing the predictions students made with the actual graphs on the graphing calculators. Help students recognize that when the base of the exponent *x* is between 0 and 1, the exponential function is an exponential decay function. When the base of the exponent *x* is greater than 1, the exponential function is an exponential growth function. Ask:

- *How can we tell by looking at an exponential function if it is a growth or decay function?*

Read the rules for the Function Game together as a class and divide students into partners or pairs of partners. You may want to model a round of play before having partners begin playing the game. Circulate as students play the game to informally assess understanding. Use the *Student Snapshot* observation tool to record notes. Discuss as a class any questions that arise during the game to clarify understanding.

10. **a)** $y = \left(\frac{1}{2}\right)^x$ is an exponential decay function because the *y*-values decrease rapidly initially and then more slowly as the *x*-values decrease.

   **b)** Answers will vary. The graphs are similar in their varied rate of change. In the graph of $y = 2^x$, the *y*-values initially increase slowly and then increase more rapidly as the *x*-values increase. In the graph of $y = 2^{-x}$, the *y*-values initially decrease rapidly and then decrease more slowly as the *x*-values decrease. Both graphs do not cross the *x*-axis.

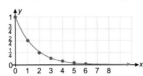

# Exponential Decay Functions

**MATHEMATICALLY SPEAKING**

▸ exponential decay

The exponential function $y = \left(\frac{1}{2}\right)^x$ is an example of exponential decay. You graphed this function in the paper-folding activity to show the relationship between the number of folds and the area of the smallest section formed.

**10. a)** Why do you think this is called an exponential *decay* function?

**b)** With a partner, compare this graph with the graph of $y = 2^x$. How are they alike? How are they different?

**c)** Can the *y*-value for this function ever be zero? Explain.

**d)** Together, discuss the rate of change for this function.

## Heat 'Em Up!

At the food court of the Discovery Center, shop owners have to keep their hot drinks hot! The drinks cannot stand too long or they will have to be reheated. How long does it take before they need to be reheated?

Try this class experiment. Put a cup of boiling water on the counter. Use a food thermometer to measure the temperature of the water every thirty seconds for five minutes. Record your data in a table where *x* represents time and *y* represents the temperature.

**11. a)** Predict whether the graph of this function is linear, quadratic or exponential by looking at the table.

**b)** Graph the function to check your prediction. Note that because you are using real data and there may be errors in timing and temperature measurements, your graph may not exactly fit a particular curve that we have studied. However, one of those curves should be a fairly good model.

**12. a)** Predict how the shape of the graph of $y = \left(\frac{1}{3}\right)^x$ will compare to the graph of $y = 3^x$.

**❓ Hint**
See page 169

**b)** Compare using your graphing calculator.

**c)** No, the *y*-values will get closer and closer to zero as *x* increases but will never reach zero. As the value for the exponent, *x*, increases, the value for *y* will always be a fraction with 1 as the numerator. A fraction with 1 in the numerator will never be equal to zero.

**d)** The rate of change is varying. As the negative *x*-values increase, the *y*-values initially decrease rapidly and then decrease more slowly as you move toward positive *x*-values.

**11. a)** Predictions will vary. The graph of this function is an example of exponential decay. (For more information, research Newton's Law of Cooling.)

**b)** Answers will vary. The graph will decrease from the initial hot temperature but will never go below the value of the current room temperature.

**12. a)** $y = 3^x$

| x | y |
|---|---|
| −3 | $\frac{1}{27}$ |
| −1 | $\frac{1}{9}$ |
| 1 | $\frac{1}{3}$ |
| 0 | 1 |
| 1 | 3 |
| 2 | 9 |
| 3 | 27 |

$y = \left(\frac{1}{3}\right)^x$

| x | y |
|---|---|
| −3 | 27 |
| −1 | 9 |
| 1 | 3 |
| 0 | 1 |
| 1 | $\frac{1}{3}$ |
| 2 | $\frac{1}{9}$ |
| 3 | $\frac{1}{27}$ |

**b)**

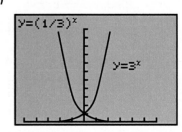

Responses will vary depending on predictions made.

**13. a)** Predictions will vary. Possible predictions include: Both graphs will intersect the *y*-axis at the point (0, 1). The graph of $y = 3^x$ will rise more steeply than the graph of $y = 2^x$ as the positive *x*-values increase. The curve for the graph of $y = 3^x$ will lie above the curve for the graph of $y = 2^x$ when *x*-values are positive. As the negative values of *x* decrease, both graphs get closer and closer to, but never reach, zero. The graph for $y = 2^x$ will have greater values for *y* when the *x*-values are negative. Therefore, the curve for the graph of $y = 2^x$ will lie above the curve of the graph $y = 3^x$ when *x*-values are negative.

| $y = 3^{x2}$ | |
|---|---|
| **x** | **y** |
| −3 | $\frac{1}{27}$ |
| −2 | $\frac{1}{9}$ |
| 1 | $\frac{1}{3}$ |
| 0 | 1 |
| 1 | 3 |
| 2 | 9 |
| 3 | 27 |

| $y = 3^{x2}$ | |
|---|---|
| **x** | **y** |
| −3 | $\frac{1}{8}$ |
| −2 | $\frac{1}{4}$ |
| −1 | $\frac{1}{2}$ |
| 0 | 1 |
| 1 | 2 |
| 2 | 4 |
| 3 | 8 |

**b)** The graphs will have the point (0, 1) in common.

---

**13. a)** With your partner, predict how the shape of the graph $y = 3^x$ will compare to the graph of $y = 2^x$.

**b)** Will these graphs have any points in common?

 **Hint**
See page 169

See page 169

**c)** Graph $y = 2^x$ and $y = 3^x$ using your graphing calculator.

**d)** Were your predictions correct? Explain.

**14.** Play the Function Game.

**GAME** · · · · · · · · **Function Game** · · · · · · ·

Players: **2 players or 2 teams of 2 partners each**

Materials: **playing cards**

Directions:

- Shuffle cards and pass out the entire deck, alternating cards to each player or team.
- The object of the game is to get as many sets of three-of-a-kind functions as possible.
- Players look at the cards they have in their hand and determine if they have any sets.
- A set is a group of three cards described below. The function can be represented with a graph, table or equation. The point value for the set of three cards is given in parentheses.

  Any three quadratic functions (1)
  Any three exponential functions (1)
  Any three linear functions (1)
  Any three quadratic functions that have negative coefficients for $x^2$ (5)
  Any three quadratic functions that have graphs facing upward (5)
  Any three exponential growth functions (5)
  Any three exponential decay functions (5)
  Any three linear functions with positive slopes (5)
  Any three linear functions with negative slopes (5)
  Three cards that represent the exact same function (10)

- Once all sets that can be made are created, the extra cards are put in the middle of the table and the player or team with the least number of sets sees if another set can be made from this pile of cards. Players (or teams) alternate turns until no more sets can be made. Players (or teams) count up their points. Each of these sets is worth 1 point.
- All cards are then reshuffled and dealt again. The first player or team to reach 25 points wins the game.

 **NOTE** The cards that make up each set do not have to represent the same function, but rather the same *type* of function.

**c)**

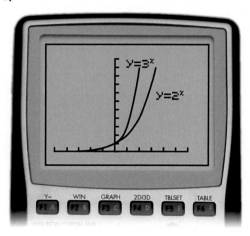

**d)** Answers will vary depending on predictions made.

## Wrap It Up

You may have heard people talking about how something is "growing exponentially." Discuss what they are referring to and explain what exponential growth is mathematically. Mention rate of change in your explanation.

**MATHEMATICALLY SPEAKING**

▶ explicit rule
▶ exponential decay
▶ exponential function
▶ exponential growth
▶ recursive rule

14. Students will play the **Function Game**. In this game they match graphs, tables and equations of linear, quadratic and exponential functions.

## Wrap It Up

Responses will vary. Students should include the following key ideas in the discussion:

- "Growing exponentially" means increasing in value slowly at first and then very quickly.

- Exponential growth means as the value of the independent variable, $x$, increases, the value of the dependent variable, $y$, increases slowly at first and then more rapidly. The rate of growth changes dramatically as the values of the independent variable steadily increase or decrease.

### Reflect

Use these questions to help you reflect on the lesson and plan for future instruction.

- What strategies do students use to identify exponential growth and exponential decay functions?

- How accurately can students predict the graph of an exponential function?

See corresponding assessments in Assessment Resources.

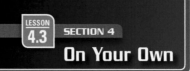
**MATERIALS LIST**
▸ Graphing calculator
▸ Graph paper
▸ Internet
▸ Food thermometers

**Write About It**

1. Tiffany thinks $y = x$ and $y = 2^x$ are both linear functions, because they both rise upward from left to right on a graph. Explain to Tiffany why she is wrong. Include the relationships between the variables, the shapes of the graphs and rate of change for each of the functions in your explanation.

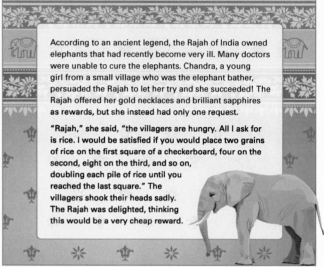

According to an ancient legend, the Rajah of India owned elephants that had recently become very ill. Many doctors were unable to cure the elephants. Chandra, a young girl from a small village who was the elephant bather, persuaded the Rajah to let her try and she succeeded! The Rajah offered her gold necklaces and brilliant sapphires as rewards, but she instead had only one request.

"Rajah," she said, "the villagers are hungry. All I ask for is rice. I would be satisfied if you would place two grains of rice on the first square of a checkerboard, four on the second, eight on the third, and so on, doubling each pile of rice until you reached the last square." The villagers shook their heads sadly. The Rajah was delighted, thinking this would be a very cheap reward.

Adapted from Barry, D. (1994). The Rajah's Rice: A Mathematical Folktale from India, New York: W.H. Freeman and Company

Read the story above.

2. What do you think? Was this a wise decision on Chandra's part? Defend your answer. In your answer, explain how this relates to exponential functions.

**? Hint**
See page 169

## On Your Own

**Write About It**

1. Answers will vary. Possible response:

- Tiffany is correct that $y = x$ is a linear function. It has a graph that is a straight line. There is a steady rate of change between the variables; as $x$ increases by 1, $y$ increases by 1. The line intersects both axes at $(0, 0)$.

- Tiffany is incorrect about $y = 2^x$. This is an exponential function. The graph of $y = 2^x$ is an exponential growth curve, not a straight line. The rate of change varies with $y$-values initially increasing slowly and then increasing more rapidly as the $x$-values increase at a steady rate. It has a $y$-intercept of $(0, 1)$ and never crosses the $x$-axis.

2. Yes, this was a wise decision. The amount on the $n^{th}$ square would be 2 to the $n$ power. The number of grains of rice Chandra would receive on the last square alone is 18,446,744,073,709,551,616 or about $1.8447 \times 10^{19}$. (This problem is similar to the problem about the grandmother who invests twice as much money each year in an account.) This amount is enough rice to fill the great volcano, Mt. Kilimanjaro!

3. Match each graph with the correct equation.

a) $y = 4^x$        c) $y = 4x$

b) $y = \left(\frac{1}{4}\right)x$     d) $y = 4x^2$

**1.**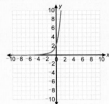

**3.**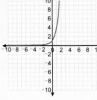

**5.**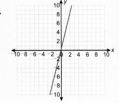

**2.**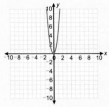

**4.**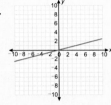

4. You are offered a babysitting day job. You will be paid 1¢ for the first day, 2¢ for the second day, 4¢ for the third day and so on, with the amount doubling each day. What is the minimum number of days you would agree to do this job? Explain your reasoning and give the total amount you would be paid.

 Think Beyond

5. Moore's Law, named after Gordon Moore, the cofounder of Intel Corporation, states that the speed and power of a computer doubles every two years because of the increasing number of transistors (tiny switches) that each computer chip is able to contain. He expects this model to work well up to 2017. A good model for this is $y = 2{,}300(1 + 0.38)^x$, where $y$ represents the number of transistors and $x$ represents the number of years since 1971.

a) Using this model, find the number of transistors in a computer chip in 1990, in 2000 and in 2008.

b) What implications might this have for an organization like the Newton Discovery Center?

Gordon E. Moore, Co-founder, Intel Corporation.

**3. a)** 3

**b)** 4

**c)** 5

**d)** 2

4. Answers will vary. The exponential equation for the babysitting situation is $y = 2^{(x-1)}$, where $x$ represents the number of days of babysitting and $y$ represents the total number of cents earned on the $x^{th}$ day. In the table below, the third column gives the amount of money earned on the $x^{th}$ day in dollars. The final column gives the running total earned for $x$ days:

$$\frac{\$(2 \cdot 2^{(x-1)} - 1)}{100} \text{ or } \frac{\$(2^x - 1)}{100}.$$

| x | y | Amount Earned in Dollars | Total Amount Earned |
|---|---|---|---|
| 1 | 1 | $0.01 | $0.01 |
| 2 | 2 | $0.02 | $0.03 |
| 3 | 4 | $0.04 | $0.07 |
| 4 | 8 | $0.08 | $0.15 |
| 5 | 16 | $0.16 | $0.31 |
| 6 | 32 | $0.32 | $0.63 |
| 7 | 64 | $0.64 | $1.27 |
| 8 | 128 | $1.28 | $2.55 |
| 9 | 256 | $2.56 | $5.11 |
| 10 | 512 | $5.12 | $10.23 |
| 11 | 1,024 | $10.24 | $20.47 |
| 12 | 2,048 | $20.48 | $40.95 |
| 13 | 4,096 | $40.96 | $81.91 |
| 14 | 8,192 | $81.92 | $163.83 |
| 15 | 16,384 | $163.84 | $327.67 |
| 16 | 32,768 | $327.68 | $655.35 |
| 17 | 65,536 | $655.36 | $1,310.71 |
| 18 | 131,072 | $1,310.72 | $2,221.43 |
| 19 | 262,144 | $2,221.44 | $5,242.87 |
| 20 | 524,288 | $5,242.88 | $10,485.75 |

Accept answers that are justified with sound reasoning. Encourage students to consider the number of hours they think they would be babysitting per day and a reasonable rate per hour for babysitting. For example, after the tenth day of babysitting the average daily rate over the 10 days is still only $1 per day, while after 15 days the average rate is about $22.

 **NOTE** Lesson Guide 4.3A: *Babysitting Job Earnings* is available for those students who may need support organizing data in a table.

5. a) The number of transistors per chip:
   - in 1990 is approximately 1,045,756.
   - in 2000 is approximately 26,195,177.
   - in 2008 is approximately 344,551,410.

   b) Since the speed and power of computers increase dramatically due to the rapid rise in the number of transistors per chip each year, they become obsolete quickly. The Newton Discovery Center will need to consider the replacement of computers in their budget.

**6. a)** Predictions will vary. Possible predictions include:

Both graphs will intersect the *y*-axis at the point (0, 1). The graph of $y = 4^x$ will rise more steeply than the graph of $y = 3^x$ as the positive *x*-values increase from left to right. The curve for the graph of $y = 4^x$ will lie above the curve for the graph of $y = 3^x$ when *x*-values are positive. As the negative values of *x* decrease, both graphs get closer and closer to, but never reach, zero. The graph for $y = 3^x$ will have greater values for *y* when the *x*-values are negative. Therefore, the curve for the graph of $y = 3^x$ will lie above the curve of the graph of $y = 4^x$ when *x*-values are negative.

| $y = 3x^2$ | |
|---|---|
| **x** | **y** |
| −3 | $\frac{1}{27}$ |
| −2 | $\frac{1}{9}$ |
| −1 | $\frac{1}{3}$ |
| 0 | 1 |
| 1 | 3 |
| 2 | 9 |
| 3 | 27 |

| $y = 4^x$ | |
|---|---|
| **x** | **y** |
| −4 | $\frac{1}{256}$ |
| −3 | $\frac{1}{64}$ |
| −2 | $\frac{1}{16}$ |
| −1 | $\frac{1}{4}$ |
| 0 | 1 |
| 1 | 4 |
| 2 | 16 |
| 3 | 64 |
| 4 | 256 |

**b)** Predictions will vary. Possible predictions include:

Both graphs will intersect the *y*-axis at the point (0, 1). The curve of the graph of $y = 4^x$ will rise rapidly as the *x*-values increase. The curve of the graph of $y = \left(\frac{1}{4}\right)^x$ will rise rapidly as the *x*-values decrease. The two curves are symmetric about the *y*-axis.

| $y = 4^x$ | |
|---|---|
| **x** | **y** |
| −4 | $\frac{1}{256}$ |
| −3 | $\frac{1}{64}$ |
| −2 | $\frac{1}{16}$ |
| −1 | $\frac{1}{4}$ |
| 0 | 1 |
| 1 | 4 |
| 2 | 16 |
| 3 | 64 |
| 4 | 256 |

| $y = \frac{1}{4}^x$ | |
|---|---|
| **x** | **y** |
| −4 | 256 |
| −3 | 64 |
| −2 | 16 |
| −1 | 4 |
| 0 | 1 |
| 1 | $\frac{1}{4}$ |
| 2 | $\frac{1}{16}$ |
| 3 | $\frac{1}{64}$ |
| 4 | $\frac{1}{256}$ |

**c)** Responses will vary depending on predictions made. The graph is below.

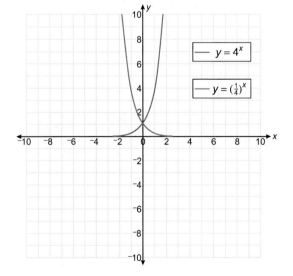

**6. a)** Predict how the graph of $y = 4^x$ will compare to the graph of $y = 3^x$.

**b)** Predict how will it compare to the graph of $y = \left(\frac{1}{4}\right)^x$.

**c)** Graph the equations $y = 4^x$ and $y = \left(\frac{1}{4}\right)^x$ on the same coordinate grid. Refine and/or add on to your predictions, if necessary.

**7.** Predict how the graphs of $y = \left(\frac{1}{5}\right)^x$ and $y = \left(\frac{1}{10}\right)^x$ are alike and how they are different. Graph both on the same axes using your graphing calculator. Were your predictions correct?

**8. a)** Predict how the graph of $y = 3^x$ will compare to the graph of $y = 3x^2$.

What will each graph look like? Will they have any points in common? Why or why not?

**b)** Graph both equations on the same axes using your graphing calculator. Were your predictions correct?

**9.** Tell whether each table or equation represents a linear, quadratic or exponential function.

**a)**

| x | y |
|---|---|
| −3 | 3 |
| −2 | 2 |
| −1 | 1 |
| 0 | 0 |
| 1 | −1 |
| 2 | −2 |

**b)** $y = \frac{1}{2}x + 7x - 5$

**c)** $A = x(2x - 4)$

**d)** $y = \left(\frac{5}{8}\right)^x$

**e)**

| x | y |
|---|---|
| 0 | 1 |
| 1 | 10 |
| 2 | 100 |
| 3 | 1,000 |
| 4 | 10,000 |
| 5 | 100,000 |

---

**7.** Predictions will vary. Possible predictions include:

Both graphs have curves that rise more rapidly as the *x*-values decrease. The graph of $y = \left(\frac{1}{10}\right)^x$ will rise more steeply than the graph of $y = \left(\frac{1}{5}\right)^x$ as the *x*-values below 0 decrease. The curve for the graph of $y = \left(\frac{1}{10}\right)^x$ will lie above the curve for the graph of $y = \left(\frac{1}{5}\right)^x$ when *x*-values are negative. The graph for $y = \left(\frac{1}{5}\right)^x$ will fall less steeply than the graph of $y = \left(\frac{1}{10}\right)^x$ as *x*-values above 0 increase. Therefore, the curve for the graph of $y = \left(\frac{1}{5}\right)^x$ will lie above the curve of the graph of $y = \left(\frac{1}{10}\right)^x$ when *x*-values are positive.

| $y = \left(\frac{1}{5}\right)^x$ | |
|---|---|
| **x** | **y** |
| −3 | 125 |
| −2 | 25 |
| −1 | 5 |
| 0 | 1 |
| 1 | $\frac{1}{5}$ |
| 2 | $\frac{1}{25}$ |
| 3 | $\frac{1}{125}$ |

| $y = \frac{1}{4}^x$ | |
|---|---|
| **x** | **y** |
| −3 | 1,000 |
| −2 | 100 |
| −1 | 10 |
| 0 | 1 |
| 1 | $\frac{1}{10}$ |
| 2 | $\frac{1}{100}$ |
| 3 | $\frac{1}{1,000}$ |

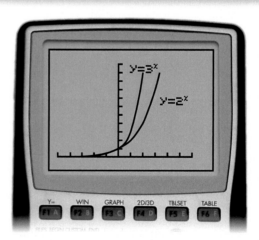

Responses will vary depending on predictions made.

**8. a)** Predictions will vary. Possible predictions include:

The graph of $y = 3^x$ will intersect the $y$-axis at the point (0, 1). The curve of the graph will rise rapidly as the positive $x$-values increase. The graph of $y = 3x^2$ will be a parabola that intersects the $y$-axis at the point (0, 0). The graphs will have two points in common—(1, 3) and (3, 27) —because the curves intersect on both sides of the $y$-axis.

| $y = 3x$ | |
|:---:|:---:|
| **$x$** | **$y$** |
| −3 | $\frac{1}{27}$ |
| −2 | $\frac{1}{9}$ |
| −1 | $\frac{1}{3}$ |
| 0 | 1 |
| 1 | 3 |
| 2 | 9 |
| 3 | 27 |

| $y = 3x^2$ | |
|:---:|:---:|
| **$x$** | **$y$** |
| −3 | 27 |
| −2 | 12 |
| −1 | 3 |
| 0 | 0 |
| 1 | 3 |
| 2 | 12 |
| 3 | 27 |

**b)** Responses will vary depending on predictions made

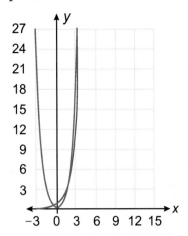

**9. a)** linear function ($y = -x$)

**b)** linear function ($y = 7.5x - 5$)

**c)** quadratic function ($A = 2x^2 - 4x$)

**d)** exponential (decay) function ($y = \left(\frac{5^x}{8}\right)$)

**e)** exponential (growth) function ($y = 10^x$)

**f)** linear function ($y = -5x$)

**Think Beyond**

**a)** Predictions will vary. The graph for $y = 2 \cdot 2^x$ will be a curve that lies above the graph of $y = 2^x$. The $y$-values for the graph of $y = 2 \cdot 2^x$ will be two times greater than the corresponding $y$-values of the graph of $y = 2^x$. The graph of $y = 2 \cdot 2^x$ will intersect the $y$-axis at (0, 2) while the graph of $y = 2^x$ intersects the $y$-axis at (0, 1). Both graphs have curves that rise rapidly as the $x$-values increase.

| $y = 2 \cdot 2^x$ | |
|---|---|
| **x** | **y** |
| −3 | $\frac{1}{4}$ |
| −2 | $\frac{1}{2}$ |
| −1 | 1 |
| 0 | 2 |
| 1 | 4 |
| 2 | 8 |
| 3 | 16 |

**b)**

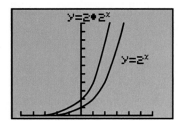

**f)**

| x | y |
|---|---|
| -3 | 15 |
| -2 | 10 |
| -1 | 5 |
| 0 | 0 |
| 1 | -5 |

 **Think Beyond**

10. **a)** Predict how the graph of $y = 2 \cdot 2^x$ will compare to the graph of $y = 2^x$.

   **b)** Compare using your graphing calculator.

 **Think Beyond**

11. **a)** Predict the shape of the graph of $y = 2^{-x}$.

   **b)** How will it compare to the graph of $y = 2^x$?

   **c)** How will it compare to the graph of $y = \left(\frac{1}{2}\right)^x$?

   **d)** Graph each equation on the same axes. Refine and/or add on to the predictions, if necessary.

**Think Back**

12. If each letter is represented by the opposite of its order in the alphabet (that is, $a = -1$, $b = -2$ and so on) and a word's value is the sum of the value of its letters, is it true that *math* > *candy*?

13. It takes a certain bacteria 16 minutes to double in number. If there are 7,012,524 bacteria at 5 pm, what is the best estimate, in millions, of the number of bacteria at 5:48 pm on the same day?

   **A.** 14        **C.** 35

   **B.** 28        **D.** 56

14. In the 1988 Olympics, Janet Evans from the United States won the 400-meter freestyle swimming event with a record time of 4:03.88 (this means 4 minutes, 3.88 seconds). East Germany's Heike Friedrich came in second with a time of 4:05.94.

   **a)** What was the difference in their times?

   **b)** What percent of Evans's total time was this difference (to the nearest hundredth of a percent)?

15. In the 1992 Olympics, Janet Evans's time in the 400-meter freestyle was 4:07.37, earning her second place. How much slower was her time in 1992 than in 1988?

11.  **Think Beyond**

**a)** The graph of $y = 2^{-x}$ will be an exponential decay curve. Its *y*-values will decrease in value quickly as the negative *x*-values increase and then more slowly as the positive *x*-values continue to increase by 1. The graph will intersect the *y*-axis at the point (0, 1).

**b)** The graph of $y = 2^x$ will be an exponential growth curve that is a reflection of the graph $y = 2^{-x}$ about the *y*-axis.

**c)** The graph of $y = 2^{-x}$ will be identical to the graph of $y = \left(\frac{1}{2}\right)^x$ since $y = 2^{-x} = \frac{1}{2}^x = \left(\frac{1}{2}\right)^x$.

**d)**

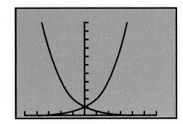

16. In May 2006, Laure Manaudou of France finally broke Janet Evans's 17-year record in the 400-meter freestyle, with a time of 4 minutes, 3.03 seconds at the French national championships.

a) What was the difference between Manaudou's time and Janet Evans's record?

b) What percent of Evans's total time is this difference?

Photo © Jim Callaway. Used by permission. See www.jimcallaway.com.

Optional Technology Lesson for this section available at www.mymathinnovations.com

Think Back

12. *math* = $-13 + -1 + -20 + -8 = -42$

*candy* = $-3 + -1 + -14 + -4 + -25 = -47$

$-42 > -47$; therefore, *math* > *candy* is true.

13. **D.** 56

14. a) Janet won by 2.06 seconds.

b) $2.06 \div 243.88 = 0.0084$ or 0.84%

15. Janet's 1993 Olympic time was 3.49 seconds slower.

16. a) Laure broke Janet's 1988 Olympic record by 0.85 second.

b) This represents $0.85 \div 243.88 = 0.003485$ or 0.35% percent of Janet's record time.

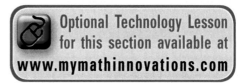

Optional Technology Lesson for this section available at www.mymathinnovations.com

| Number of Folds | Number of Sections Formed | Area of the Smallest Section |
|:---:|:---:|:---:|
| 0 | 1 | 1 |
| 1 | 2 | $\frac{1}{2}$ |
| 2 | | |
| 3 | | |
| 4 | | |
| $n$ | | |

| Time | Temperature |
|---|---|
| Start | |
| 30 seconds | |
| 1 minute | |
| 1 minute 30 seconds | |
| 2 minutes | |
| 2 minutes 30 seconds | |
| 3 minutes | |
| 3 minutes 30 seconds | |
| 4 minutes | |
| 4 minutes 30 seconds | |
| 5 minutes | |

$$y = -x^2$$

$$y = -3x^2 - 3$$

$$y = x^2 + 3$$

$$y = x^2$$

$$y = -2x^2$$

$$y = -3x - 1$$

| | |
|---|---|
| **The Function Game** | **The Function Game** |
| **The Function Game** | **The Function Game** |
| **The Function Game** | **The Function Game** |

| | |
|---|---|
| $y = x + 1$ | $y = \left(\dfrac{1}{3}\right)^x$ |
| $y = -3x$ | $y = 2^x$ |
| $y = 3^x$ | $y = \left(\dfrac{1}{2}\right)^x$ |

# The Function Game

# The Function Game

# The Function Game

# The Function Game

# The Function Game

# The Function Game

$$y = x^2 - 1$$

| x | y |
|---|---|
| −2 | −4 |
| −1 | −1 |
| 0 | 0 |
| 1 | −1 |
| 2 | −4 |

$$y = -x + 1$$

| x | y |
|---|---|
| −3 | 8 |
| −2 | 5 |
| −1 | 2 |
| 0 | −1 |
| 1 | −4 |

$$y = 2x$$

| x | y |
|---|---|
| −2 | −15 |
| −1 | −6 |
| 0 | −3 |
| 1 | −6 |
| 2 | −15 |

# The Function Game

# The Function Game

# The Function Game

# The Function Game

# The Function Game

# The Function Game

| x | y |
|---|---|
| 0 | 1 |
| 1 | 3 |
| 2 | 9 |
| 3 | 27 |

| x | y |
|---|---|
| 0 | 1 |
| 1 | 2 |
| 2 | 4 |
| 3 | 8 |
| 4 | 16 |

| x | y |
|---|---|
| 0 | 1 |
| 1 | $\frac{1}{3}$ |
| 2 | $\frac{1}{9}$ |
| 3 | $\frac{1}{27}$ |

| x | y |
|---|---|
| −2 | 7 |
| −1 | 4 |
| 0 | 3 |
| 1 | 4 |
| 2 | 7 |

| x | y |
|---|---|
| −4 | −3 |
| −3 | −2 |
| −2 | −1 |
| −1 | 0 |
| 0 | 1 |

| x | y |
|---|---|
| −4 | −8 |
| −2 | −4 |
| 0 | 0 |
| 1 | 2 |
| 2 | 4 |

# The Function Game

# The Function Game

# The Function Game

# The Function Game

# The Function Game

# The Function Game

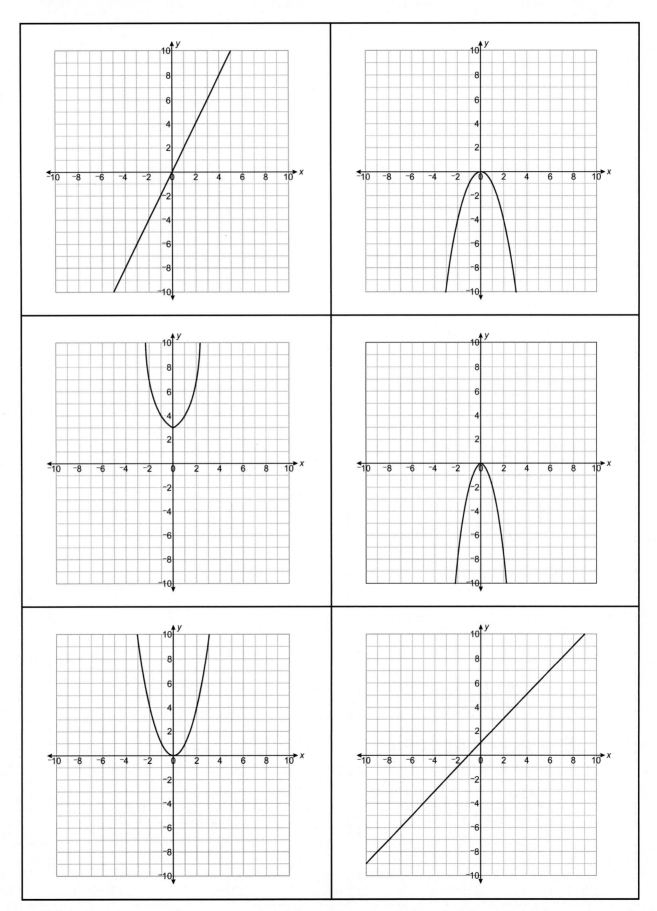

# The Function Game

# The Function Game

# The Function Game

# The Function Game

# The Function Game

# The Function Game

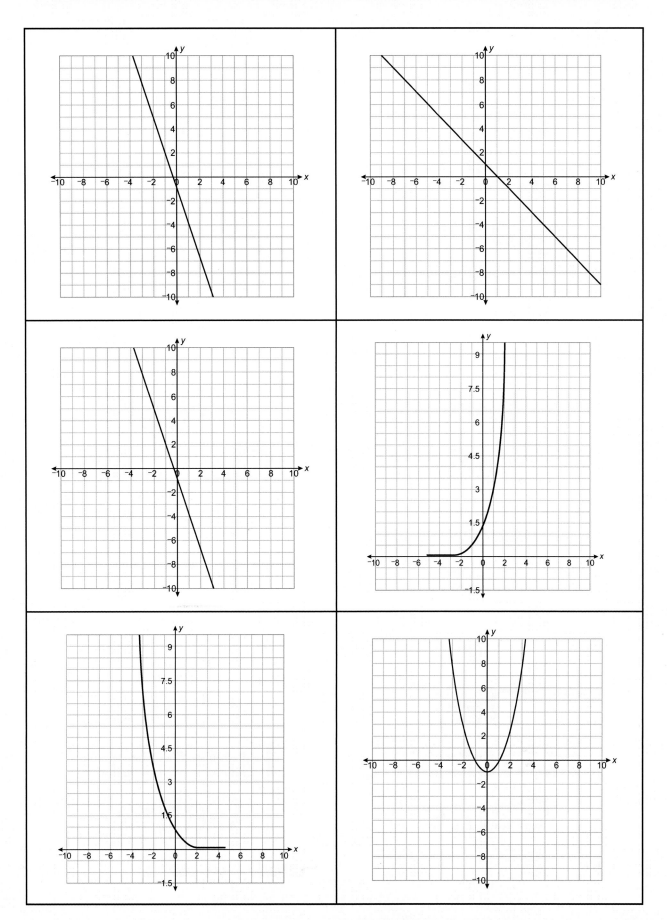

# The Function Game

# The Function Game

# The Function Game

# The Function Game

# The Function Game

# The Function Game

| x | y | Amount Earned in Dollars | Total Amount Earned |
|---|---|---|---|
| 1 | 1 | $0.01 | $0.01 |
| 2 | 2 | $0.02 | $0.03 |
| 3 | 4 | $0.04 | $0.07 |
|   |   |   |   |
|   |   |   |   |
|   |   |   |   |
|   |   |   |   |
|   |   |   |   |
|   |   |   |   |
|   |   |   |   |
|   |   |   |   |
|   |   |   |   |
|   |   |   |   |
|   |   |   |   |
|   |   |   |   |
|   |   |   |   |
|   |   |   |   |
|   |   |   |   |
|   |   |   |   |

# Sum It Up

In this section, you explored quadratic and exponential functions and their graphs. The following are important ideas that you learned in this section.

## Quadratic Functions

- A quadratic function is function in which one of the variables is raised to the second power and this is the highest power of the function. Example: $y = x^2$

- The graph of the function $y = x^2$ is a parabola. Its curve is symmetrical. This means if you fold along the line of symmetry, the two sides of the curve will match up perfectly. The turning point of the graph on the line of symmetry is called the vertex.

The line of symmetry of the parabola below is the $y$-axis. The vertex is $(0, 0)$.

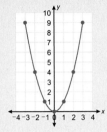

The graph below shows $y = -x^2 + 4$.

The line of symmetry is the $y$-axis. The vertex is $(0, 4)$. The negative coefficient of the $x^2$ term means that the parabola will open downward instead of upward.

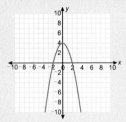

The Sum It Up summarizes the important mathematics students should have learned in this section. Encourage students to use this Sum It Up as they complete the Study Guide and prepare for quizzes and tests.

## Solving Quadratic Equations

■ Use the order of operations (**P**lease **E**xcuse **M**y **D**ear **A**unt **S**ally) to evaluate expressions and solve equations with exponents.

Example: Solve for $A$ when $x = -3$: $A = 5x^2$.

$A = 5(-3)^2$      Exponents first.

$A = 5(9) = 45$      Then multiplication.

■ To solve a quadratic equation, find the square root of the variable.

Example: $x^2 = 196$

$\pm\sqrt{x^2} = \pm\sqrt{196}$

$x = 14$ and $\pm 14$

## Exponential Functions

■ An exponential function has a variable as an exponent.

■ The exponential function $y = 2^x$, graphed below, is an example of exponential growth.

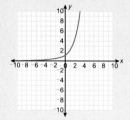

■ The exponential function $y = \left(\frac{1}{2}\right)^n$, graphed below, is an example of exponential decay.

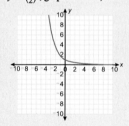

# Study Guide

**Solve It: Focusing on Equations, Inequalities and Exponents**

## Part 1. What did you learn?

1. Use the words in the Section 4 Sum It Up to fill in the blanks below.

   A _____ function is a function that represents a
   relationship between two variables in which the highest
   exponent of one of the variables is 2. The graph of the function
   $y = x^2$ is a _____ . The curve is symmetrical. If you fold
   along the _____ , the two sides of the curve will match
   up perfectly. The lowest point of an upward-opening parabola
   and the highest point of a downward-opening parabola are each
   called the _____ of that parabola.

# Study Guide

1.  1  quadratic

    2  parabola

    3  axis of symmetry

    4  vertex

2. Match each equation in Column A with the correct description in Column B, the matching table of values in Column C and the corresponding graph in Column D.

| Column A | Column B | Column C | | Column D |
|---|---|---|---|---|
| a. $y = 3^x$ | e. quadratic | i. | | m. |

i.

| x | y |
|---|---|
| -2 | $\frac{1}{9}$ |
| -1 | $\frac{1}{3}$ |
| 0 | 1 |
| 1 | 3 |
| 2 | 9 |

j.

| x | y |
|---|---|
| -2 | 12 |
| -1 | 3 |
| 0 | 0 |
| 1 | 3 |
| 2 | 12 |

b. $y = 3x^2$ — f. exponential growth

k.

| x | y |
|---|---|
| -2 | 9 |
| -1 | 3 |
| 0 | 1 |
| 1 | $\frac{1}{3}$ |
| 2 | $\frac{1}{9}$ |

c. $y = \frac{1}{3}x$ — g. linear

l.

| x | y |
|---|---|
| -2 | -6 |
| -1 | -3 |
| 0 | 0 |
| 1 | 3 |
| 2 | 6 |

d. $y = 3x$ — h. exponential decay

3. Using the correct order of operations, substitute the value for the variable and solve the equation.

   a. Solve for $A$ when $x = 4$: $A = 3x^2$.

   b. Solve for $a$ when $b = 4$: $3a = 6(b^2 - 1)$.

   c. Solve for $y$ when $x = -1$: $y = -2x^3$

2.  a, f, i, n
    b, e, j, p
    c, h, k, m
    d, g, l, o

3.  a. $A = 48$

    b. $a = 30$

    c. $y = 2$

4. Evaluate each of the following:

   a. $\sqrt{144}$

   b. $-\sqrt{49}$

   c. $2\sqrt{100} - \sqrt{36}$

5. Represent the function $y = 2x^2 - 1$ using a table of values and a graph.

6. Without graphing, tell how the graphs of the functions $y = x^2$ and $y = -x^2$ will compare.

7. Without graphing, find the vertex and the equation for the axis of symmetry of each function below.

   a. $y = -4x^2$

   b. $y = -4x^2 - 2$

   c. $y = -4x^2 + 2$

8. The area of a swimming pool is 1,600 square feet and the ratio of the length of the square-shaped shallow end to the length of the deep end is 1:3. Find the length of the deep end and the shallow end.

**Part 2. What went wrong?**

9. Jorge evaluated the equation $A = 6x^2$ when $x = 2$ by doing the following: $6(2)^2 = 12^2 = 144$. His teacher marked his answer wrong. Why? What could you say or do to help Jorge find the correct answer?

---

4. **a.** 12

   **b.** $-7$

   **c.** 14

5.

| x | y |
|---|---|
| −2 | 7 |
| −1 | 1 |
| 0 | −1 |
| 1 | 1 |
| 2 | 7 |

6. Both graphs will be parabolas with the same axis of symmetry and vertex. The graph of $y = x^2$ will open up but the graph of $y = -x^2$ will open down.

7. **a.** The axis of symmetry is the $y$-axis ($x = 0$) and the vertex is (0, 0).

   **b.** The axis of symmetry is the $y$-axis ($x = 0$) and the vertex is (0, −2).

   **c.** The axis of symmetry is the $y$-axis ($x = 0$) and the vertex is (0, 2).

8. 20 feet and 60 feet

9. Student answers will vary. Possible answer: Jorge did not follow the order of operations. He multiplied 6 by 2 first, but he needs to square 2 before multiplying the result by 6. I would remind Jorge to follow the order of operations which states that we evaluate exponents before multiplying. The correct answer is 24 since $2 \cdot 2 = 4$ and $4 \cdot 6 = 24$.

Solve It: Focusing on Equations,
Inequalities and Exponents

## Part 1: What did you learn?

### SECTION 1

1. Try the following Mathmagic trick. Fill in the missing parts so that the final answer is always 1.

| Step | Words | Diagram | Expression |
|---|---|---|---|
| 1 | Choose your favorite number between 1 and 10. | $n$ | |
| 2 | | | $n + n + 1$ |
| 3 | | $n$ $n$ $+1$ $+1$ $+1$ | |
| 4 | Add your original number. | | |
| 5 | | | $n + 1$ |
| 6 | | | 1 |

2. Write a Mathmagic trick that uses the additive inverse property and the distributive property of multiplication over addition.

| Step | Words | Diagram | Expression |
|---|---|---|---|
| 1 | | | |
| 2 | | | |
| 3 | | | |
| 4 | | | |
| 5 | | | |
| 6 | | | |
| 7 | | | |

1.

| Step | Words | Diagram | Expression |
|---|---|---|---|
| 1 | Choose your favorite number between 1 and 10. | $n$ | $n$ |
| 2 | **Add one more than your original number.** | $n$ $+n$ $+1$ | $n + n + 1$ |
| 3 | **Add 2.** | $n$ $+n$ $+1$ $+1$ $+1$ | $2n + 3$ |
| 4 | Add your original number. | $n$ $+n$ $+n$ $+1$ $+1$ $+1$ | $3n + 3$ |
| 5 | **Divide by 3.** | $n$ $+1$ | $n + 1$ |
| 6 | **Subtract your original number.** | 1 | 1 |

**2.** Answers will vary. Possible answer.

| Step | Words | Diagram | Expression |
|------|-------|---------|------------|
| 1 | Choose your favorite number between 1 and 10. | $n$ | $n$ |
| 2 | Add 3. | $n$ +1 +1 +1 | $n + 3$ |
| 3 | Double. | $n$ +1 +1 +1 <br> $n$ +1 +1 +1 | $2(n + 3) = 2n + 6$ |
| 4 | Subtract 6. | $n$  $n$ | $2n$ |
| 5 | Divide by 2. | $n$ | $n$ |
| 6 | Write your final result. | $n$ | $n$ |

**3. a.** 30

   **b.** $1\frac{3}{4}$

   **c.** 13

**4.**

| Bar diagram | Algebraic properties and rules |
|---|---|
| $-60$<br><br>$a-4$ \| $a-4$ \| $a-4$ \| $a-4$ \| $a-4$ \| $a-4$<br>$-10$ \| $-10$ \| $-10$ \| $-10$ \| $-10$ \| $-10$<br><br>$a = {}^-6$ | $6(a-4) = {}^-60$<br>$6a + {}^-24 = {}^-60$<br>$6a + {}^-24 + 24 = {}^-60 + 24$<br>$6a = {}^-36$<br>$\frac{1}{6} \cdot 6a = 36 \cdot \frac{1}{6}$<br>$a = {}^-6$ |
| $110$<br><br>$2b+3$ \| $2b+3$ \| $2b+3$ \| $11$<br>$99$ \| $11$<br>$33$ \| $33$ \| $33$ \| $11$<br><br>$2b + 3 = 33$<br>$b = 15$ | $3(2b + 3) + 11 = 110$<br>$6b + 9 + 11 = 110$<br>$6b + 20 = 110$<br>$6b + 20 + {}^-20 = 110 + {}^-20$<br>$6b = 90$<br>$\frac{1}{6} \cdot 6b = 90 \cdot \frac{1}{6}$<br>$b = 15$ |
| $22$<br><br>$-2c + 4$ \| $10$<br>$12$ \| $10$<br>$8$ \| $4$ \| $10$<br><br>$-2c = 8$<br>$c = {}^-4$ | $10 - (2c - 4) = 22$<br>$10 - 2c + 4 = 22$<br>$14 - 2c = 22$<br>$14 + {}^-2c + {}^-14 = 22 + {}^-14$<br>$^-2c = 8$<br>$-\frac{1}{2} \cdot 2c = 8 \cdot \frac{1}{2}$<br>$c = {}^-4$ |

**5.**  a, h
   b, m
   c, j
   d, k
   e, n
   f, l
   g, i

**6.**

| | |
|---|---|
| $21 - 4x = {}^-16x - 15$ | given |
| $21 + {}^-4x = {}^-16x + {}^-15$ | rewrite subtraction as addition of the opposite |
| $21 + {}^-4x + 4x = {}^-16x + {}^-15 + 4x$ | addition property of equality |
| $21 = {}^-12x + {}^-15$ | simplify |
| $21 + 15 = {}^-12x + {}^-15 + 15$ | addition property of equality |
| $36 = {}^-12x$ | simplify |
| $-\frac{1}{12} \cdot 36 = {}^-12x \cdot -\frac{1}{12}$ | multiplication property of equality |
| $^-3 = x$ | solution |

**7.**

$$6(3 - x) = 12x + 54$$
$$18 - 6x = 12x + 54$$
$$18 - 6x + 6x = 12x + 54 + 6x$$
$$18 = 18x + 54$$
$$18 + {}^-54 = 18x + 54 + {}^-54$$
$$^-36 = 18x$$
$$^-2 = x$$

8. Write an inequality for each of these statements.

    a. You must be 55" or taller to go on this ride.

    b. Salaries start at $40,000 and have a maximum of $100,000.

    c. Speed must be greater than 45 mph but no more than 65 mph.

    d. We must have more than 10 chaperones but no more than 16 to go on the field trip.

    e. The cost will be at least $65 but no more than $100.

9. For each statement below, write the statement in symbols and graph all solutions on a number line.

    a. $a$ is greater than $-\frac{10}{3}$.

    b. $b$ is less than or equal to $-4$ but greater than $-10.5$.

    c. $d$ is not greater than $-\frac{4}{3}$.

10. You plan to buy a bicycle that will cost at least $180. You have saved $38 and your parents have given you $50.

    a. Write an inequality to find how much more money, $m$, you need to save.

    b. Solve your inequality.

    c. Graph your inequality on a number line.

11. Find the missing entries in the chart below.

| | Standard Notation | Scientific Notation |
|---|---|---|
| a. | | $5.618 \times 10^5$ |
| b. | 37,000,000,000 | |
| c. | 0.000,56 | |
| d. | | $1.908 \times 10^{-5}$ |

8. a. $h \geq 55$ where $h$ is your height

    b. $40{,}000 \leq s \leq 100{,}000$ where $s$ is salary

    c. $45 < s \geq 65$, where $s$ is speed

    d. $10 < c \leq 16$, where $c$ is the number of parents or guardians

    e. $65 \leq c \leq 100$ where $c$ is the cost

9. a. $a > -\frac{10}{3}$

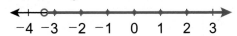

    b. $-10.5 < b \leq -4$

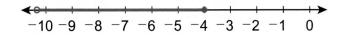

c. $d \leq -\frac{4}{3}$

10. a. $m + 38 + 50 \geq 180$

    b. $m \geq 92$

    c.

11. a. 561,800

    b. $3.7 \times 10^{10}$

    c. $5.6 \times 10^{-4}$

    d. 0.00001908

12. Find a number, $x$, that satisfies each inequality. Write your answers in scientific notation.

   a. $35.6 \times 10^3 < x < 6.45 \times 10^5$

   b. $0.653 \times 10^4 < x < 0.658 \times 10^4$

   c. $7.9 \times 10^{15} < x < 7.91 \times 10^{15}$

13. Simplify using scientific notation and the rules for exponents.

   a. $47,000,000 \times 10^7$

   b. $(4 \times 10^9)(6 \times 10^{12})$

   c. $\frac{75 \times 10^{20}}{3 \times 10^{18}}$

   e. $\frac{2.4 \times 10^6}{8 \times 10^{-2}}$

14. A light-year is 5,865,696,000,000 miles. Mercury is 36 million miles from the sun. Approximately how many light-years is this?

15. Order the following lengths from shortest to longest.

   $6.8 \times 10^{-5}$ centimeters, 0.000008 meter, 8 nanometers, $4.5 \times 10^{12}$ millimeters

16. Find the value that should replace each question mark.

   a. $2^4 \cdot 2^2 \cdot 2^3 = 2^?$

   b. $\frac{3^6}{3^2} = 3^?$

   c. $25^2 \cdot 5^3 = 2^?$

**SECTION 4**

17. Use the correct order of operations to solve $V = (2x)^3$ for $V$ when $x = 4$. Show your work.

---

12. Answers will vary. Possible answers are given below.

   a. $4.1 \times 10^5$

   b. $6.57 \times 10^3$

   c. $7.905 \times 10^{15}$

13. a. $4.7 \times 10^{14}$

   b. $2.4 \times 10^{22}$

   c. $2.5 \times 10^3$

   d. $3 \times 10^6$

14. About $6.1 \times 10^{-6}$

15. 8 nanometers, $6.8 \times 10^{-5}$ centimeters, 0.000008 meter, $4.5 \times 10^{12}$ millimeters

16. a. 9

   b. 3

   c. 7

17. $Z = (2x)^3$
    $Z = (2(4))^3$
    $Z = (8)^3$
    $Z = 512$

18. Represent each function below using a table of values and a graph.

**a.** $y = 3x$

**b.** $y = x^2$

**c.** $y = 3^x$

19. Identify each equation in Question 18 as linear, quadratic or exponential. Explain how the tables and graphs of these functions are similar and different.

**18.**

**a.** $y = 3x$

| x | y |
|---|---|
| −3 | −9 |
| −2 | −6 |
| −1 | −3 |
| 0 | 0 |
| 1 | 3 |
| 2 | 6 |
| 3 | 9 |

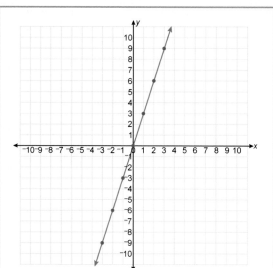

**b.** $y = x^2$

| x | y |
|---|---|
| −3 | 9 |
| −2 | 4 |
| −1 | 1 |
| 0 | 0 |
| 1 | 1 |
| 2 | 4 |
| 3 | 9 |

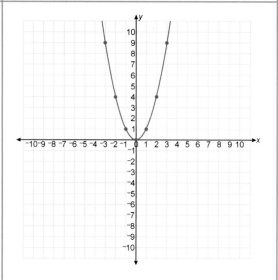

**c.** $y = 3^x$

| x | y |
|---|---|
| −3 | $\frac{1}{27}$ |
| −2 | $\frac{1}{9}$ |
| −1 | $\frac{1}{3}$ |
| 0 | 1 |
| 1 | 3 |
| 2 | 9 |
| 3 | 27 |

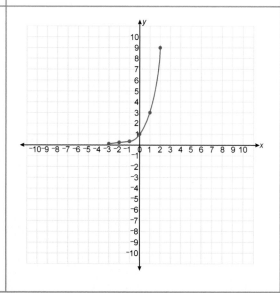

19. Graph *a* is linear. Graph *b* is quadratic. Graph *c* is exponential. Explanations will vary. Possible explanation: The *y*-values in the linear and exponential tables are increasing. In the linear function, the increase is constant. The *y*-values in the table of the quadratic function decrease and increase. The graphs of the linear and exponential graphs go from left to the upper right. The graph of the quadratic function goes down and then up.

20. Identify the line of symmetry and vertex of the parabola of the function $y = 2x^2 + 4$.

21. Which would you rather receive: $2 on the first day of the month, $4 on the second day of the month, $8 on the 3rd day of the month and so on, doubling the amount each day for a 28-day month; or one lump sum of $1,000,000? Show or explain how you made your choice and give the total amount you would be paid.

## Part 2. What went wrong?

22. Mickey tried to solve the equation $2(3x + 2) - 4x = -8$. Here is what he did:

$$2(3x + 2) - 4x = -8$$
$$6x + 2 + {}^-4x = {}^-8$$
$$2x + 2 = {}^-8$$
$$2x + 2 + {}^-2 = {}^-8 + {}^-2$$
$$2x = {}^-10$$
$$\frac{1}{2} \cdot 2x = {}^-10 \cdot \frac{1}{2}$$
$$x = {}^-5$$

What error did Mickey make? What would you say or do to help Mickey find and fix his mistake?

20. Line of symmetry is $x = 0$ and vertex is (0, 4).

21. The first deal is better. Explanations will vary. Possible explanation: On the 28th day alone, you would receive $2^{28}$ or approximately 250 million dollars.

22. Explanations will vary. Possible explanation: Mickey made his error as soon as he tried to apply the distributive property of multiplication over addition. He wrote $2(3x + 2)$ as equal to $6x + 2$. This is wrong.
I would tell Mickey that he needs to multiply 2 by each term in the parentheses. This would give him $6x + 4 + {}^-4x = {}^-8$ as his second line. This would lead to a final answer of $x = {}^-6$.

23. Explanations will vary. Possible explanation: Verona should draw the circle on the 4 but leave the circle open. The open circle shows that the solution set begins with all numbers greater than 4, but does not include 4.

**23.** Verona solved the equation $2x - 6 > 2$ and got $x > 4$. Her teacher told her to graph her solution on a number line. Her teacher told her to draw the open circle on the 4, but Verona thinks the circle should be drawn after the 4 since $x$ can't be 4. What do you think? Explain your reasoning.

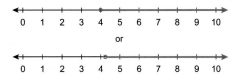

or

**24.** Jerry thinks all three of the following expressions are equivalent: $7^{-2}$, $-7^2$, $(-7)^2$. His friend Adam thinks none of them are equivalent. Who do you agree with? Why?

**24.** Explanations will vary. Possible explanation: I agree with his friend Adam. $7^{-2}$ means the reciprocal of $7^2$. Since $7^2$ equals 49, $7^{-2}$ equals $\frac{1}{49}$. $-7^2$ means the opposite of $7^2$. Since $7^2$ equals 49, $-7^2$ equals $-49$. $(-7)^2$ means $-7$ times itself which is 49. Looking at the three answers, $\frac{1}{49}$, 49, $-49$, we can see that they are all different.

**addition property of equality** The property that states that if the same number is added to both sides of an equation, the expressions on each side remain equal.

**Example**

For all real numbers $a$, $b$ and $c$, if $a = b$ then
$$a + c = b + c.$$

$$x + 4 = 19$$
$$x + 4 + {}^-4 = 19 + {}^-4 \quad \text{Add } -4 \text{ to both sides.}$$
$$x + 0 = 15$$
$$x = 15$$

---

**addition property of inequality** The property that states that adding the same number to both sides of an inequality does not change the inequality.

**Example**

For all real numbers $a$, $b$ and $c$, if $a > b$ then
$$a + c > b + c.$$

$$x + 7 > 23$$
$$x + 7 + {}^-7 > 23 + {}^-7 \quad \text{Add } -7 \text{ to both sides.}$$
$$x + 0 > 16$$
$$x > 16$$

---

**additive identity property** The property that states that adding 0 to a number or expression does not change the value of that number or expression.

**Example**

For all real numbers $a$, $a + 0 = a$.

$${}^-2 + 0 = {}^-2$$
$$(3x + 5) + 0 = 3x + 5$$

---

**additive inverse property** The property that states that the sum of a number and its additive inverse is equal to 0.

**Example**

For all real numbers $a$, $a + (-a) = 0$.

$$6 + (-6) = 0$$
$$(-10) + 10 = 0$$

---

**algebraic expression** An expression that contains at least one variable.

**Example**

$$2x$$
$$3(8 - 2x) + 15$$

---

**astronomical unit (AU)** A unit of length used to measure distances in the solar system. An AU is the average distance between the sun and Earth (approximately 93 million miles or 150 million kilometers).

**Example**

A light-year is 63,240 AU.

---

**bar diagram** A diagram using bars of equal length to represent equal expressions or quantities.

**Example**

$$4(79) + t = 475$$

| 79 | 79 | 79 | 79 | $t$ |
|----|----|----|----|-----|
| 475 | | | | |

**base (of an exponential expression)** The factor of a repeated multiplication when expressed in exponential form. In an exponential expression of the form $x^y$, $x$ is the base.

**Example**

$2^3 = 2 \cdot 2 \cdot 2$     2 is the base.

$5^2 = 5 \cdot 5$     5 is the base.

$10^x$     10 is the base.

---

**constant** A value that does not vary.

**Example**

In the expression $x + 3$, 3 is a constant.

In the formula $A = \pi r^2$, $\pi$ is a constant.

---

**distributive property of multiplication over addition** The property that states that the product of a sum and a number is the sum of the products of that number and each addend.

**Example**

For all real numbers $a$, $b$ and $c$, $a \cdot (b + c) = ab + ac$

$3 \cdot (5 + 8) = (3 \cdot 5) + (3 \cdot 8)$

$2 \cdot (3x + 5 + y) = 6x + 10 + 2y$

---

**equation** A mathematical sentence stating that two expressions are equal.

**Example**

$5 + 2 = 7$

$3(10 + 2) = 30 + 6$

$5x = 15$

---

**equivalent expressions** Expressions that can be rewritten in the same form as one another. Expressions that simplify to an equal value for all values of the variable(s) they contain.

**Example**

$l + l + w + w$ and $2l + 2w$ are equivalent expressions for the perimeter of a rectangle.

---

**explicit rule** A rule that directly defines the output variable in terms of the input variable.

**Example**

Situation: I open a savings account with $10, and then deposit $50 each month.

Explicit Rule: $A = 10 + 50n$; $A$ is the amount in the account after $n$ months of deposits. $A$ is the output variable and $n$ is the input variable.

---

**exponent** The raised number or expression indicating the number of times a number or expression is used as a factor in repeated multiplication. In an exponential expression of the form $a^b$, $b$ is the exponent.

**Example**

$2^3 = 2 \cdot 2 \cdot 2 = 8$     The exponent is 3.

$(3r)^2 = (3r)(3r) = 9r^2$     The exponent is 2.

**exponential decay** An exponentially decreasing relationship.

**Example**
The function $y = \left(\frac{1}{4}\right)^x$ represents a relationship of exponential decay.

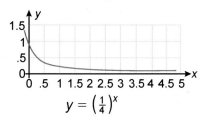

$$y = \left(\frac{1}{4}\right)^x$$

---

**exponential function** A function of the form $y = a^x$ where $a > 0$ and $a \neq 1$.

**Example**
$$y = 5x$$
$$y = \left(\frac{1}{3}\right)x$$

---

**exponential growth** An exponentially increasing relationship.

**Example**
The function $y = 3^x$ represents a relationship of exponential growth.

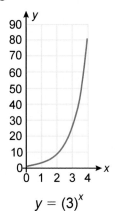

$$y = (3)^x$$

---

**factor (an expression)** To rewrite an expression as a product of factors.

**Example**
$$5x - 10 = 5(x - 2)$$
$$6x^2 - 3x = 3x(2x - 1)$$

---

**function** A relationship between two variables, in which each value of the independent (input) variable is matched to only one value of the dependent (output) variable.

**Example**
Function: $y = 2x + 3$

| Input (x) | −2 | −1 | 0 | 1 | 2 | 3 |
|---|---|---|---|---|---|---|
| Output (y) | −1 | 1 | 3 | 5 | 7 | 9 |

---

**greatest common factor (GCF) (greatest common divisor)** The greatest (largest) factor of two or more numbers.

**Example**
The factors of 20 are 1, 2, 4, 5, 10 and 20.

The factors of 50 are 1, 2, 5, 10, 25 and 50.

The GCF of 20 and 50 is 10.

**grouping symbols** Symbols used to group portions of an expression or equation. All grouping symbols act as parentheses when following the order of operations.

**Example**

Brackets [ ] and parentheses ( ) are used to group terms:

$$[5 + 2x(3 - x) - 4] + 10.$$

The division bar is used to group terms:

$$\frac{5 + 3x}{2x - 5}.$$

**inequality** A statement containing the symbols > (greater than), < (less than), ≥ (greater than or equal to), ≤ (less than or equal to) or ≠ (not equal to) to indicate how one quantity relates to another.

**Example**

$$x > 2$$

$$-1 < 7$$

The value of any 3 coins is ≥ 3 cents.

**light-year** A unit of length used to measure distances in space; the distance that light travels in one year (approximately 9,460,730,472,580.8 km; 5,878,625,373,183,61 miles; or 63,240 AU).

**Example**

The earth is $1.51 \times 10^{-5}$ or 0.0000151 light-years from the sun.

**like terms** Terms in an expression or equation that include the same variable(s) raised to the same power(s); like terms can be combined to simplify expressions and equations.

**Example**

In the expression $3 + 4x + 6 + 7x$, 3 and 6 are like terms, and $4x$ and $7x$ are like terms. Since $3 + 6 = 9$ and $4x + 7x = 11x$, we can simplify this expression as $9 + 11x$.

In the expression $3xy + 4x^2y - 7xy^2 + 2x^2y$, the $4x^2y$ and $2x^2y$ are like terms and combine to be $6x^2y$. The expression simplifies to $3xy + 6x^2y - 7xy^2$.

**line of symmetry** A line dividing a figure into two parts, each of which is a mirror image of the other.

**Example**

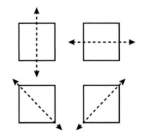

**mantissa (in scientific notation)** The number from 1 up to but not including 10 (≥ 1 and < 10) that is multiplied by a power of 10 when expressing a value in scientific notation.

**Example**

$1.2 \times 10^2$      1.2 is the mantissa.

$3.215 \times 10^4$      3.215 is the mantissa.

**micrometer** A unit of length equal to one millionth of a meter or $1 \times 10^{-6}$ meter.

**Example**

0.000001 meter = 1 micrometer

0.001 millimeter = 1 micrometer

**micron** Another name for a micrometer.

**multiplication property of equality** The property that states that if the same number multiplies both sides of an equation, the expressions on each side remain equal

**Example**
For all real numbers $a$, $b$ and $c$, if $a = b$ then
$$a \bullet c = b \bullet c.$$
$$3x = 27$$
$$\left(\tfrac{1}{3}\right)(3x) = \left(\tfrac{1}{3}\right)(27) \qquad \text{Multiply both sides by } \tfrac{1}{3}.$$
$$x = 9$$

**multiplication property of inequality for multiplication by a positive number** The property that states that multiplying both sides of an inequality by the same positive number does not change the inequality.

**Example**
For all real numbers $a$, $b$ and $c$, if $a > b$ and $c > 0$ then $a \bullet c > b \bullet c.$
$$120 > 10x$$
$$\left(\tfrac{1}{10}\right)(120) > \left(\tfrac{1}{10}\right)(10x) \quad \text{Multiply both sides by } \tfrac{1}{10}.$$
$$12 > x$$

**multiplication property of inequality for multiplication by a negative number** The property that states that multiplying both sides of an inequality by the same negative number reverses the inequality.

**Example**
For all real numbers $a$, $b$ and $c$, if $a > b$ and $c < 0$ then $a \bullet c < b \bullet c.$
$$-5x > 25$$
$$\left(-\tfrac{1}{5}\right)(-5x) < \left(-\tfrac{1}{5}\right)(25) \quad \text{Multiply both sides by } -\tfrac{1}{5}.$$
$$x < -5$$

**multiplicative identity property** The property that states that multiplying a number or expression by 1 does not change the value of the number or expression.

**Example**
For all real numbers $a$, $a \bullet 1 = a.$
$$15 \bullet 1 = 15$$
$$(3x + 2y) \bullet 1 = (3x + 2y)$$

**multiplicative inverse property** The property that states that the product of a number and its inverse (reciprocal) is 1.

**Example**
For all real numbers $a$ where $a \neq 0$, $\left(\tfrac{1}{a}\right)(a) = 1$
$$\left(\tfrac{1}{7}\right)(7) = 1$$

**nanometer** A measure of length equal to $1 \times 10^{-9}$ meter.

**Example**
$0.000000001$ meter $= 1$ nanometer

**nanotechnology** A new area of scientific study broadly addressing the smallest parts of matter that scientists can manipulate.

**order of operations** A prescribed order for evaluating expressions and solving equations:
1) perform all operations within parentheses
2) simplify all expressions with exponents
3) multiply and divide in order from left to right
4) add and subtract in order from left to right.
The mnemonic Please Excuse My Dear Aunt Sally (PEMDAS) indicates the sequence of the order of operations.

**Example**

$4 + (8 - 3)^2$

$4 + (5)^2$      perform operation within parentheses

$4 + 25$      simplify expression with exponent

$29$      add from left to right

---

**parabola** The graph of a quadratic function.

**Example**

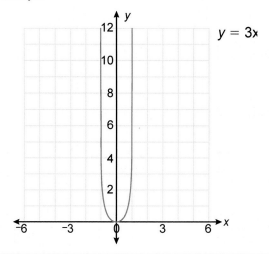

$y = 3x^2$

---

**power** The result of raising a base to an exponent. In the power $a^b$, $a$ is the base, $b$ is the exponent and the expression is read "$a$ raised to the $b^{th}$ power" or "$a$ to the $b$."

**Example**

$2^3 = 2 \cdot 2 \cdot 2 = 8$      2 raised to the 3$^{rd}$ power is 8.

$5^4 = 5 \cdot 5 \cdot 5 \cdot 5 = 625$    5 to the 4$^{th}$ power is 625.

---

**quadratic equation** An equation in one variable in which the greatest exponent of that variable is 2. A quadratic equation can be written in the form $0 = ax^2 + bx + c$ where $a \neq 0$.

**Example**

$x^2 = 81$

$2x^2 + 5x + 1 = 0$

---

**quadratic function** A function in which one variable is related to a quadratic expression of another variable. A quadratic function can be written in the form $y = ax^2 + bx + c$ where $a \neq 0$.

**Example**

$y = 3x^2$

$y = {}^-2x^2 + 5x - 3$

$y = x^2 - 10$

---

**radical sign** A symbol used to indicate the principle or positive square root.

**Example**

$\sqrt{16} = 4$

If $x^2 = 9$, then $x = \pm\sqrt{9} = \pm3$. $\sqrt{9} = 3$.

**ratio** A comparison of two quantities, $a$ and $b$, stated as "$a$ to $b$" and represented as $a : b$ or $\frac{a}{b}$.

**Example**

With 4 girls and 3 boys, the ratio of girls to boys is $4 : 3$ or $\frac{4}{3}$.

---

**recursive rule** A rule that is applied to the result of a previous application of itself; the input value is a previous output value of the rule.

**Example**

Situation: I open a savings account with $10 and deposit $50 each month. Therefore, each month my balance is $50 more than the previous month.

Recursive Rule: *New = Previous* + 50; initial amount of $10.

---

**replacement set** The set of numbers from which values may be chosen for variable substitution in a given mathematical expression or statement.

**Example**

$2y - 3 > 15$    $y$ could be any number. (Only $y > 9$ are members of the solution set.)

$y = \frac{1}{x}$    $x \neq 0$ ($x$ can be all numbers except 0.)

---

**scientific notation** A notation system to express numbers as a product of a number between 1 and 10 (the mantissa) and a power of ten.

**Example**

542 is written as $5.42 \times 10^2$.

1,497 is written as $1.497 \times 10^3$.

0.004 is written as $4 \times 10^{-3}$.

---

**solution (or solution set)** A number (or set of numbers) that produces a true statement when substituted for a variable (or variables) in a mathematical sentence (equation or inequality). The answer to a mathematical problem.

**Example**

$y = 2(10)$    $y = 20$ (The only solution is 20.)

$2x + 3 = 10$    $x = 3.5$ (The only solution is 3.5.)

$4y > 8$    $y > 2$    (All numbers greater than 2 are in the solution set.)

---

**square root** A solution $x$ to the equation $x^2 = n$ for a given value of $n$.

**Example**

2 is a square root of 4 since $2^2 = 4$

$-5$ is a square root of 25 since $(-5)^2 = 25$

---

**standard notation** A notation system to express numbers using the place value of digits in a base-ten system.

**Example**

542 represents 5 hundreds, 4 tens and 2 ones.
1,497 represents 1 thousand, 4 hundreds, 9 tens and 7 ones.
0.004 represents 4 thousandths.

---

**symbol "(AU)" astronomical unit**

**Example**

1 AU < 93,000,000 miles.

A light-year is 63,240 AU.

---

**symbol ">"** Greater than.

**Example**

$5 > 2$

$(10 + n) > 10$, when $n$ is a positive number.

**symbol "≥"** Greater than or equal to.

**Example**

If $j \geq 63$ inches, where $j$ is Jessica's height in inches, then Jessica is 63 inches tall or taller.

The number of coins that sum to $1.00 is $\geq 1$.

---

**symbol "<"** Less than.

**Example**

$2 < 7$

If $x + 2 < 5$, then $x < 3$.

---

**symbol "≤"** Less than or equal to.

**Example**

If $m \leq 14$, where $m$ is Mark's age in years, then Mark is 14 years old or younger.

The amount of cereal in a 14-ounce box is $\leq 14$ ounces.

---

**symbol "≠"** Not equal to.

**Example**

$3 \neq 7$

$x \neq 6$

---

**symbol "√"** Radical sign. Principle or positive square root.

---

**vertex (of a parabola)** The point on the graph of a parabola where the graph turns (from decreasing to increasing or from increasing to decreasing); the maximum point of a downward-opening parabola or the minimum point on an upward-opening parabola.

**Example**

The vertex of the parabola below is at $(0, 4)$.

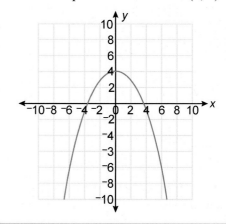

## Lesson 1.1

### Magic Tricks . . . or Are They?

**Page 2, Question 1:** Did you get the this answer? How many of your classmates got this answer?

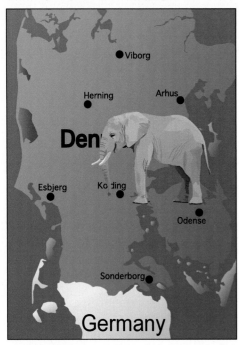

### Using the Distributive Property

**Page 6, Question 7f:** Remember, the product of two negative numbers is a positive number.

## Lesson 1.2

### One Equation—Three Solutions?

**Page 15, Question 2b:** Remember to use the correct order of operations.

### On Your Own

**Page 20, Question 3c:** Jeff must buy full containers of dough.

**Page 24, Question 12:** Draw a picture to help you.

**Page 25, Question 15:** Use 3.14 for $\pi$

## Lesson 1.3

### Using Properties to Solve Equations

**Page 29, Question 4c:** $-4$ is the same as $+ (-4)$. Distribute $-4$ over the parentheses.

### Combining Like Terms with Variables

**Page 30, Question 5d:** $y = 1 \cdot y$

## Lesson 1.4

### Solving Equations with variables on both sides of the equal sign

**Page 40, Question 3b:** Remember $z = 1 \cdot z$ or $1z$ so $3z - 1z = 2z$

**Page 40, Question 3d:** Distribute 5 first.

### On Your Own

**Page 42, Question 5:** Recall the formula for circumference: $C = \pi d$.

## Lesson 2.1

### Reading Backward and Forward

**Page 56, Question 11:** Use a number line to help you.

**Page 56, Question 12b:** Make sure your answers make sense in the situation.

### Combining Inequalities

**Page 57, Question 16e:** Non-integer values are fractions and decimals that are not included in the set of integers. For example, $\frac{1}{2}$, 0.02, $-1.78$, 65.32

### On Your Own

**Page 61, Question 9a:** "Between 86 and 92" includes neither 86 nor 92.

## Lesson 2.2

### On Your Own

**Page 70, Question 6b:** When you get off the last ride, you don't need to spend 7 more minutes in line.

## Lesson 3.1

**The Solar System Exhibit**
> **Page 79, Question 1:** 1 kilometer is approximately 0.6 mile.

**Finding Distances in Our Solar System**
> **Page 81, Question 7:** 1 mile is approximately 1.6 kilometers.

**On Your Own**
> **Page 87, Question 11b:** Find the speed of the space shuttle in miles per second.


## Lesson 3.4

**Scaling Down in a Nano-World**
> **Page 108, Question 10:** 1 millimeter = 0.001 m


## Lesson 4.1

**Evaluating Equations with Exponents**
> **Page 122, Question 7f:** Use 3.14 for $\pi$.

> **Page 122, Question 8:** Draw a diagram of the pool.

**On Your Own**
> **Page 124, Question 2c:** Use 3.14 for $\pi$.


## Lesson 4.3

**Getting the Word Out**
> **Page 137, Question 3a:** Remember, any number raised to the zero power is 1.

**Heat 'Em Up!**
> **Page 139, Question 12a:** Make a table of values for the functions to help you predict.

> **Page 140, Question 13b:** Make a table of values for the function to help you predict.

**On Your Own**
> **Page 142, Question 2:** A checkerboard has 64 squares.

# P

parabola  129, 147, *165*
  curve and vertex of  129A, 133
PEMDAS  (See *order of operations.*)
powers of 10  165. (See also *nano [10⁻⁹], power of zero.*)
  dividing with  114C
  multiplying with  90, 91
  patterns with  114A
  with negative exponents  106
power of zero  105
properties  34. (See also *like terms.*)
  addition property of equality  T20, 28, 46, 160
  addition property of inequality  T26, 64, 73, 154, 160
  additive identity property  28, 46, 154, 160
  additive inverse property  T20, 28, 29, 46, 154, 160
  associative property of multiplication  T20, 91
  commutative property of multiplication  T20, 91
  distributive  T20, 5, 11, 46, 154
  identity properties  T20
  multiplication over addition  6, 9
  multiplication property of equality  T20, 28, 29, 46, 154, 164
  multiplication property of inequality for multiplication by a negative number  T26, 64, 73, 164
  multiplication property of inequality for multiplication by a positive number  T26, 64, 73, 164
  multiplicative identity property  28, 154, 164
  multiplicative inverse property  T20, 28, 46, 154, 164
  solve equations using  27, 29

# Q

quadratic equation  T31, 127, 128, 129A, 165. (See also *function, quadratic function.*)
  solve, 148
quadratic function  T31, 128, 129, 165. (See also *function.*)
  comparing  130
  tables  134C
quantities, comparing  (See *inequalities.*)
questioning techniques  (See also *Five Ws and an H Mathematical Questions, Talk Moves.*)
  focusing  T7
  funneling  T7

# R

radical sign  121, 165. (See also *square root, symbols.*)
ratio (to compare quantities)  97, 166
recursive rule  135, 137, 166. (See also *explicit rule.*)
replacement set  54, 73, 166. (See also *equations, inequalities, solution set.*)

# S

scientific notation  80, 91, 166. (See also *astronomical unit, standard notation.*)
  base  80, 92
  exponent  80
  mantissa  80, *163*
  mass in  84
  simplify using  98
simplify  (See also *distributive property, expressions.*)
  algebraic equations  4
  numerator and denominator  17
  using scientific notation  98
slope-intercept form  37, 126B, 130B. (See also *equations.*)
solution  26. (See also *equations, inequalities.*)
  of inequalities  51
solution set  T26, 54, 166. (See also *replacement set.*)
  graphing  55
square root  120, 121, 166. (See also *radical sign, symbols.*)
  of variable  148
standard notation  T30, 81, 91, 166. (See also *astronomical unit, scientific notation.*)
Student Snapshot  T11
symbols
  chart  53, 72
  Egyptian ("astonished man")  103
  grouping  T22, 16
  "greater than" ($>$)  *166*
  "greater than or equal to" ($\geq$)  51, *167*
  "less than" ($<$)  51, *167*
  "less than or equal to" ($\leq$)  51, *167*
  nano ($10^{-9}$)  **104**
  "not equal to" ($\neq$)  51, *167*
  radical sign ($\sqrt{}$)  121, *167*